A Conscience in Conflict

THE LIFE OF

ST. GEORGE JACKSON MIVART

ST. GEORGE JACKSON MIVART

A Conscience in Conflict

THE LIFE OF

ST. GEORGE JACKSON MIVART

By Jacob W. Gruber

PUBLISHED FOR
TEMPLE UNIVERSITY PUBLICATIONS
BY COLUMBIA UNIVERSITY PRESS
NEW YORK 1960

To SHIRLEY

PREFACE

The history of science since the Middle Ages is a record of man's continuing attempt to explain the cosmological phenomena of his experience in natural and regular terms. It is, in a sense, a record of his search for security through prediction and consequent control of the forces of a cosmos whose subject he is.

As the science of the seventeenth century sought to naturalize and regularize the heavenly universe of the spheres, that of the nineteenth century sought the solution to the riddle of life and its variety.

History is a cumulative process, the surge of culture through time. It is a concatenation of persons, ideas, and events. History is personal in that it is men who make it. It is men who are the activators of events and the purveyors of ideas. It is men who live and create their culture; and in their lives is reflected the continuing, the ever-changing stream of history.

Few periods in the history of science are as significant as the middle quarters of the nineteenth century. The significance of these few decades lies not so much in the fact that modern biology was born then as in the transitional character of the period. These were the painful years of labor whose intellectual convulsions brought forth a new conception in the sciences of life. It was in these decades that the rigidified biologies of Linnaeus, Cuvier, and Owen were challenged by the dynamism of Darwin's evolution. This was a period of transition, of flux, of intellectual chaos and confusion.

The lives of those who lived and fought the intellectual battles of nineteenth-century science mirror the characteristics of the period. Whatever their philosophical allegiances, they personalize the conflicts from which emerged the philosophical and methodological foundations upon which modern biology rests.

Only those who personify the extremes in this conflict are remembered today, almost a century after their arguments began to float away on the historical stream. Darwin, Owen, Huxley, Haeckel—these are the names that are remembered; for they symbolize the sharply divergent views, the antitheses, in that "battle of the century." The memory of man, too full, casts off the others—the armor-bearers, the fire tenders, the mediators. These have been lost in the abridgment of history past, in the peculiar shorthand of the historian for whom only the "important" names make history.

One of these lesser figures was St. George Jackson Mivart. From the work of a whole lifetime there is occasionally recalled a single paper or book or, more often, a phrase discharged in the heat of controversy.

In attempting to trace out the life of Mivart, I hoped to add some detail to the rough and sometimes blurred etching of a period in the history of science whose outlines, whose major figures, are almost too well known. Mivart was not a giant in his intellectual community; nor was he a pygmy. Faced by the pressure of the extremes, he sought, as did so many others, to resolve his intellectual conflicts in compromise. He was unwilling to give up all of the past for the promise of the future. And in his attempt to synthesize the truths of both, he gained the favor of the adherents of neither. His was a life of controversy in the interests of the truth he sought, a search conducted with honesty, sincerity, and courage.

My concern with Mivart is not so much with the man as with the mind. Aside from the fact that few details of his life have been preserved in the face of the rejection of his work, the literal details of biography do not well serve the purposes of intellectual description. Although it is possible that his social experiences, trivial as they might have been, determined his intellectual production, it is the latter with which I have been concerned, for it is the latter that contributed to the reservoir of our past.

In gathering the widely scattered and often sparse materials necessary for this attempted reconstruction of a mind, I have had to depend upon the help of many individuals. Most of them are unknown to me except by correspondence. All of them, however, have given freely of their time, their advice, and their encouragement. There are some whose special help cannot go unnoticed.

I wish to thank those who willingly assumed the roles of informants and volunteer researchers, searching out for me the tidbits of information in places inaccessible to me: Sir John Murray of the London publishing house which bears his name, who supplied me with the first appreciable number of unpublished Mivart letters; Sir Shane Leslie, who regarded his help as a "labour of love" and who offered encouragement and interest along the way; Henry Tristram, the archivist of the Newman Collection in the Birmingham Oratory, who kindly made available the Newman-Mivart correspondence in his keeping, the Fathers of the Birmingham Oratory, who own the copyright, and Thomas Nelson and Sons Ltd., who are about to publish a complete edition of Cardinal Newman's letters, for permission to use them; Sir Francis Meynell and his sister, Mrs. Olivia Sowerby, who made available to me the extant correspondence between Mivart and his good friends, the Wilfrid Meynells; Mr. Nigel Abercrombie, the biographer of Edmund Bishop, who found for me the important Mivart-Bishop letters, and the Abbot of Downside who has permitted me to use them; Mr. G. C. Lowry, clerk to the Governors of the Imperial College of Science and Technology, who provided me with copies of the letters in the Huxley collection pertaining to Mivart, and Mrs. Rosalind Huxley for her kind permission to use them; Mr. A. C. Townsend of the British Museum, to whom I am indebted for copies of Mivart's letters to Owen, and the Trustees of the British Museum (Natural History), who have permitted me to quote from the letters of Owen, Darwin, and Wallace; and the Linnean, Zoological, and Royal Societies of London which, through their respective secretaries, provided me with whatever pertinent material they had. To all of these I owe a debt of gratitude for their graciousness in supplying me with material otherwise unavailable.

The frontispiece has been reproduced by permission of The

Linnean Society of London from a portrait of Mivart presented to the Society in 1901.

There are also those whose aid was less specific although no less important: Dr. Loren C. Eiseley, Provost of the University of Pennsylvania, to whose influence I owe my interest not only in the history of science but in the men who made it, and who arranged for funds from the Research Fund of the Department of Anthropology to aid in this study; Dr. and Mrs. A. I. Hallowell and Dr. Samuel N. Kramer, who talked me through my difficulties and, through their enthusiasm, urged me on; Dr. Hughbert Hamilton, editor of Temple University Publications, without whose advice this account of Mivart would exist only in the privacy of the manuscript; and Miss Elisabeth Shoemaker, of Columbia University Press.

No work of this sort could have been done without the aid of libraries. The Sullivan Memorial Library of Temple University, particularly its reference division, provided a base of operations, securing for me those sources not locally available. The libraries of the University of Pennsylvania, Villanova College, the Philadelphia Academy of Natural Sciences, and Georgetown University of Washington, D. C., were also valuable sources of help and reference.

CONTENTS

A Conscience in Conflict

THE LIFE OF

ST. GEORGE JACKSON MIVART

PROLOGUE

Less than a year before the funeral caisson of Queen Victoria rolled heavily through London's streets, there had been another death and another burial. On April 7, 1900, a windswept, squally day in London, a small band, self-conscious in its grief and duty, almost tragic in its semisecrecy, accompanied the body of St. George Mivart to the unhallowed catacombs of Kensal Green Cemetery where, without benefit of clergy, in almost dull simplicity, the service was hurriedly completed.

Ex umbris et imaginibus in veritatem read the inscription on his coffin. Out of the shadows into truth. How fitting an epitaph for the life of a man! How much more fitting for that of a scientist of Victoria's reign, pressing through the shades of traditional myth and prejudice in his search for truth.

The muffled roll of the drums accompanying Victoria's funeral cortege signaled the end of one of the most remarkable eras in the history of man. During the more than sixty years of her reign the face of western civilization had changed even as had that of England's queen. In the arts, in science, in politics and social awareness, in man's whole conception of his worth, his purpose, and his place, the world of the newborn twentieth century was far different from the world of Victoria's birth and subsequent coronation. The long—sometimes apparently endless—rule of Victoria spanned a period of birth and growth and transition of such magnitude and significance that its fertility as a source of investigations into human history and culture is almost inexhaustible.

But history is not made by a single monarch, even one so illustrious as Victoria. She was but a symbol of the millions of persons who were born, who lived out their lives, who worked and thought and fought, who died, while she occupied the throne. The history of man is a history of men, each of whom—some less, some more—contributed to, as each reflected, that stream of time and human events that we call history. The character of an age is the product of those who lived it. The life of St. George Mivart fits the Victorian era. Born a decade before its opening, he died at its close. In all his life, in the work he did and in the controversies in which he engaged, he reflected the conflicting currents of thought and feeling which marked the age. He was both scientist and theist; and as both he was righteous. In all, he was a Victorian.

I. CONVERSION

From a social, political, and economic point of view, England, in the year 1827, was on the verge of a great transformation. She was poised, in a superficial calm, between a period that had all but passed—a period of landed estates and agrarian aristocracy—and those furious years which marked the first culmination of the Industrial Revolution. But like a chrysalis emerging from its sheltering cocoon as it feels the promptings of spring, England, buffeted by the winds from a radically changing world scene, was beginning to stir from the comfortable complacency of its tradition-bound agricultural past.

The natural sciences reflected the apparent stability of the social order. The divine system embodying truth was still the goal of the natural philosopher. Physics and astronomy, the twin majesties of eighteenth-century science, still maintained their hegemony in the hierarchy of natural philosophy; but the laws of physics, the knowledge of mechanics, which had during the preceding two centuries so patiently been brought to bear upon the workings of the universe, had not as yet been applied to living forms.

Organic chemistry, the knowledge of which provided the key for the explanation of fundamental life processes, was still veiled by the darkness of ignorance. The whole area of physiology and the essential identity of the utilization and conservation of energy in both organic and inorganic substances were as yet part of the future.

Hardly sciences at all, biology and geology, from whose data much of the distinction of nineteenth-century science was derived, were still heavily impregnated with theological meanings;

and they were yet the fields of dilettantes and amateurs most of whom sought through their efforts to glorify a personal, omnipresent, omnipotent, and often capricious God. Cuvier was still alive, the last great representative of the eighteenth-century naturalist; and his influence was still the most powerful of any man in the field of science. And Lamarck was still alive, that neglected genius, blind and forgotten, his theories of transformation born too soon to disturb the illusory calm.

Signs of change there were. Genesis was weakening in the face of the pressures of a developing geology.[1] While modified hypotheses of cataclysm and catastrophe were to remain respectable for a generation, the common-sense geology of the uniformitarian was about to reach its maturity through the facile pen of Lyell. Von Baer was opening the world of embryology which was to become one of the solid buttresses of the new biology. The sciences of life were being born.

More significant, however, than the embryonic developments in any particular field of science was the slow emergence of a different approach to the phenomena of nature, a new point of view, a new methodology. The truths—absolute and divine— born of the mind, the goal of the eighteenth-century natural philosopher, slowly gave way to the finite truths of the senses. The laboratory—whatever its dimensions—was replacing the study.

Science in the nineteenth century was undoubtedly successful. It was to open up a world of miracles beside which those of the medieval world paled into insignificance. But the miracles were illusory. When fixed with the eye of the investigator, when viewed with the aid of the new methodology, the miracles ordered themselves into law; but in their orderliness they lost none of their wonder. At times the urge to make laws sped too fast and a host of ideas and theories emerged—each supposedly the answer, the solution to the ever-present puzzle of Nature. Like a child with a jigsaw puzzle, half of whose pieces are missing, the scientist of the nineteenth century sought the solution with the confidence of a confident age but, because of the lack of some pieces and the distortion of others, he often failed. Failure, however, was but the price of progress, a tentative detour on the road to perfection. Huxley expressed the spirit of the new age of science when, just prior to the publication of Darwin's *Origin,* he wrote enthusiastically to Hooker: "I look forward to a great revolution being effected. Depend upon it, in natural history, as in everything else, when the English mind fully determines to work a thing out, it will do it better than any other. I firmly believe in the advent of an English epoch in science and art, which will lick the Augustan . . . into fits." [2] With this new apostle's creed as the watchword, there could be little room for the doubter whose uncertainties were translated into a querulous criticism.

It was during this period of transition, in the years of superficial intellectual calm signaling the imminence of change, that St. George Jackson Mivart was born. Neither a true son of the Enlightenment nor yet the child of that hardheaded, work-ridden utilitarianism precipitated by a maturing English industrialism, he later showed inconsistencies in belief and action that reflected the intellectual crises and conflicts of his time.

Many of Mivart's interests, particularly as they apply to the natural world, are traceable to his father, James Edward Mivart, who also gave him the means to indulge them.

Born in 1771,[3] the elder Mivart was for several years employed as a chef in the house of one of the great English country families; and in this period of gustatory excellence he became famous. Capitalizing on both his fame and his abilities, he invested his savings in 1816 in the construction of a small private hotel in Grosvenor Square which was later to become the celebrated Claridge's of London. Here Mivart was born, the fourth child, on November 30, 1827.

The elder Mivart's venture into the hotel business was a successful and profitable one, as the Mivart Hotel soon became famous, like its successor, as the temporary residence of nobility and royalty, a hotel one of whose unique features was the possession of a bathroom. Added to his acumen as both successful businessman and host, however, was a keen interest in the intellectual and social developments of his day; and it was from these interests that his son derived his early acquaintance with the scientific and literary world of his later years. But the Mivart home, like so many of this period and this class, was torn by the often conflicting currents of the worldly sophistication of the father and the religious orthodoxy of a retiring mother.

Mivart was born in his parents' middle age; his father was forty-seven and his mother forty-two, and for both it was a second marriage. James Mivart was a man of the world, well traveled and cosmopolitan. He loved the theater and, an amateur actor himself, formed fast friendships with members of the theatrical profession. Mivart's mother, on the other hand, had a character the antithesis of her husband's. Of Scotch and Irish descent, Caroline Georgina Cunningham was of the stuff of which the Victorian reaction was made. "She was," goes the description of one who knew her, "of strongly religious bias, and in the later years at Brook Street, rather uneasy in her somewhat lively surroundings. Like her husband she had a decided inclination for literature, and a curiously retentive memory. . . . She was of a very charitable disposition, giving freely to the poor, and spending much time in visiting the sick and needy." [4]

The influence of an indulgent and intellectually stimulating father is unmistakable in Mivart's life and was frequently acknowledged by him. James Mivart was the guide whose own interests are mirrored over and over again in the activities of the son. He was the enlightened cosmopolite who, through his own varied acquaintances and activities, set the pattern for his son's intellectual development. In short, it was from his father that Mivart derived his zest for learning as well as the wherewithal to make his life a continuing process of that cultivation of knowledge which was to him the ultimate goal of civilized man. It was something more than stereotyped filial devotion which prompted Mivart toward the end of his life to dedicate one of his last books "To the dear memory of my father James Edward Mivart, who by his toil freed me from sordid cares while he ever encouraged me to love and work for science." [5] Here, as in many cases, the boy was father to the man.

Mivart's boyhood was a peripatetic one as he moved through the prescribed educational stages of the time. From a ladies' school at the age of six to Mr. Dempster's and the Clapham School of Dr. Laing the boy moved on, interested more in the position of the meat course on the menu than in Latin verbs, remembering more the discipline of the stomach than that of the intellect. But there was fun too—trips to the theater with his father; a boyhood trip to France with his family, every detail of which he was able to recall long afterwards; and the boyish acquaintance with the famous figures of continental aristocracy as they rested in the elegance of his father's hotel.

And then there was his natural history and his collecting, the great joy of his early years as it was the mainstay of his later life. "My taste for Zoology," Mivart later wrote in a rare mood of reminiscence,

led me to begin to form a little collection. From my earliest years I had this love which was greatly developed by the following circumstances: My father had had presented to him Queen Caroline of Brunswick's copy of the large original edition of Buffon's Histoire Naturelle and this was readily accessible to me. I was very fond of examining the plates, and early began to copy some. Again and again I began to write a book of Natural History myself, always leading off with 'the lion' though I had a great liking for apes. I copied not only external forms but also anatomical figures. It was in the colouring of two figures of tigers that I first found out my colour blindness. . . . My earliest animal pet was a little smooth terrier "Trip," which was kept at Addison Road, but about this time I got my first monkey, a macaque, afterwards followed by a cebus, a marmoset and a green monkey. As I grew older my father encouraged my taste for natural history, allowing me to buy specimens freely, considering our means. He used to go with me now and then to Stevens' Auction Rooms, King Street, Covent Garden, and bid for me and allow me to bid. I thus began my ultimately fine collection of reptiles. On one occasion we returned from Paris with a variety of mammalian skins and an excellent named collection of coleoptera. My father not only encouraged me but opposed those who would have discouraged me. . . . [6]

From his father's friends he often received the kindly and sometimes patronizing instructional favors granted the young by the old. Yarrell the naturalist, Waterhouse, secretary to the Zoological Society of London, the prolific Dr. Gray of the British Museum, Gould the ornithologist, C. Linnaeus Martin, Lord Farnham, and finally Richard Owen himself—all these were the masters of pre-Darwinian natural history in England. His whole childhood was a circle of circumstances which, ringing him and capitalizing on his interests, thrust Mivart into the still peaceful arena of science.

A scientist—more particularly a naturalist—he was to become, but it was a slow process, indirect, haphazard, and undisciplined. In these still early years of the nineteenth century there was no direct road to the goal of naturalist. For most the pursuit of the life sciences was the hobby of gentlemen, the avocation of physicians, or the labor of experienced handymen, working under the direction of others. The place of natural science was reflected in the training of its practitioners. An occasional course at the university in systematic botany or zoology (biology itself was a word unused and meaningless), a few lectures in geology, or an apprenticeship in an anatomy laboratory—these were the heterogeneous matrices from which the giants of modern biology emerged. For some few there were the collecting excursions and expeditions—always fraught with sacrifice—which tempered the searcher of nature in the fires of unknown and uncharted intellectual experiences whose perils formed that discipline and intellectual independence which was the mark of the great naturalist. In sum, it was a disorganized kind of training, where each could be his own master, subject only to the dictates of observation joined with reason.

To spend his life in the service of science, to follow the path of the Grays, the Owens, the Waterhouses, and the Buffons was undoubtedly Mivart's ultimate goal. But there were the nearer, the stronger, the more cloying demands of position and social fitness. Son of a tradesman with means and reputation, Mivart required the status of gentleman, a social step whose inevitability was assumed. For this, there was the more formal and more traditional education of the public schools and the universities.

After attending Clapham, therefore, Mivart moved on to Harrow. But here his stay was short and disappointing; he "learnt nothing" during his ten-month stay except to escape the hazing of older boys. A few brief months followed at Clapham Grammar School "where I was nearer to my parents' reach as my health was unsatisfactory." And then on to King's College at London to prepare for Oxford. All of this was a normal educational process and one increasingly characteristic in the lives of many young men of his circumstances and of his day.

2

This quite normal and relatively easy path to prestige and position in English society was, however, blocked when in 1844, at the age of sixteen, Mivart entered the communion of the Roman Catholic Church. So significant was this act of adolescence for Mivart's future that it must be regarded as one of the major events of his life. A generation later an act such as this would have had little consequence and would have occasioned little concern. But in England of the 1840s the Catholic community was not yet recovered from a host of legal and popular discriminatory practices which have been the lot of the religious minority of many nations in many times.

Although the Catholic population at this time was small—certainly no more than a hundred thousand in all of England—the tradition established in the time of Henry VIII and Elizabeth I subjected members of the faith to a complex of social, political, and educational restrictions. In the 1840s, while Catholics had only recently been granted the right to hold political office or to accept commissions in the army, they, like the Dissenters, were still excluded, both as teachers and students, from the universities. In addition, even in the enlightenment of the nineteenth century, Catholics were occasionally the victims of popular persecution. The Catholic community formed a small isolated enclave, regarded, and to a certain extent regarding itself, as "wholly external to English society." Movingly, Newman later described the pathetic appearance presented by these Catholic remnants in the early nineteenth century:

One and all of us can bear witness to the fact of the utter contempt into which Catholicism had fallen by the time that we were born. . . . No longer the Catholic Church in the country—nay, no longer, I may say, a Catholic community; but a few adherents of the old religion, moving silently and sorrowfully about, as memorials of what had been. "The Roman Catholics"—not a sect, not even an interest, as men conceived it; not a body, however small, representative of the great communion abroad—but a mere handful of individuals, who might be counted like the pebbles and *detritus* of the great deluge, and who, forsooth, merely happened to retain a creed which, in its day indeed, was the profession of a Church. Here, a set of poor Irishmen, coming and going at harvest time, or a colony of them lodged in a miserable quarter of the vast metropolis. There, perhaps, an elderly person seen walking in the streets, grave and solitary, and strange, though noble in bearing, and said to be of good family, and a "Roman Catholic." An old-fashioned house of gloomy appearance, closed in with high walls, with an iron gate and yews, and the report attaching to it that "Roman Catholics" lived there; but who they were or what they did, or what was meant by calling them Roman Catholics, no one could tell—though it had an unpleasant sound, and told of form and superstition. . . . Such were Catholics in England, found in corners, and alleys, and cellars, and the housetops, or in the recesses of the country; cut off from the populous world around them, and dimly seen, as if through a mist, or in a twilight, as ghosts flitting to and fro, by the high Protestants, the lords of the earth. At length so feeble did they become, so utterly contemptible, that contempt gave birth to pity, and the more generous of their tyrants actually began to wish to bestow upon them some favour. . . .[7]

Subject to an ecclesiastical hierarchy responsible only to Rome, the Catholic community had its own educational institutions, its own values and its own seemingly vain hopes for the eventual conversion of England and the restoration of the pre-Elizabethan condition of Roman Catholic universality.

Mivart's conversion, while still in his teens, to this faith of no social standing whose members were so isolated by the various restrictive practices to which they were subject was the most significant act of his early years. And yet it was essentially the act of a romantic adolescent hungering as did so many during these years for a faith that was absolute and true.

The period of Mivart's youth was one of religious questioning and controversy. The Catholic question was of increasing importance; it was a manifestation of the growing schism between the secularity of "Low Church" Anglicans and the ritual mysteries of the High Church party. The Tractarians of Oxford with Newman as their intellectual leader were inevitably moving from the mundane practicality of an Anglicanism under Low Church influence toward the pomp and traditional catholicity of Rome. In the utilitarianism of the burgeoning Victorian age, Catholicism seemed the last refuge for the faith of the romantic spirit.

Mivart's conversion illustrates the attraction which, in one form or another, Catholicism—whether that of the Pope or of Pusey—had for so many. For the dons of Oxford, the steps, slow and hesitant as they were, toward Rome were guided by reason; Mivart, however, was borne to his conversion by the strength of his adolescent emotions. The strong evangelical piety of his mother had surrounded him; but it was not enough to satisfy the need for the aesthetic trappings of his theistic beliefs. For him his conversion represented a choice of the container for his theism. Even in his later years when his devotion to Catholicism was demonstrated in his every act, it was the externals of the Church—its rituals, its language, and its architecture—which chiefly concerned him.

Throughout 1842 and 1843, both at Clapham and at King's College, he was often in the company of Tractarians. Ward, Wingfield, Oakley, and Brewer—intellectual giants to the boy not yet a man. Each was, in his own way, talking through the difficulties of conversion. And from each Mivart heard the arguments, the condemnations, the rationalizations, the dreams.

By late 1843 his decision had virtually been made, requiring only the occasion. While at King's College he boarded with Dr. Brewer who "professed to hold all Roman doctrines except that of Papal Supremacy." But still it was Anglicanism. "At this time," Mivart noted years later, "I had gone so far as to have a *Garden of the Soul* and I habitually said the "Memorare", though I duly attended Anglican worship. I recollect receiving Communion with great devotion at St. Paul's Knightsbridge, indeed, I have rarely felt greater devotion since." [8] In donning the finery of the High Church, he had begun his conversion.

During the spring of 1844, having read Pugin's [9] architectural arguments in favor of Catholicism, Mivart decided on a tour of the Catholic churches recently built under the influence of

Pugin's Neo-Gothic style.   He had "hungered and thirsted" to see these; and he also desired "to obtain some practical knowledge of the Catholic Church, to understand its working, and to make acquaintance with some members of its clergy." Symbolically, the tour began on Easter Monday in Birmingham whose St. Chad's was the first Catholic cathedral consecrated in England since the Reformation.   While the exterior was a "little disappointing," the over-all effect surpassed his expectations.

As he examined with satisfaction the adjoining bishop's house, the Reverend John Moore, head priest of the mission, entered.   After introductions, he asked, "Are you a Catholic?"

"No."

"Why not?"

"I hardly know."

The final step had almost been taken.   Mivart had already "almost" convinced himself of the truth of Catholicism and "but few difficulties remained." [10]

The tour continued.   The Convent of the Sisters of Mercy at Handsworth with Father Moore as guide and discussant, the Church of St. Giles at Cheadle, Alton Towers, Lichfield Cathedral, and then, advised by Father Moore, Nottingham. Here he dined with Bishops Walsh and Wiseman, the leaders of the Catholic mission in England.   With them as guides he visited the Church of St. Barnabas and then went by train to Derby and the Church there.   Returning to Birmingham, again with Father Moore as guide, he visited the Catholic College at Oscott, which was to be the central retreat for the converts from the Oxford Movement.

When this short tour ended at Oscott the conversion was virtually accomplished.   Back in London, Mivart searched his soul while he attended both Protestant and Catholic services, one sometimes immediately following the other.   It was a period of turmoil made no less difficult by the concern of his parents over the move which appeared imminent.   Indignant in the face of the contemplated conversion, his father threatened to disown him should he become a Catholic.   "But I felt he was much too kind and indulgent to carry out any such threat, however much he might mean it when he said it." [11]

"On May 24th I went to St. Bernard's Cistercian Monastery. . . . A lay brother showed me around and I saw Father Bernard Palmer, the prior. I was much impressed with the air of reality about the whole thing. After my visit I went on to Birmingham where, on the morning of the 25th, Mr. Moore all but persuaded me to become a Catholic there and then." Instead Mivart wrote his parents telling them of his decision and waited in the bishop's house for the inevitable reaction.

On the 27th, while sitting at dinner in the refectory, I was called to my mother who had come down by the first available train full of distress and anxiety. So great was her trouble that I could not refuse to return home with her and wait a little. Delighted at my consent, she very willingly went with me to see the church which I was very anxious should, as well as the clergy, impress her favourably. The church did please her, as also did the Rev. Mr. Leith, whom we found at prayer within it. . . . She seemed to like all except Mr. Moore, whom she very naturally distrusted, saying he looked "a regular Jesuit."

On the 28th we returned to Brook Street where I endeavoured to please my father and mother as much as possible, and at their request went to call on our parish minister, the Rev. Mr. Cooper, at his house, to listen to all his arguments against the Church of Rome. I was amazed, and am so still, at my own success with him. He seemed unable to reply to my arguments, and gave my father to understand that his opinion was that my father had better let me go as it seemed to be God's Will.

On June 1st, my father received a letter from Dr. Wiseman which, coming as it did upon Mr. Cooper's expression of opinion, decided him to let me go. Accordingly I set off as quickly as possible for the third time. . . . My father having been called away to the City on some important business, I could not see him before I left home. To my great joy, however, he came to Euston Square Station and saw me. I was in the train about to start when he appeared and said very kindly, "I felt I must come and say, God bless you, before you left London."

On my arrival at Birmingham I was welcomed at the Bishop's house and there remained. . . . [12]

On the following day, Mivart declared his faith in the Roman Catholic Church. The act of conversion was a public event.

Nervously, after High Mass, he faced the congregation of St. Chad's. Standing beneath the arch of the rood screen, dwarfed by the magnificence of Pugin's Gothic interior, he read out the articles of the Creed of Pius IV, concluding with the powerful commitment, "I do, at this present, freely profess and truly hold this true Catholic faith, without which no one can be saved; and I promise most constantly to retain and confess the same entire and inviolate, with God's assistance, to the end of my life. And I will take care, as far as in me lies, that it shall be taught, and preached by my subjects, or by those the care of whom shall appertain to me in my office. This I promise, vow and swear—so help me God, and these holy Gospels of God." [13]

It was done.

The congregation crowded round to have a nearer view of this young convert to their disabilities. For Mivart the conclusion of this sacred profession was the end of his search; he had found a faith. The waverings of his adolescence had ceased; he knew the rock which was to be his lifelong refuge and the reference point for all he was to do and be.

Mivart's conversion made attendance at Oxford—or any other university—impossible; for attendance at these still required a religious test as prerequisite. Consequently, after a two-month tour of France, with Father Moore again as both companion and guide, he took up residence, on October 21, 1844, at St. Mary's College at Oscott. Six years before St. Mary's had been rebuilt to serve as one of the few parochial colleges in England designed to rekindle "the zeal and piety of a community which had become worn out by the penal laws and was too much disposed to a policy of compromise with their Protestant neighbours." [14] Its program according to the Catholic Directory for 1843 was described as embracing "besides the classical languages, French, Italian, and German, which are taught to all who pursue the ordinary course of studies, mathematics and natural philosophy, assisted by very complete apparatus, as well as history, geography, elocution, and other branches of learning, becoming either a scholar or gentleman. . . ." It was for English Catholicism more than a college. The missionary zeal of its president, Nicholas Wiseman, later first archbishop under the reconstituted English Catholic hierarchy, made of St. Mary's a congregating place as well as a haven for many of the converts from the Oxford Movement. Here it was that they received their instruction prior to their final confirmation. In the published records for 1845 one can read: [15]

This was a memorable year in the history of Oscott on account of the large number of converts from the established church to whom Oscott opened her hospitable doors. On the 11th of May, Bishop Wiseman administered the Sacrament of Confirmation to Benjamin Bitland and St. George Mivart, and on the 15th of August, to William Ward, John D. Dalgairns, Frederick Bowles, and Richard Stanton. The 9th of October [to] Newman [who] was conditionally baptized at Littlemore by Fr. Dominic.

These are names which were the symbols of a revivified Catholicism in England in the later nineteenth century.

3

Mivart's stay at Oscott was not a long one, for on January 15, 1846, he began the study of law at Lincoln's Inn, one of the four Inns of Court in London devoted to the training of barristers-at-law. Five years later, on January 30, 1851, he was called to the bar after having fulfilled the requirements for the degree of barrister-at-law.

What prompted Mivart to a career in law can only be a matter of conjecture, although one may see in the England and its values of the mid-nineteenth century certain pressures which tended to impel him toward a course of study seemingly so alien to his professed interests in science, architecture, and history.

Within the new class structure which had crystallized as a consequence of the impact of an urban-centered industrialism upon a rural aristocracy, membership in a particular class carried with it certain behavioral requirements and restrictions. Some of these were theoretically economic, manifesting themselves in a limitation of the fields of occupational activity. For a gentleman of the rising middle class, to whom a profession for financial reward was of little concern, the work in which he was engaged was a matter of prestige rather than one of financial reward. The professions suitable for an English gentleman were law, medicine, and the ministry.[16] Natural science, at best, was regarded more as an adjunct of medicine than as a science in its own right.

Of the acceptable professions, only law was open to Mivart, whose father's success had made him a gentleman. Since careers in both medicine and the church required attendance at a university, these professions, for all practical purposes, were closed to Catholics. Only the institutions of legal education, the Inns of Court, traditionally independent of governmental affiliation and control, required no religious test for membership.

As voluntary associations, the Inns of Court acted as clubs, additions to whose personnel required only the approval of the membership. Lincoln's Inn, like the three other Inns of Court in London, demanded only that the candidate be personally "known . . . as a gentleman of character and responsibility," and that he be believed "to be a fit person to be admitted a Member of the Honourable Society of Lincoln's Inn, and be called to the Bar." [17]

Although the availability of a legal education in his suddenly restricted sphere of professional activity may well have been the primary factor in Mivart's turn to law, a still more personal element may be considered. Both the character of the course of study and the traditions which surrounded the Inns of Court were such that they may have had a strong appeal to the young man in his late teens on whom the artistic and religious traditions of the Middle Ages had made so strong an impression.

Preparation for admittance to the bar at the Inns of Court was a leisurely affair. These law schools, never formally organized, had a medieval origin and flavor. Aside from certain financial obligations, formal requirements were few, each student gaining the greater part of his education in the law through private study. During Mivart's stay as a student at Lincoln's Inn, a new regulation stipulated only "that Students of this Inn, having attained the age of twenty-three years, may be called to the Bar after the expiration of five years from admission, twelve terms having been kept, nine exercises performed and a Certificate produced of attendance on two courses of Lectures." [18] Although by contemporary definition these requirements appear somewhat strict, in actual fact they were not. To "keep a term" the student had only to dine three times in the Common Hall of the Inn; the exercises at Lincoln's Inn were formal presentations in Norman French before four barristers. Even in Mivart's day, "these exercises [were] a mere matter of form, retained for the purpose of making the bar acquainted with the names and persons of the students." [19]

There was an emotionally satisfying flavor about such a course, apart from all considerations of financial and social gain which might derive from its completion. And in Lincoln's Inn Mivart found a direct link with the past to which he was so much addicted. For in addition to the traditional character of the legal curriculum and the panoply with which it was conducted, Lincoln's Inn, alone of all the Inns of Court, occupied the site and the buildings of a medieval abbey. Here perhaps he could experience vicariously a partial fulfilment of longings half expressed years later when, in a letter to Wilfrid Meynell, he wrote: "In my wanderings I have halted on the banks of the Dart and there made acquaintance with Buckfast Abbey and its edifying monks. If ever I become a monk it is there I shall plant myself. I am much interested in the place." [20]

Having achieved the degree—and the distinction—of barrister-at-law, Mivart appears never to have practiced the profession for which he was formally prepared.

He soon returned to the study of science, admittedly his first and lifelong love. In his too-short sketch of his friend, A. R. Wallace remarked:

Even more than Darwin, Mivart was almost a self-taught biologist. . . . When about five and twenty, he began to take an interest in anatomy, and determined to study it systematically; and he one day told me that when he announced his intention, his father remarked, "Well, you never have earned a penny yet, and I suppose you never will." This rather put him on his mettle, and shortly afterwards he wrote an article for some periodical,[21] and on receiving a liberal honorarium he produced the cheque, jokingly telling his father he had earned it to prove that his prediction was a wrong one.[22]

From anatomy he moved on to comparative anatomy and eventually to systematic zoology, the field to which most of his later scientific papers and monographs have reference. It was from this threefold foundation that he later developed his interests in and contributions to what he referred to as "philosophical anatomy," which in modern terms would be called "theoretical biology."

The sources of these interests appear much earlier, however. Buffon, philosopher as well as depicter of Nature, had been one of his boyhood heroes; and his father's fellowship in the Zoological Society provided the means for instruction and counsel from its professional staff. Waterhouse gave him lessons in mammalian zoology, C. Linnaeus Martin provided him "elementary notions" of physiology and comparative anatomy, and Charles Pritchard introduced him to botany at Clapham. Haphazard and unplanned as his scientific instruction was during his boyhood, it was more rounded than that received by the great majority of his contemporaries.

The most important influence of these early years, however, was undoubtedly that of Richard Owen, the Cuvier of English science, the most able naturalist of his generation. This association too was the result of the scientific interest of Mivart's father. The nature of the association may be gleaned from a note which Mivart wrote to Owen in 1880, long after the system of Owen had been submerged by the new biology of Darwin's disciples. "In the year 1846," he wrote, "I used to tease you with questions on comparative anatomy. Time does not seem to alter our relations . . . though I regret to say I do not see you as often now as I did then." [23] The relationship established as a young man was never lost; it was one of the most powerful directives in Mivart's subsequent work in science, in religion, and in philosophy. The authority of Owen was not infrequently invoked to buttress some new fact that had been observed or some disputed thesis.

From Owen directly, as from Buffon indirectly, Mivart derived not only an immense amount of technical data but also a point of view toward the world of nature which he never lost and the importance of which he stresses in a tribute written in

1893. "By the clear and emphatic distinction he made between *Analogy* and *Homology*," he wrote of the recently deceased Owen, "by his account of special and general homologies, and by his exposition of serial and lateral homologies, he spread abroad in England the perception that a deep significance underlies the structure of animals—a significance for which no stress or strain, and no influence of heredity, and certainly no mere practical utility, can account." [24]

Like a sudden clarifying inspiration, the concept of analogy and homology—particularly the latter—provided the young philosophical-minded Mivart with a plan by which the individual data with which he was so abundantly familiar could be arranged. As Darwin's doctrine of evolution was the generalization through which Huxley could bring meaning and order to his data, so, in the generalizations of Owen, Mivart found the purpose which clothed with flesh the skeleton formed of the isolated facts of comparative anatomy.

The mystery and latent meaning of homologies within the individual organism—lateral, serial, and vertical—were to entrance Mivart throughout his scientific lifetime. There is hardly a general publication of his in the field of biology in which he does not stress the importance of this concept for an understanding of the origin of species, of the development of life, of life itself. He scanned the literature of pathology to find instances by which he could show the intimate relationship existing between symmetrically arranged segments of the organism. Such relationships and the symmetry which they expressed were for him a final blow to any purely utilitarian, environmental, or secular explanation of the organization and development of the organism. They implied rather a mysterious internal plan which operated to create through some inner control a harmoniously structured individual. And just as the homologies evident *within* the organism testified to some so far incomprehensible planning agent or device, so did the homologies demonstrable *between* organisms of different species, orders, and classes testify to some similar—perhaps identical—guiding plan throughout the organic universe. On the basis of the evidence derived from both intra- and inter-individual homologies, Mivart felt that no mere interaction between organism and environment was capable of producing such phenomena; rather it appeared to him "that each organism has an innate tendency to develop in a symmetrical manner, and that this tendency is controlled and subordinated by the action of external conditions, and not that this symmetry is superinduced *ab externo.* In fact, . . . each organism has its own internal and special laws of growth and development." [25]

Much more than the significant concepts of analogy and homology did he derive from Owen. The concept of an inherent tendency of organisms to change irrespective of external conditions, the keystone of Mivart's evolutionary structure, was itself fully expressed by Owen in his *Anatomy of Vertebrates* and, indeed, had been anticipated by various statements of Owen's during the preceding decade. Despite protestations that he arrived at this view "in complete independence," it is not improbable that in this too Mivart reflected the philosophical views of Owen, who, like his protégé, felt constrained, in the final analysis, to explain his data in terms of his own theological conceptions. Even his belief in evolution as a general principle of nature and his subsequent ready acceptance of its general affirmation in Darwin's *Origin* may have their source in his intellectual and personal ties with Owen. For he writes to Owen in 1872 with respect to a forthcoming article: "I took the opportunity of doing a simple act of justice—viz: bearing witness to your distinct enunciation of the evolution of species by the operation of ordinary secondary laws before even the 'Origin of Species' saw the light—I distinctly recollect the circumstance: we were standing on the right hand side of the Museum of the College of Surgeons—the first hall you enter." [26]

Even more significant than the particular mechanisms and concepts by which Mivart ordered his data was the over-all view of nature and natural processes which he derived from Owen and which tended to support, since they were congruent with, his own theologically inspired views. Owen was essentially a direct descendant of the natural philosophers of the eighteenth century. Not content with the simple delineation and description of the phenomena apparent in the world of perceptive reality, a field in which he was an acknowledged master, he, like his predecessors, sought to merge—at times to submerge—the observational data into an all-inclusive philosophical scheme applicable to and explanatory of the whole world of nature. It is this intimate relationship between philosophy and science which was so vehemently rejected by Darwin and Huxley and their followers. While rejecting, as unsupported by all verifiable data, Owen's vertebral theory of the skull as well as his more general, but limited, theory of evolution based upon primordial archetypes, Mivart did assume the essence of all such speculations, i.e., the existence of some ill-defined, guiding agent in nature through whom the process of evolution proceeded upon its predestined path, aided by the operation of knowable secondary causes. As a compromise between the emerging science and the existing theology such a view could be extremely satisfying.

There was a considerable amount of mysticism, an enthusiastic and sometimes ecstatic approach to nature in Mivart's outlook to which the transcendental philosophical anatomy, of which Owen was the English spokesman, had an emotional appeal. This was an appeal not unlike that which drew him toward Catholicism. His was a desire to know truth; and his approach to the consummation of that desire was essentially through the use of deductive techniques and the application of broad a priori generalizations to the empirically derived data.

A decade of close association with Thomas Henry Huxley provided the balance. Although he was interested in the problems of philosophy, Huxley made every effort to effect a complete separation between philosophy and science. For him —and it is this view which marks the beginning of the new biology—a sharp line marked the border between the provinces of empirical and metaphysical knowledge; and if the latter intruded upon the former both were corrupted.

II. SCIENCE

"The first time I saw Professor Huxley," Mivart wrote late in his life, when all conflicts had been resolved by death,

was in January 1858 at the Royal Institution, where he was giving a course of lectures on *The Principles of Biology*. It is almost needless to say that his teaching, both its manner and matter, made a profound impression on me. . . . It was on the 22nd of February, 1859, that I was introduced to him in the Paleontological and Mineral Gallery of the British Museum. . . . Thenceforth I saw Professor Huxley at not infrequent intervals—as he resided in the same region—but it was not till the autumn of 1861 that neighbourly goodwill began to ripen into intimacy, and we occasionally took a walk together. On these rare and highly valued occasions I became more and more impressed with the lucidity of his thought and the admirable clearness with which he gave expression to it, with the extent and varied nature of his reading, and his evidently exceptional power of memory.[1]

The personal enthusiasm generated by these early contacts pervaded the attitude of Mivart to the spokesman of Darwinism for the rest of his life, although later disagreements, personal and philosophical, destroyed the early intimacies. It is not surprising that Huxley should have had such an effect. Who of the younger naturalists with intellects not yet chained by the rigid universe of Cuvier and Owen and their disciples could resist the ever-changing tableaux of nature which Huxley, with the *Origin* as his backdrop, so forcefully and persuasively presented? Who could resist his honesty, his obvious sincerity, in stripping all the "hollow pretense" from the scientific constructions of his dated contemporaries?

It was in the years immediately following the publication of the *Origin* that his influence on Mivart was so great; and these years reflect Huxley at his scientific best. In the prime of life, still youthful, he represented the enthusiasm of the young as they pitted their still labile hopes and aspirations against the crystallized ideologies of a generation past. These are the years of his confident battles with Owen, with Wilberforce, with the whole structure of orthodoxy and rigidity. He must have been an enchanting and—to his generation—an inspiring figure, this David, as he met the Goliaths astride the paths of a changing order. Bowed by ever recurring financial responsibilities to a rapidly growing family and inspired beyond measure by the vistas laid open to the devotee of the new biology, he threw his entire being, during these years, into his confident and competent search for truth. These were the years of his maturing and of his greatness; no later periods in his life approach this one in the creativeness of his outlook or in the zeal he displayed toward the propagation of scientific faith.

And in these years Huxley was Mivart's friend, "a good friend indeed—firm, generous, energetic, loyal and affectionate." [2] But even more than friend, he was teacher, guide, intellectual confidant, and master.

Two years after his first meeting with Huxley, Mivart became his student and attended his lectures "for years." Even as late as the early 1870s, when he had already broken with the ideological school of which Huxley was chief, and just prior to the final personal break between them, he was attending, when able, Huxley's lectures to the workingmen. Although already possessing professional competence and recognition, he still retained to some extent the status of student with Huxley. "The great value of Huxley's anatomical ideas," he wrote in his reminiscences of Huxley, "and the admirable clearness with which he explained them, led me in the autumn of 1861 to seek admission as a student to his course of lectures at the School of Mines in Jermyn Street. . . . He welcomed my application with greatest cordiality, save that he insisted I should be only an honorary student, or, rather, should assist at his lectures as a friend. I availed myself of his permission on the very next day, and subsequently attended almost all of his lectures there and elsewhere, so that he one day said to me, 'I shall call you my "constant reader." ' To be such a reader was to me an inestimable privilege, and so I shall ever consider it." [3] Years later, in attempting to recapture, after a decade of social separation, the old intimacy destroyed by his vehement rejection of Darwinism, Mivart referred to this relationship with a sense of longing. "I *read* you," he wrote to Huxley on the last day of 1886, "when the opportunity offers, as, in old times, I used to *hear* you. Do you recollect you said you used to call me your 'constant reader'?" [4] The two men were, however, too many years, too many ideas, too many bitter words apart for the classroom intimacy of the younger, perhaps better, years to return.

Mivart also noted in his remembrance of his relationship with Huxley the strengthening professional and social bonds between them and the intellectual stimulation which was their result:

My constant attendance at Huxley's lectures naturally augmented our intimacy, and family visits and social meals together further increased it. The more I knew of him, the more fond I became of him; and he was often kind enough, after a Hunterian Lecture, to politely evade the advances of others and, having disentangled himself, walk alone with me from Lincoln's Inn to St. John's Wood.

Many an amicable discussion took place between us on such subjects as serial and bilateral symmetry in animals and problems connected therewith; man's place in Nature as regards his intellectual faculty; evolution, Darwinian and other; the independent evolution of similar structures; the possibility of the medusa having been an ancestral form of man; and various questions of philosophy and religion.

It was in 1866 that he delivered a memorable address to the students of St. Mary's Hospital School,[5] and about that time a project was on foot between him, myself, Tyndall, and one or two more, to form a small scientific and philosophic club. . . . This project was a frequent subject of our discussion in our walks. The institution was sketched out on broad lines, the one qualification for membership proposed being a personal devotion to some branch of science and an interest in philosophy. . . . The project, however, fell through, though the discussions carried on about it may, I think, have in some measure helped in the development of the well-known Metaphysical Society of three years later.[6]

It was Huxley who, with Owen, aided Mivart in gaining his first professional position. It was Huxley who presided when, on November 22, 1864, Mivart read his first scientific paper before the Zoological Society of London. And it was Huxley who communicated Mivart's monograph on the appendicular skeleton of Primates to the Royal Society and successfully campaigned for the publication of that study in the scientifically exclusive *Proceedings* of that body. Referring to the latter event, Mivart wrote, "One day when I was at work at the College of Surgeons, he came to me from the Royal Society Council, and told me gaily: 'It is to be published; *totus, teres, atque rotundus!*'" [7]

Huxley's importance during this crucial decade in the development of Mivart's world-view—as in that of his whole generation—lay in his emphasis upon the primary nature of observable phenomena as truths in themselves without regard to their compatibility with preconceived hypotheses. It was through such an appeal that Mivart's philosophizing was curbed. But although Mivart could acknowledge the worth of such an approach; although he could epitomize this emphasis upon the describable detail in both his technical and popular writings, he could never deprive himself of that ultimate and universal truth as a—indeed *the*—goal of scientific investigation. Nor could he refrain from a constant flight from the facts into the tempting regions of mystical speculation. Just as many of his works illustrate his recognition of the value of the observable data, so do they demonstrate his inability to confine himself to the limits they impose.

For Huxley the function of science and the goal of the scientist were the gradual expansion, through empirical techniques, of the light of knowledge and understanding into the infinite mists of the unknown. "All human inquiry," he wrote, in a beautifully worded and movingly expressive statement of his faith,

must stop somewhere; all our knowledge and all our investigation cannot take us beyond the limits set by the finite and restricted character of our faculties, or destroy the endless unknown, which accompanies, like its shadow, the endless procession of phenomena.

So far as I can venture to offer an opinion on such a matter, the purpose of our being in existence, the highest object that human beings can set before themselves, is not the pursuit of any such chimera as the annihilation of the unknown; but it is simply the unwearied endeavour to remove its boundaries a little further from our little sphere of action.[8]

It was a utilitarian, common-sense induction, rather than a philosophical and speculative deduction, which held out the greatest hope for an understanding of the universe in which man existed.

For Mivart, however, Huxley's student and friend, that goal was rather the illumination of a known and finite intelligence —God—the proof of whose existence lay in its most perfect— and yet how imperfect!—representation, the human mind. Like Samuel Wilberforce, writing against Darwin under Owen's tutelage, he was "as sure as he was of his own existence that the God of Truth is at once the God of Nature and the God of Revelation." [9] Like the eighteenth-century rationalists, whose intellectual heir he was, philosophy and science were twin tools of the human mind, through the use of which absolute truth could be exposed to view and understanding.

The irreconcilability of these two conceptions of the task of intelligence in the post-Darwinian years was the rock upon which Mivart's attachment to the new science foundered.

2

These years of his friendship and dependence upon Huxley were the years of Mivart's apprenticeship in natural science.

It was during this period that his ties to natural science and its professional practitioners were formalized through his election into the fellowship of those scientific societies which, through the periodic exchange of ideas and information at their meetings and in their journals, provided the atmosphere in which nineteenth-century science thrived and the media through which it was expressed. A member of the Royal Institution since 1849, he became a Fellow of the Zoological Society in 1858. Four years later, on March 20, 1862, he was elected a Fellow of the Linnean Society; and, finally, he was granted a certificate of election into the Fellowship of the Royal Society of London on June 3, 1869.[10]

It was also during this decade that Mivart began his professional career as a teaching biologist. In 1862, with the recommendations of both Owen and Huxley to support his candidacy, he was appointed, first, Lecturer, and then, Professor of Comparative Anatomy at St. Mary's Hospital Medical School in London. This post he filled until his resignation twenty-two years later.

These, too, were the years of his best and most thoughtful scientific work. It was this work in his laboratory and its published results which marked Mivart as a man to watch, a biologist of promise, worthy of his teachers. The decade after his first real association with Huxley marks a period of growth during which Mivart secured by patient and painstaking research the reputation from which his later more controversial —and more speculative—pronouncements derived their support and authority. Although the tempo of his writing increased in later decades, at no later period was his competence as a researcher so apparent—as judged by both the number and quality of his published works. While the diffuse and often superficial character of many of his later writings could lead with some justification to the charge that he wrote "for mere effect," his articles and monographs of the 1860s were solid contributions to both the descriptive and theoretical aspects of biology.

From 1864, when his first article appeared, through 1870, Mivart published, alone or as a collaborator, twenty-three separate articles of technical content, most of which appeared in the *Proceedings of the Zoological Society of London*. The core of this collection, each item of which displayed Mivart's skill as comparative anatomist and/or systematist, dealt with the Primates. In this interest and emphasis, he followed, as he often did throughout his scientific life, the path pioneered by Huxley in the years immediately following the publication of the *Origin;* and he reflects the consequent interest in the structural relationships of the Primates.

In the 1860s this order of which man is so recognizably a

part was one of the least known of the mammals. Except for a few random memoirs—in the main osteological—based upon single specimens, little was known of the anthropoid apes individually; and less was known of their comparative anatomy. Huxley, in 1863, described the slow and painful accumulation of knowledge with respect to these manlike apes from the first notice they received in 1598. One need only read that relatively barren history to understand the pathos of his concluding paragraph: "Two centuries and a half have passed away [since the first mention of the great apes] . . . and it has taken nearly that time to arrive at the clear result that there are four distinct kinds of Anthropoids." [11] The paucity of information regarding the most manlike of the nonhuman Primates was more than matched by the lack of data concerning the least manlike, the lemurs.

The publication of the *Origin,* however, underscored the prevalent ignorance regarding the Primate order; for with the new philosophical bases which evolution provided the Linnaean system of classification, the Primates, as the order in which man was included, assumed a new and overriding importance. No longer was a comparative anatomy of Primates necessary only for the illumination of the eighteenth-century "chain of being." More important to those who could read with understanding the message of the *Origin* was the light that could be shed upon the origins of man; more significant was the potential solution of *that* recurring mystery in the history of the human intellect.

The new emphasis was reflected in Huxley; certainly he played a significant role in its generation. Beginning in 1860 and culminating in his *On Man's Place in Nature* in 1863 and in his Hunterian Lectures of the following year, he devoted most of his research energies to the establishment of a comparative anatomy of the Primates. Dealing primarily with the anthropoid apes, Huxley, as in most of his biological research, laid down the broad lines of investigation for other more disciplined workers to follow. As in most of his work, he also generated the enthusiasm and provided the inspiration, regardless of the value of his own specific contributions, for more detailed researches. He was a teacher in every positive sense of the word; and it was his students, his disciples who, in following the leads he provided, constructed, with a patience of which Huxley himself was incapable, the body of biological knowledge which is the glory of post-Darwinian biology.

As one of Huxley's protégés during this period of Primate interest, Mivart devoted his own research capacities primarily to the systematics of the Primates as an order; and, more particularly, to the classification, through comparative anatomy, of that little-known segment of the order to which he was to apply the collective term *Lemuroidea.*

These researches produced a series of papers and memoirs on the comparative anatomy—more particularly, comparative osteology—and the classification of Primates which, collectively, represent Mivart's most important contribution in the field of inductive biology.

Brief as it was, this series represents the most complete and comprehensive study of the osteology of the Primates for most of the century, and, with his series on the lemuroids, it established Mivart's reputation as one of the few authorities of his generation on the structural relationships within the whole of that troublesome order. Others had written osteological descriptions and had made limited comparisons between individual segments of that group; "but the valuable treatises of these authors," noted Mivart, "yet leave much to be desired, because they relate only to the highest forms of the Order, and some distinctions resulting from such limited comparisons are apt to disappear, and the anatomical value of others to decrease when the survey is considerably extended." [12] Until Mivart, no one had so thoroughly and in so much detail reviewed the osteology of the Primates.

It was through his intense knowledge of this most important but heretofore little understood order that Mivart was able to construct a definition of the Primates as valid today as it was three quarters of a century ago. [13] In 1873, with his Primate research already behind him, he characterized the varied members of that order as

unguiculate, claviculate placental mammals, with orbits encircled by bone; three kinds of teeth, at least at one time of life; brain always with a posterior lobe and calcarine fissure; the innermost digits of at least one pair of digits opposable; hallux with a flat nail or none; a well-developed caecum; penis pendulous; testes scrotal; always two pectoral mammae.[14]

Mivart's emphasis upon the skeleton reflects a limitation which he was never able to overcome and which, as the post-Darwinian years brought biology to its maturity, became an increasingly greater liability to him. Despite his acknowledged competence in osteology, he virtually ignored in his personal research the myological problems of the class in which he was so much interested—the mammals.

The reasons for such a lack of competence or interest are unclear. Whatever the reasons, however, Mivart's inability to move along with a changing biology, in which the data from dissection and microscopic anatomy were coming to supplant those from skeletal investigations as the primary focus in research, contributed to his eventual dissociation from the field of research biology as a whole.

So long as the data of biology consisted primarily of osteological descriptions and comparisons, so long as the subjects of descriptive biology were those "skin and bone" specimens contributed by the collector, so long as the ontogenetic stages of the whole organism were considered unimportant in the solution of biological problems—only so long could Mivart's emphasis on the skeleton be considered significant and valuable. And, viewed in the context of an Owen- or a Cuvier-dominated zoology, they were both significant and valuable. But in the changing intellectual milieu of the mid-nineteenth century, of which Darwinism was a single expression, it was the organism as a functioning entity, as a dynamic whole, which was the focus of investigation; any skeleton, although its description was valuable as a datum, represented simply a moment in an ever-changing continuum. It was not that skeletal studies were unimportant, but rather that their importance stemmed from an understanding of the whole organism of which the skeleton was but a part. As the static naturalism of Linnaeus and his followers gave way in the latter half of the nineteenth century to the more dynamic ecological biology inspired by and expressed in the *Origin*, interest in the skeleton, representative of the staticity of form, was gradually supplanted by an interest in a physiological anatomy which epitomized the dynamism of function.

Mivart was not unaware of the changes in conception which were infusing post-Darwinian biology with a new vigor. In adapting himself to them, however, he was a victim of his own limitations, physical and philosophical. The fact that he was color-blind undoubtedly restricted the area of his own anatomical research; but still more important were the outmoded philosophical conceptions with which he approached the study of zoology. To him a reality was a reality—whether it was the skeleton, a part of the skeleton, or the whole organism. To him, the skeleton could be significant of itself, demonstrating the laws which hold creation together; it represented a class of data equivalent to, rather than related to, the data of non-osteological anatomy. Of course, he was not alone in such a view. The techniques of specimen collecting tended to emphasize the importance of the skeleton as against the more perishable parts of the organism. It was the skeleton alone which was preserved in fossil deposits; and it was the skeleton, with sometimes the pelt, which the collector was most able to transmit. With conditions so favorable for the exploitation of the skeleton, not only in anatomical description but in system building as well, it is little wonder that this preserved core should be given so high a value.

These early studies of Mivart's in the skeletal anatomy of the Primates were valuable contributions to the swiftly expanding biology of the immediate post-Darwinian period; but their value lies in the data they provided. When used, however, as Mivart sometimes used them, as the major planks upon which to construct a theoretical system, they lose that value in the distortion of overemphasis.

Taken as a group, these Primate studies of the 1860s are essentially Darwinian in their orientation; and they lend substance to Mivart's note in 1872 that "In common with so many others, I was, at one time, a hearty and thoroughgoing disciple of Mr. Darwin, and I accepted from him the view that Natural Selection was '*the* origin of species.' It was only by degrees, and through the evidence of a multitude of biological facts, that an opposite conclusion was gradually forced upon me." [15]

He became impressed with the difficulty of developing evolutionary lines similar to those simple "family trees" which were springing up on all sides in the wake of the Darwinian impact upon systematics. To a systematics that had been essentially two-dimensional the concept of evolution added the necessary dimension of time; to a systematics in which a "natural" group depended for its being upon immediately observable structural similarities Darwinism added the criterion of genetic affinity, an affinity expressing a community of origin and relationship by descent. With evolution, these historical relationships became the focus of a classificatory scheme; and it was the structural traits which, in their similarities, affirmed these relationships through the assumed equation of similarity in form to similarity in origin.

By the time of his last Primate monograph, published in 1873, the initial Darwinian-inspired enthusiasms had already waned in the face of the difficulties of reconciling an increasingly complex body of comparative data with the starkly simple evolutionary trees. The Primates still remained "a group . . . sharply marked off from every other order of Mammals, . . . a coherent whole in spite of the diversity existing between the two subordinal sections into which it is divided." [16] But the basis for the cohesion of its diverse members was gradually shifted from a Darwinian frame of reference to an older, more traditional, more conservative Linnaean scheme.

The crucial investigative problem, the contemplation of which signalized the shift in orientation, was that of the evaluation of those hosts of differences which provide the variety within the organic universe. Mivart used his article "On *Lepilemur* and *Cheirogaleus* and the Zoological Rank of the Lemuroidea" as the means of recasting his classificatory ideas:

Experience has more and more persuaded me that the number of similar structures which have arisen independently is prodigious. The elaborate investigations of my friend Mr. Parker constantly bring before us an increasing number of complex cross relations and more and more entangled interdependencies; and I am convinced that by means of such careful and minute researches many of the genealogical trees which have been developed with the rapidity of the fabled "bean-stalk" are destined to enjoy an existence little less ephemeral. *The notion that "similarity of structure" necessarily implies "genetic affinity" can no longer be ranked as a biological* axiom (Italics mine—J. G.).[17]

Here, then, was the dilemma. Within the Darwinian context, similarities of inherited structures were assumed to be indications of community of descent; such community of descent was then the foundation upon which "natural" classificatory categories were constructed; these "natural" categories then explained the similarity of structure. Although such reasoning could be regarded as sound, it was certainly circular. One could support it by faith in the evolutionary doctrine or, scientifically, by proof that all inherited, i.e., cross-generational, traits stemmed from the same genetic source.

Mivart was not convinced by the faith argument. And he had come to regard the scientific argument as untenable in the face of the data. He had become convinced that similar structures can and do arise independently. As he searched the lost horizons from which the organic universe had sprung, he saw a multitude of paths along each of which the life forms did, on occasion, make similar adjustments to life's demands. Thus to their descendants—the raw materials of the systematist—was bequeathed a bewildering complexity of traits some of which testified to common ancestry, some of which were of independent origin, and some of which—the least puzzling of all—were unique. The introduction of this concept of parallel evolution destroyed the efficacy of the tree as a genealogical symbol. Although he had used it himself, he was forced to admit: "The affinities of the animal kingdom, or even the Mammalian class, can never be represented by the symbol of a tree. Rather, I believe, we should conceive the existence of a grove of trees, closely approximated, greatly differing in age and size, with their branches interlaced in a most complex entanglement." [18]

The possibilities of parallel development loomed so large in Mivart's thinking that he was tempted to see its importance everywhere. Reversing an earlier judgment, he noted as his final word on Primate relationships that their various defining characters "taken together . . . render it in the highest degree improbable that the Lemuroids and Apes took origin from any common root-form not equally a progenitor of other Mammalian orders. Consequently, if genetic affinity is to be our standard, the *Lemuroidea* should rank as a distinct order." [19] But he went even further in denying phylogenetic affinities. It seemed to him "highly probable" that the New World and Old World Monkeys "are no diverging offshoots from some common Ape-parents but that they have arisen in an independence as complete as that between the origin of either of them and the origin of the Lemuroids or Carnivores. . . ." [20]

If, then, the independent development of similar structures made it difficult, if not impossible, to construct a phylogeny upon genetic affinities, the promise of the Darwinians was but a chimera, offering nothing of immediate value to the practicing systematist. It was the structural relationships which must provide the basis of classification, without immediate reference to phylogeny. For Mivart the criteria of the classifier must be workability and convenience. "If any two groups of animals can easily be joined together in a larger aggregation capable of distinct definition by numerous characters, easily discernible and drawn from structures important in the economy of life, then I submit such groups should be joined, provided they do not constitute a whole inconvenient and unmanageable from the number of its subdivisions." [21] Whatever the genealogical relationships involved or suggested, the systematist can, in the one case, break down a category into separate taxonomic units if its member groups become too large to handle; or he may, in another case, join two or more separate phyla into a single taxonomic group if the smallness of their numbers justifies it.

"I would urge," he wrote as his concluding statement on classification,

that the more prudent course is to give to genetic considerations a decidedly subordinate place in questions of classification. . . . A judicious scepticism seems to me to be somewhat needed at the present moment. The considerations here advanced are by no means intended to support the assertion that views as to genetic affinity are mere dreams. Far from so believing I conceive the theory of evolution to be probably true; and, if so, real genetic affinity must exist, and when it can be securely detected must be most important. But the response of organization to need being such as it is . . . the discrimination between genetic and adaptive families must long, if not ever, continue a work of extreme delicacy and difficulty. The hasty way in which a few detected (often superficial) resemblances have of late, from time to time, been made to do duty as sufficient evidence of affinity and descent, seems to me to be unscientific as well as unphilosophical.[22]

With some justice, Mivart was attempting to curb the oversimplified excesses which flowed from the initial enthusiasm engendered by the *Origin;* but in doing so he was retreating into the security of Linnaean systematics with its concern for the elucidation of the two-dimensional, time-lacking design of the organic world.

This statement, as indeed the whole article of which it was a part, published in the *Transactions of the Zoological Society,* represents Mivart's scientific reconversion to pre-Darwinian natural history.

The theory of evolution which it espouses is so limited as to be compatible with the most rigid system of special creation. It is an evolution in a much older sense of the word, an unfolding of a preordained line of development. In sustaining it, Mivart reverted to a theoretical concept which Owen had made fashionable, the idea of the archetype as the basis for organic design. His brief but intense courtship of Darwinism was over.

III. COMPROMISE

Mivart's rejection of Darwinism did not occur as the result of a single revelatory act. It was the hardly realized end product of a growing disillusionment. To him the promises of a new biology were illusory: the new generalizations were unable to meet the test which the developing data imposed. Disillusionment with ideas is an experience harrowing enough; when coupled with the fall of heroes, it becomes soul-shaking. Mivart seems never to have forgotten the various circumstances which led to his estrangement from that body of ideas and men which was science in the later decades of the nineteenth century. In a moving passage, written towards the end of his life, he described the mental conflict which plagued him during these years:

It was in 1868 that difficulties as to the theory of Natural Selection began to take shape in my mind, and they were strongly reinforced by the arguments of one who became, and remains, as gratitude demands, a highly valued friend, whose acquaintance I made at Professor Huxley's lectures, at which love of science had also made him a regular attendant. This was the Rev. W. W. Roberts. . . . The arguments he again and again urged upon me were the difficulties, or rather the impossibilities, on the Darwinian system, of accounting for the origin of the human intellect, and above all for its moral intuitions—not its moral *sentiments,* but its ethical *judgments.*

For the rest of that year and the first half of the next I was perplexed and distressed as to what line I should take in a matter so important, and which more and more appeared to me one I was bound to enter upon controversially.

After many painful days and much meditation and discussion my mind was made up, and I felt it my duty first of all to go straight to

Professor Huxley and tell him all my thoughts, feelings, and intentions in the matter without the slightest reserve, including what it seemed to me I must do as regarded the theological aspect of the question. Never before or since have I had a more painful experience than fell to my lot in his room at the School of Mines on that 15th. of June, 1869. As soon as I had made my meaning clear, his countenance became transformed as I had never seen it. Yet he looked more sad and surprised than anything else. He was kind and gentle as he said regretfully, but most firmly, that nothing so united or severed men as questions such as those I had spoken of.

Nevertheless no positive breach took place, though the following day, as we were driving homewards together, the conversation became rather sharply controversial. Yet family friendly relations continued. . . . [1]

Huxley's concern was understandable. This was not a Wilberforce or a Gladstone or any of the petty snipers in the religious press whose theological rumblings barely concealed their scientific ignorance. This was a colleague whose competence was a product of his own tuition. This was a friend and associate who had been warmly embraced by the small company of Darwinians. Nor had Mivart provided grounds for any other view. In most biological matters he had followed Huxley, for whom, both as man and scientist, he had had the most profound respect. With Huxley's view he was generally in accord "for though I had not accepted Darwin's theory of 'Natural Selection,' I was neither its opponent nor convinced it was untenable." [2] For Darwin, with whom he corresponded and whom on occasion he entertained socially, he had the highest regard, personally and professionally. He considered himself his "admiring" and "sympathetic disciple," one whom he later felt Darwin thought "destined to be an active propagator of his special views." In these years he had friendly relations with Haeckel, the most enthusiastic of Darwin's followers, as well as with Wallace. He was a member of the circle; and it was no unreasonable hope which led Darwin and his supporters to count upon him to swell their ranks.

The difficulties to which Mivart alludes in the reminiscence of his old age were undoubtedly theological in their inspiration. More particularly they stemmed from man's position in the Darwinian universe.

With a caution the lack of which would have been the undoing of a man in his position, Darwin had consistently avoided any specific references to man in the *Origin* except for the often quoted, cryptic paragraph which concludes the work: "In the future," he prophesied, "I see open fields for far more important researches. Psychology will be securely based on the foundation already well laid by Mr. Herbert Spencer, that of the necessary acquirement of each mental power and capacity by gradation. Much light will be thrown on the origin of man and his history." [3]

The omission of man from the *Origin,* and the limitation of the treatment of evolution primarily to morphological characters, did permit one to accept, if he wished, evolution for non-humans only, despite the fact that Darwin, himself, by no means omitted man from his over-all evolutionary thinking. It was on this limited basis, however, that Mivart made his acceptance; and for doing so he had some precedent. Even Huxley, who at this time was the strongest scientific influence in Mivart's life, was loath to proceed beyond the limits set by Darwin in the *Origin*. In his *Essay on Man's Place in Nature* in 1863, in which he pointed out for the first time the close structural relations existing between man and the apes, the position he espoused was "a very guarded one, as the state of knowledge at that time demanded. All I had to say came to this—If there is reason to believe that the lower animals have come to be what they are, by a process of gradual modification; then, there is nothing in the structure of man to warrant us in denying that he may have come into existence by the gradual modification of a mammal of ape-like organization. . . ." [4]

Only to those who did not wish to recognize the implications of Huxley's researches and conclusions could such a statement be considered equivocal. It is certainly true that, despite the strength and force of his intimations, nowhere does he state with certainty that man is descended from an apelike ancestor; but the arguments for relationship—genealogical as well as structural—are so conclusive from the structural point of view that no one who agreed with evolution in principle or was in any way acquainted with such a doctrine, whatever he thought of natural selection, could mistake the implication. Certainly there were many who did not mistake it.

Such guarded statements were, for Mivart, acceptable as hypotheses—hypotheses, however, to which he himself was unwilling to subscribe wholeheartedly. His own work had indicated to him not only the close relationship existing between man and the apes, but also the possibility, if not the probability, that man *had* evolved from some apelike progenitor. His conception of the evolution of man, however, differed from that of the Darwinians in general in that it applied only to the structural or physical aspect of man as contrasted with his more important intellectual nature which could only be explained through some extra-evolutionary mechanism.

Regarding man and his origin, as in so much else of his thinking, Mivart was a curious blend of post-Darwinian evolutionist and pre-Darwinian creationist. He could, with genuine sincerity and conviction, agree with Huxley when the latter wrote, "I have endeavoured to show that no absolute structural line of demarcation, wider than that between the animals which immediately succeed us in the scale, can be drawn between the animal world and ourselves"; but with equal sincerity and conviction, he felt himself constrained to disagree with the corollary: "and I may add the expression of my belief that the attempt to draw a psychical distinction is equally futile, and that even the highest faculties of feeling and intellect begin to germinate in lower forms of life." [5] So long as the Darwinians either restricted themselves to the morphological structure of man and its evolution or regarded their hypotheses as to the origin of the whole man as hypotheses or "beliefs" and nothing more, so long as the hypothesis did not evolve into truth not through proof but "from being repeatedly spoken of, and being connected with celebrated and influential names" whereby "it is likely to be taken for very much more than it is really worth"[6] —so long and only so long was Mivart content, in the interests of a science which held all hypotheses valuable as stimulants to further research, to go along, restricting opposition to those areas subject to verifiable observation.

Neither the temper of the times, however, nor the exuberance and zeal of both investigators and theorizers was such as to permit so precarious a balance or so objective a view to remain for long. It soon became apparent that what had begun as a simple hypothesis, unverifiable (and consequently eternally tentative) except by analogy, was gradually assuming the proportions of fact through, Mivart felt, the very process which he had feared. In 1866 Ernst Haeckel published his *General Morphology*. Here for the first time was Darwinism carried to its logical extreme. Haeckel made it "the foundation of a consistent monistic philosophy," transcending science, in order to explain, with the "doctrine of descent" as the major theme, the origin and evolution of all life, not excluding man. Here were no reservations, no equivocation. Haeckel's was a simple statement of gross godless materialism, a statement which most of Darwin's critics had recognized as implicit in his more limited and less dire formulation. For Haeckel, man did not exist apart from the entire organic world; his uniqueness, no matter upon what it was thought to rest, was but a delusion. Intellectual and moral man was nothing but a reflection of physical man.

The furor which Haeckel's system aroused and the almost inevitable recognition that it was consistent with the concept of Darwinian evolution, if not, indeed, that same concept in a slightly different guise, was for Mivart of such consequence that he felt constrained to oppose such unwarranted, as he thought, extensions of the doctrine contained in the *Origin*. It was in all probability under such a compulsion that he determined to take the steps which led to his actual breach with the Darwinians, to verbalize "those questions" than which "nothing so united or severed men."

It was the "man question" which was the critical one. While for his associates the implications of the Darwinian hypothesis led inevitably to the view of the descent of man in his entirety, physical and psychical, for Mivart the passing years intensified his preoccupation with that "wonderful chasm" which separated man from his fellow Primates so that by 1871 he could maintain with some vehemence that man differed more from the gorilla than the latter did from the dust of the earth. As the chasm between man and the animal world became wider with the passing years so did the gulf in understanding and friendship between Mivart and the Darwinians.

2

Men of science often change their views, for their hypotheses are usually provisional—tentative hunches based upon the observational evidence as it exists at an immediate point in time. The validity of a hypothesis, since it often pertains to matters which are not directly verifiable, depends upon its compatibility with the ever-increasing fund of factual data for whose explanation it was formulated. The changes in Mivart's thinking, therefore, per se would not be a subject of interest—and surprise—were it not for the fact that these changes ran counter to the direction of the scientific thought of his period. There were many in the years after the publication of the *Origin* who deserted more speculative hypotheses for the apparently more realistic view which Darwin presented; but few were the apostates who, once having seen, closed their eyes to the new view of the organic universe. Of these Mivart, perhaps, was the most striking; for in his apostasy he was not content simply to abjure but, as he was to feel in his Catholicism, he felt it necessary with the zeal of the apostate to throw the weight of his knowledge and energies against the false Messiah.

But why was the reaction delayed so long? Others had detected the implications of Darwinism for the "man question" long before. The impossibility of including man within the Darwinian scheme had formed the basis of theologically inspired opposition from those emotion-packed days which first followed the publication of *Origin*. In one of the first reviews, in the influential *Quarterly Review*, the reviewer, though opposing the whole conception as eminently unscientific and unworthy of the reputation of its author, viewed with particular alarm its application to man:

First, then, he [Darwin] not obscurely declares that he applies his scheme of the action of natural selection to MAN [7] himself, as well as to the animals around him. Now we must say at once, and openly, that such a notion is absolutely incompatible not only with single expressions in the word of God on that subject of natural science with which it is not immediately concerned, but, which in our judgment is of far more importance, with the whole representation of that moral and spiritual condition of man which is its proper subject-matter. Man's derived supremacy over the earth; man's power of articulate speech; man's gift of reason; man's free-will and responsibility; man's fall and man's redemption; the incarnation of the Eternal Son; the indwelling of the Eternal Spirit,—all are equally and utterly irreconcilable with the degrading notion of the brute origin of him who was created in the image of God, and redeemed by the Eternal Son assuming to himself his nature.[8]

The cogency of such an argument was certainly as great in 1860 as it was in 1868.

The reasons for Mivart's delayed ideological response lay not so much, nor so consciously, in his broader acquaintance with the biological facts as in the changing character of the theological community of which he was so dedicated a member. As science was changing during these years, so too was Catholicism. As these were the years during which a new scientific orthodoxy was being defined, so were they the years of a definition of Catholic orthodoxy in matters mundane. In his attempt to hew to the orthodox line in each, he ended by being heterodox in both.

On the basis of what is known of his later relations with the Catholic community and the Church in England, Mivart was, after his conversion, an active and loyal son of the Church. Like most converts, he never lost the crusading zeal which so characterized the Catholic Revival in England in the 1840s; and in this zeal he felt a strong responsibility toward the pitiful remnant of English Catholicism whose adherents had for the centuries since the Reformation comprised a provincial community on the periphery of English life, social and intellectual. With the too few Catholic intellectuals of his time, free of both the unworldliness of the pure theologians and the smug complacency of the traditional Catholic gentry, he felt that the hope of his adopted faith lay not in a return to the papal authoritarianism of the Middle Ages but rather in an enlightened laity equipped to handle the increasingly more complex social, political, and intellectual problems of a changing era. In his insistence upon an enlightened Church constituency and its active participation in Church affairs he was expressing an attitude consistent with the liberal outlook of Victorian England.

Nor was this attitude an unreasonable one. At the time of Mivart's conversion there could be every hope, fostered by the liberal actions of Pope Pius IX, that the Catholic Revival in England was but a phase of a greater revival within the Church Universal. The character of the Church, however, and its thinking, as it was crystallized during the later reign of Pius IX at Rome and that of his ecclesiastical as well as ideological representative in England, Manning, Archbishop of Westminster, belied the early promise. The impact of the revolutionary developments in both the natural and historical sciences had forced the Church into a rigid and reactionary position in which it hoped to defeat, by ignoring it, the strongest threat to its existence since the Reformation.

During the early years of Mivart's Catholicism, those years in which he was drinking from the Darwinian-Huxleyan fountain, neither the character nor the direction of the Church in England had as yet been defined. "The Church in England," wrote the biographer of Manning, a central figure in its development "was in a transition state—always an uneasy, often a dangerous position. The hierarchy had not long been established.[9] Rights and duties had yet to be adjusted. Men had come into possession of new powers, the limits of which . . . had as yet to be ascertained. . . . Men's minds were in a ferment. New ideas were coming in; new principles of action; new life, or rather new developments of life struggling for expression. In the nature of things this new energy of action ended in a struggle for mastery. Equally, as a matter of course, there was action and reaction." [10] These years saw a succession of events, each minor in itself, of which the cumulative effect was to fashion a philosophical structure closed to contemporary movements in science and alien to the mundane intellectualism of a significant portion of the laity. In its failure to find a middle way between its traditional ideology and the developing liberalism in both thought and action, the Church rejected the latter entirely and retired to the security of a revived scholasticism.

The schism which split the Church in Europe and cast such a broad shadow upon the revived Catholic community in England after the reestablishment of the hierarchy was the never completely resolved and ever reemerging conflict between the liberal element and the group collectively, and sometimes loosely, termed the ultramontane. For the ultramontane faction the pope was supreme "over every part of the Church of Christ as well as every sovereign within its boundaries," [11] and his expression in any matter was regarded with the reverence due the personal representative of God on earth. For these, the unworldliness—more exactly, the otherworldliness—of the Church dominated its mundane expressions; and, with the scholastics, they regarded the secular to be subordinate to the religious—in truth, to exist only on the sufferance of spiritual authority. For the ultramontane the Church represented a temporal unity of truth. The words of the Fathers were revered because of the authority vested in them by divine power. As it was crystallized at the height of the Victorian era, the attitude of the ultramontane manifested itself in an "absolute opposition to all which they regarded as characteristic of the modern spirit." [12] In terms of the dualism between "naturalism" and "spiritualism," a dichotomy with which many were preoccupied partly as a result of the developments in science during the nineteenth century, the position of the ultramontane left no room for doubt: it was, overtly, "spiritualism" par excellence.

The liberal view, on the other hand, particularly as it was expressed by Döllinger in Germany and Acton, his disciple, in England in the late 1850s and early 1860s, emphasized the necessity, from an intellectual and worldly point of view, of grounding Catholic doctrine—and even dogma—on the solid foundation of scientific fact. To the liberal, Catholicism was a faith, the only true faith; but faith could exist, could be true, only if it were consistent with the data of objective science. In contrast to the ultramontane, the liberal sought to base his faith upon reason rather than upon authority. For the liberals it was the dogma of the Church which must conform, even to the point of change, to the facts which the newly reoriented sci-

ences of geology, biology, and biblical criticism were beginning
to divulge. Liberal Catholicism emphasized the freedom of
individual conscience and intellect as opposed to the authority
of an infallible hierarchy. In England, as in Germany, as it
was expressed by Acton and his supporters through the medium
of the short-lived and ill-fated *Rambler* and *Home and Foreign
Review,* liberal Catholicism "took the form of an intense faith
in scientific freedom, and a somewhat revolutionary campaign
on behalf of the reformation of Catholic theology in the light
of fashionable hypotheses in history as well as in physics." [13]

There can be little doubt as to Mivart's position in these
controversies which shook the Church of his adoption. He was
a liberal. And though at times he wavered in his liberalism,
he could say with sincerity a few years before his death: "Certainly as a Catholic, I have always been on the liberal side, and,
like the late Montalembert, I hope—however penitent I may
be at the last for many errors and shortcomings—to, at least,
die an 'impenitent liberal.' " [14]

He was a supporter of both the *Rambler* and the *Home and
Foreign Review,* the voices of liberal Catholicism; and years
later in a letter to Meynell he despaired of a Catholic press
which lacked such media of communication. His letters, both
to Newman and Meynell, bristle with denunciations of the
conservative leadership among Catholic laity and clergy alike.

Though numerically small, the liberals engaged the large
party of ultramontanes in a series of skirmishes during the
1850s and 1860s; despite the intellectual force of the argument
of the liberals and the articulateness of their leaders, they were
defeated by the ultramontanes at every turn. The engagement
between the two parties which perhaps affected Mivart most
was the argument that ended by assertion of the right of papal
authority to intrude in the realm of science. This intrusion,
successful against whatever opposition could be mustered, and
showing the background of the developing authoritarianism of
the Church played a great part in the transformation of Mivart
vis à vis Darwinism.

Until the mid-sixties there was hope among the intellectual
minority within the Catholic community that the developing

sciences could be made consistent with Catholic faith with gain to both, that the Catholic scientist could operate on a level of free inquiry unhampered by the restraints of antiquated doctrine. Such a hope was based upon the assumption, expressed earlier by St. Augustine, that the fields of science and theology were mutually exclusive, each existing upon and for a different level of phenomena and explanation. This optimistic view was fostered by the increasing emphasis during the early years of Pius IX upon science and a noticeable, almost extreme, de-emphasis of the scholastic approach, an approach that was always inimical to scientific investigation. Optimism was rampant among those few clerics and laymen who were familiar with the newer developments in the fields of natural science and biblical criticism. A new day seemed to be in the offing when Catholic intellectuals would—and could—argue on equal grounds with the less dogmatically circumscribed of their Protestant colleagues. If Catholicism were true, if its doctrines, teachings, and dogma were from an inspired source, it could not be damaged, but only perfected, by a knowledge of and a full participation in the scientific movements of the day. Such was the optimistic view; such was the hope.

The hope was short-lived Alarmed by the dangers for the Church implied by the ferment of Catholic intellectuals, Pius IX invoked censure.

"While Catholics," he wrote in the Munich Brief of December 21, 1863, "may cultivate these sciences safely, explain them, and render them useful and certain, on the other hand *they cannot do so if* their natural intellect, in investigating natural truth, does not supremely venerate the infallible intellect of God as revealed in Christianity" (i.e., Catholicism). In essence, "the Brief emphatically asserted the claims of scholastic theology and the Roman Congregations, as having authority even over the speculations of Catholic men of science." [15]

As he read the Brief while still under the scientific tutelage of Huxley and as he noted the suppression of Acton's *Review* for its advocacy of the liberal approach, Mivart may well have wondered as to *his* place in a science so circumscribed and a

faith so circumscribing. He may have thought bitterly, as Newman wrote in comment on the Brief:

I thought it was commonly said that Galileo's fault was that he
meddled with *theology,* and that, if he had confined himself to *scientific conclusions* he would have been let alone; but surely the language of the brief . . . is as if even men of science must keep *theological* conclusions before them in treating of *science.* Well I am
not likely to investigate in science—but I certainly could not write
a word upon the special controversies and difficulties of the day
with a view to defend religion from thinking physicists without
allowing them freedom of logic in their own science. So that, if I
understand this brief, it is simply a providential intimation to every
religious man, that, at this moment, we are simply to be silent,
while scientific investigation proceeds—and say not a word on questions of interpretation of scripture, etc., etc., when perplexed persons ask us.[16]

This was sufficient for the scientifically untutored cleric. But
what of the scientific investigator? What of *his* approach to
science?

The ring of authority was to be drawn still tighter. By 1865
Catholics in England were not even to know that science which
had been so delimited; by order of the English hierarchy, led
by Manning of the clergy and Ward of the laity, they were excluded from attendance at the universities, admission to which
had been won after so long a struggle. In vain did Mivart join
with other disturbed laymen in petitioning Rome to lift the
ban.[17] Rome was adamant; for Rome, it seemed, victory over
heresy lay in ignorance. Against such prejudice the liberals
could only rail in private. Wrote Newman, occupying, himself,
a precarious position between the ultramontanes and the liberals: "A great prelate . . . said to me years ago, when I said
that the laity needed instruction, guidance, tenderness, consideration, etc. etc. 'You do not know them, Dr. N., our laity
are a peaceable body—they are peaceable.' I understood him
to mean: 'They are grossly ignorant and unintellectual, and we
need not consult, or consult for, them at all.' . . . And at Rome
they treat them according to the tradition of the Middle Ages.
. . . Well, facts alone will slowly make them recognize the fact

of what a laity must be in the 19th century if it is to cope with Protestantism." [18]

And finally, as the last expression of ultramontane victory, "the infallible intellect of God" itself was defined and, in its definition, harshly limited. After months of wrangling over a foregone conclusion the Vatican Council in 1870 proclaimed the infallibility of the pope as a dogma of the Church. Though theoretically restricted to matters of faith, the new dogma, to which all Catholics must subscribe, interposed papal authority in matters of science.

With the promulgation by the Vatican Council of the dogma of papal infallibility, ultramontanism reigned supreme. Both politically and philosophically, the champions of Catholic liberalism had been defeated within the Church; and the return to the institutionalization of the Middle Ages had been completed. The recurrent menace of modernism had been repressed again.

Only those Catholics who were ignorant of the method and data of the modern sciences, only those for whom the world of the spirit transcended all else in importance—only they could be insensitive to the implications of the growing rigidity of the Church during the 1860s. Only those who believed that all that could be known was known could remain unaffected by the intrusion of Church authority into the area of intellectual discovery, discussion, and speculation. For the scientist, dedicated to the elucidation of the unknown, it meant that investigation could not be free but must ever be carried on against the backdrop, even in the shadow, of a traditional frame of reference in which general questions had all been posed and already had their answers. They could describe and they could clarify; but never could they change the system of explanation to which they were bound by faith and the infallibility of the leader of the Church.

For Mivart, both as a scientist and as a Catholic, the return to scholasticism was disturbing. He was aware, as the only Catholic scientist of note in England, of the charges of intolerance laid against the Church in her relations to science. Darwin himself was to charge Mivart with bigotry. Mivart well knew that to most of his colleagues science and Catholicism were mutually exclusive, that they felt that the Church regarded progress with hostility, refusing her members intellectual freedom and forbidding them science. To him, in the optimism of his middle years, such charges were libelous: there were Catholic scientists of note and it was on their contributions through the ages that modern science rested. For him the hoped-for status of the Catholic in science lay in demonstrating that, contrary to the thinking of her critics, the Church and her teachings were compatible with modern science. Through such a demonstration he hoped to convince the critic of the liberality of the Church and, conversely, to convince the Catholic of the respectability of science. England must produce Catholic scientists, who by the strength of their contributions would benefit both science and Church. The libel leveled against the Church would not be dissipated by platitudes and generalities emanating from Rome; it could only be disproved by the conscientious efforts of him who was both scientist and Catholic. It was by arguments in this vein that he persuaded Bertram Windle, upon his conversion, to continue his career as scientist. Urging Windle to serve his Church by becoming really eminent in his profession, he cautioned him to be scrupulously just and tolerant to scientific men of the "irreligious school" and to be always sympathetically expectant in the case of new theories. "You and I," he wrote to the perplexed convert, "having been through the fire, *know* that men may be, very sincerely and honestly, unbelievers. As a matter of justice, then, we ought to be tolerant and, as far as possible, sympathetic, and, as a matter of religious policy, doubly so." [19]

His advice to Windle, though given in 1884, illustrates Mivart's own problems in the years following the active intrusion of spiritual authority in the realms of science.

Confronted by the intellectual impasse produced by the apparently contradictory views of the universe provided by Darwinism on the one hand and Catholicism on the other, Mivart could resolve his own conflict only by a complete rejection of one position or a reconciliation of the two. Dedicated to both, he could reject neither. As the phenomena observable in nature, the subject matter of science, were true, so too were the data derived from revelation, the subject matter of religion, true. Since both represented truth, neither could be rejected without danger to that harmonious world of truth whose ultimate description and understanding were the goal of both scientist and theologian. Since both represented truth, albeit of different orders, the goal of the scientist as well as the religious philosopher, lay in the harmonious reconciliation of the two sets of data.

Mivart set himself the task of such reconciliation. The aim of his early contributions, he later wrote,

was to show the compatibility which I believed, and believe, to exist between the most advanced science and the most orthodox Christianity. As a faithful student of that science which from my earliest years has had an insuperable attraction for me, I have ever been careful to abate no jot or tittle of the just claims of Biology. As a loyal son of the Catholic Church I have been no less careful not to put forward one statement in the interests of conciliation which had not received the sanction of well-known and universally esteemed experts in theology. Having thus ventured to assume the responsible position of such a peace-maker upon certain very definite grounds, I should feel bound in honour and honesty to withdraw my apology and confess myself to have been mistaken if through new scientific discoveries, or fresh dogmatic decisions, those grounds ceased in my opinion to be capable of sustaining my argument.[20]

In compromise he found the middle way by which his twin allegiances could be reconciled, thus permitting him the continuance of the intellectual life than which he valued nothing more. The *Genesis of Species,* published early in 1871, is his monument of compromise. In it, confident of the correctness of his approach, he could write:

For the approximation we have of late made toward the solution of this problem [the origin of species], we are mainly indebted to the invaluable labours and active brains of Charles Darwin and Alfred Wallace.

Nevertheless, important as have been the impulse and direction given by those writers to both our observations and speculations, the solution will not (if the views here advocated are correct) ultimately present that aspect and character with which it has issued from the hands of those writers.

Neither, most certainly, will that solution agree in appearance or substance with the more or less crude conceptions which have been put forth by most of the opponents of Messrs. Darwin and Wallace.

Rather, judging from the more recent manifestations of thought on opposite sides, we may expect the development of some *tertium quid*—the resultant of forces coming from different quarters, and not coinciding in direction with any one of them.

. . . .

Signs of this conciliation are not wanting: opposite scientific views, opposite philosophical conceptions, and opposite religious beliefs, are rapidly tending, by their vigorous conflict, to evolve such a systematic and comprehensive view of the genesis of species as will completely harmonize with the teachings of science, philosophy and religion.[21]

By the end of the 1860s, the pressures from his laboratory and from his church had converged. As the doctrine of the latter made it necessary to question the philosophical implications of Darwinism, so did the work of the former open the way for a revision of the empirical statements. The way out was the construction of a new road, a middle road, the *tertium quid,* which, uniting the verities of both science and religion, would attain that truth which was the goal of both.

IV. ON THE GENESIS OF SPECIES

On the Genesis of Species, although scheduled for publication late in 1870, first appeared, with Macmillan as publisher, early in January, 1871. It was Mivart's first book, and came after a decade of preparation in the research laboratory. Like many of his later books, the *Genesis* reflects the thriftiness of Mivart as an author; for it was based upon a series of three articles entitled "Difficulties of the Theory of Natural Selection." This series, the first in which Mivart publicly proclaimed his disagreement with Darwinism, had been published a year and a half earlier in *The Month,* an influential, semipopular Catholic journal.

In writing the *Genesis,* Mivart had two main objectives. "My first object," he later wrote [1] in reply to Huxley's critical blast, "was to show that the Darwinian theory is untenable, and that natural selection is not *the* origin of species. This was and is my conviction purely as a man of science, and I maintain it upon scientific grounds only. My second object was to demonstrate that nothing even in Mr. Darwin's theory, as then put forth, and *a fortiori* in evolution generally, was necessarily antagonistic to Christianity."

While it was to the accomplishment of the first goal that the series of 1869 was dedicated, the *Genesis* had the more general task of incorporating the scientific objections to Darwinism as well as the truths which the Darwinian theory contained into an evolutionary system consistent with Catholic belief.

The scientific objections to Darwinism raised in the *Genesis* can be grouped into six major categories, each supported by a virtual catalogue of biological data:

1. *The inability of natural selection to account for the incipient stages of useful structures.* Accepting the Darwinian argument that advantageous structures were gradually built up through natural selection, Mivart asked how the original "infinitesimal" deviation from the preadaptive norm was selected out, particularly in those cases in which nothing but the already highly elaborated variation is advantageous. Thus, "if, as most Darwinians would probably assume, the primeval vertebrate creature was . . . apodal, how are the preservation and development of the first rudiments of limbs to be accounted for—such rudiments being, on the hypothesis in question, infinitesimal and functionless." [2] To explain such incipient structures required, for Mivart, either a directing force, foreseeing the development of the completed organ or, failing that, a sudden change which in one stroke produced, full-blown, that organ. "That minute, fortuitous, and indefinite [i. e. directionless] variations could have brought about such special forms and modifications . . . seems to contradict not imagination, but reason." [3] And he concluded this argument with his own, more circumscribed, conception of natural selection:

"Natural Selection", simply and by itself, is potent to explain the maintenance or the further extension and development of favorable variations, which are at once sufficiently considerable to be useful from the first to the individual possessing them. But Natural Selection utterly fails to account for the conservation and development of the minute and rudimentary beginnings, the slight and infinitesimal commencements of structures, however useful those structures may afterward become.[4]

2. *The independent origin of similar structures.* Since, on the Darwinian basis, structural specializations result from the unique interaction in time and space of organism and environment, it is to be expected, Mivart noted, that similar functional adaptations will occur through a variety of structural specializations, or, as he stated it, "similar ends being attained by dissimilar means." Thus, to answer the need of locomotion, many structural types had originated. But what of those cases, such as the parallel structural resemblances between marsupial and placental mammals, where the similar means of attaining sim-

ilar ends cannot be traced to unity of ancestry or heredity? For Mivart, such parallel developments could not be due exclusively to the action of natural selection "because the number of possible variations is indefinitely great, and it is therefore an indefinitely great number to one against a similar series of variations occurring and being similarly preserved in any two independent instances." [5]

3. *The importance of saltations in evolution.* The problem of the degree of the variations involved in evolutionary processes was always a knotty one. Darwin had considered the possibility of macrochanges or saltations as the important ones for the construction of new organic types and had rejected them in favor of microchanges or minute variations. Assuming that the doctrine of natural selection rests upon minute variations alone, Mivart adduced a number of instances of saltations which breed true as an argument against the exclusive action of the Darwinian principle. Moreover, he utilized the gaps in the palaeontological record as well as the then current limited conceptions of geological time to support his view that evolution occurs through saltations independent of the operation of natural selection. Not only has there not been sufficient time for the evolution of all forms from a few original ones through the selection of minute and fortuitous variations, he argued, but the palaeontological "evidence is as yet against the modification of species by 'Natural Selection' alone, because not only are minutely transitional forms generally absent, but they are absent in cases where we might certainly *a priori* have expected them to be present." [6] Thus, "there are . . . abundant instances to prove that considerable modifications may suddenly develop themselves either due to external conditions or to obscure internal causes in the organisms which exhibit them." [7] These are either *non*-fortuitous variations which are insignificant and minute or variations which are developed with comparative suddenness and are of appreciable size and importance. In either case, he maintained that natural selection was insufficient to explain them.

4. *The development of useless organs.* Natural selection is essentially a utilitarian mechanism, i. e., it develops in the species those organs which are useful to the individual organism

in its exploitation of its particular environmental situation. But how, asked Mivart, can one explain the development of organs which are apparently useless and sometimes harmful to the organism through natural selection? In one of his earliest anatomical works, he had been struck by the aborted index finger of the potto, one of the lemuroids. Even then, he and his collaborator had remarked:

How this mutilation can have aided in the struggle for life, we must confess, baffles our conjectures on the subject; for that any appreciable gain to the individual can have resulted from the slightly-lessened degree of required nourishment thence resulting (i.e. from the suppression), seems to us to be an almost absurd proposition.[8]

Similarly, in the earlier development of the wings of birds from the terrestial limb, would not the early phases of such a development have been disadvantageous for either a terrestial or an aerial habitat?

5. *Specific stability and orthogenetic trends.* On the assumption that natural selection operates on an indefinitely varying population, how is one to account for the fact that major types appear to maintain a relative stability? Why does it "appear that there are barriers which oppose change in certain directions [as well as] positive tendencies to development along certain special lines?"[9] For certainly, Mivart wrote in an unpardonable statement, "upon the theory of Natural Selection all birds have a common origin, from which they diverged by infinitesimal changes, so that we ought to meet with sufficient changes to warrant the belief that a hornbill could be produced from a hummingbird, proportionate time being allowed."[10]

6. *The unity of the organism.* Each individual organism is a totality composed of parts each of which has a special relationship to each other and to the whole. This unity of relationships is *the* organism and is the expression of an individuating cohesive power internal to the organism and thus separate from any of its external relationships upon which natural selection must depend. With reference to this somewhat mystical concept of the organism, Mivart wrote:

It is here contended that the relationships borne one to another by various component parts imply the existence of some innate, internal condition conveniently spoken of as a power or tendency, which is quite as mysterious as is any innate condition, power, or tendency, resulting in the orderly evolution of the successive specific manifestations. These relationships, as also this developmental power, will doubtless, in a certain sense, be somewhat further explained as science advances. But the result will be merely a shifting of the inexplicability a point backward, by the intercalation of another step between the action of the internal condition or power and its external result. In the meantime, even if by "Natural Selection" we could eliminate the puzzles of the "origin of species", yet other phenomena . . . would still remain unexplained and as yet inexplicable. It is not improbable that, could we arrive at the causes conditioning all the complex inter-relations between the several parts of one animal, we should at the same time obtain the key to unlock the secrets of specific origination.[11]

Together, this series of appropriately illustrated objections constituted

a cumulative argument . . . against the prevalent action of "Natural Selection", which, to the mind of the author, is conclusive. As before observed, he was not originally disposed to reject Mr. Darwin's fascinating theory. Reiterated endeavours to solve its difficulties have, however, had the effect of convincing him that that theory as the one or as the leading explanation of the successive evolution and manifestation of specific forms is untenable. At the same time he admits fully that "Natural Selection" acts and must act, and that it plays in the organic world a certain though a secondary and subordinate part.[12]

It is a measure of Mivart's competence that each of these points is a valid one. Each touches a major problem in the development of an over-all evolutionary scheme. Each represents an area the understanding of which was to inspire a host of future biological researches. It is strange, however, and somewhat tragic, that this "cumulative argument" was not applicable to the theory of natural selection as both Darwin and his followers conceived it.

Any theory of organic evolution is applicable to a single problem in biology. This problem is the origin of species, however the term species is itself defined. Any theory of organic evolution asserts that species arise or originate through change, as the modified descendants of some antecedent species. However, a theory of organic evolution, to be reasonably complete, must contain not only the philosophical principle of change through descent as an assumption, but it must also suggest the mechanism through which that change occurs. The more universally applicable that mechanism is to the facts of observation, the more universal the theory itself.

Evolution as a philosophical principle has a long history, which some writers have traced back to the early philosophies of ancient Greece. It was a factor in the intellectual disputations of the eighteenth century. As a datum in natural science, the idea of evolution—and consequently its history—is relatively unimportant; what is important is the mechanism through which the changes in species take place. When such changes are sought in natural processes, evolution becomes a principle in natural science. Such natural explanations of the cause of evolution were suggested, but with remarkably little documentation, by occasional savants in both the eighteenth and the early nineteenth centuries. It was Darwin, however, who related the whole process of evolution, as a universal process, to the observable interaction of organism and environment through his acceptance of the principle of natural selection as *the* mechanism of evolution. Divine guidance, vitalistic urges, nonphysical factors of all sorts were thus ruled out as explanatory factors and their place was taken by the environment in which and through which every organism, individually and as populations, maintains existence. Darwin is quite explicit concerning the effect of the environment in producing evolutionary change and/or originating species:

Let it be borne in mind in what an endless number of strange peculiarities our domestic productions, and, in a lesser degree, those under nature vary; and how strong the hereditary principle is. . . . Let it be borne in mind how infinitely complex and close-fitting are the mutual relations of all organic beings to each other and to their physical conditions of life. Can it, then, be thought improbable, seeing that variations useful to man have undoubtedly occurred, that other variations useful in some way to each being in the great and complex battle of life should sometimes occur in the course of thousands of generations? If such do occur, can we doubt (remembering that many more individuals are born than can possibly survive) that individuals having any advantage, however slight, over

others, would have the best chance of surviving and of procreating
their kind? On the other hand, we may feel sure that any variation
in the least degree injurious would be rigidly destroyed. This preservation of favourable variations and the rejection of injurious variations I call Natural Selection.[13]

But of the variations themselves which constitute the building
blocks for the construction of new species, he was able to say
only that "Our ignorance of the laws of variation is profound.
Not in one case out of a hundred can we pretend to assign any
reason why this or that part differs, more or less, from the same
part in the parents." [14]

Notwithstanding this ignorance of the causes of variation,
Darwin's natural selection exists as a valid mechanism for the
explanation of the evolutionary process; but it exists as such
only on one level of explanation. For a complete system of
evolution, one which explains all of the pertinent phenomena,
such a single-level explanation, while operationally valid in
terms of the circumscribed data, is insufficient. One may
probe below the level of species variation and origination upon
which Darwinism is based and ask: "Since individual variations
within the species are the prerequisites for species variation,
what are the causes or principles involved by which they can
be explained?" To this question, genetics gives an answer in
mutations; and thus a second level of phenomena can be explained within a natural system of evolution. But what of
the other fundamental levels? If individual variations are explained through mutations, what of the entities which mutate?
And so on to the ultimate principle from which the ever more
observable levels of explanation are derived. Thus, ultimately,
the mechanism of evolution becomes a philosophical problem.

One can, however, regard each level of explanation as discrete from the others, and regard the explanation of the problems of each as distinct. This is the course which the Darwinians took, and so, generalizing from Darwin's specific contribution, they regarded the problem of evolution as "solved" when
the definition of that problem was confined to the "origin of
species."

It was precisely here that Mivart diverged from his erstwhile colleagues. He could not be content with the solution on the single level of species variation; and therefore, as he often stated, he could not regard natural selection as *the* origin of species although he was willing to recognize it as a significant principle, perhaps the only principle, operative in the formation of species once intraspecific variations were assumed.

Philosophically Mivart was an evolutionist and regarded species change as inherent in nature. Moreover, he took great pains to demonstrate that he was not opposed to the theory of natural selection per se, but was opposed to it only as the primary or sole explanation for the origin of species. It was his object, he wrote, "to maintain the position that 'Natural Selection' acts, and indeed must act, but that still, in order that we may be able to account for the production of known kinds of animals and plants, it requires to be supplemented by the action of some other natural law or laws as yet undiscovered." [15] Continuing in the same vein, he put his case in brief as follows:

Admitting then organic and other evolution, and that new forms of animals and plants (new species, genera, etc.) have from time to time been evolved from preceding plants and animals, it follows, if the views here advocated are true, that this evolution has not taken place by the action of "Natural Selection" *alone*, but through it (among other influences) aided by the concurrent action of some other natural law or laws, at present undiscovered; and probably that the genesis of species takes place partly, perhaps mainly, through laws which may be most conveniently spoken of as special powers and tendencies existing in each organism; and partly through influences exerted on each by surrounding conditions and agencies organic and inorganic, terrestrial and cosmical, among which the "survival of the fittest" plays a certain but subordinate part.[16]

While the Darwinians tended to make too disparate the levels of explanation in the erection of a coherent system of evolution, Mivart tended to confuse those levels, regarding as valid in the case of one of them criticisms directed at the arguments derived from another.

It is significant of the difference in point of view that, whereas Darwin was content to open only slightly the curtains on his organic drama, Mivart felt it necessary to draw them quickly to the wings. What Mivart was concerned with were all the deeper levels of explanation, those which underlie intraspecific variation and, in contemporary terms, the structure and behavior of the genes.   None of his arguments apply solely to the level of species variation, for which Mivart accepted natural selection as a valid mechanism.

Mivart, however, was not altogether to blame for this confusion of the levels of explanation.   Although in general his meaning is clear, Darwin himself is sometimes guilty of clouding the issue with respect to just what his mechanism does.   In his language he sometimes confuses the individual with the population of which it is a part, thus giving the impression that natural selection has a direct modifying effect upon the organism itself.

Certainly his followers were aware of his meaning.   Huxley vigorously defended Darwin's right to circumscribe the phenomena to be explained; and later, Poulton, in a passage which could well have been directed at Mivart's criticisms had it occurred twenty years earlier, explicitly makes that distinction. "Now, certain writers," he wrote,

have thought to undermine the theory of Natural Selection by arguing that the important and essential factor of individual variation is not explained by the theory which rests upon it.   True, it is not; but for the theory of Natural Selection, the explanation does not signify.   So long as individual variation is present, so long as it is hereditary, it does not signify how it is produced. . . .   So long as it is there, it is available, and Natural Selection can make use of it. . . .   So long as it is a fact essential to organic nature that one individual must be different from another, and so long as these differences are hereditary, so long may Natural Selection have abundant material for its work, even though it does not itself explain how that individual difference is produced.[17]

Had Mivart confined his attention solely to the level of species variation, he would, with one exception, have been forced to accept the Darwinian principle of natural selection in much the same way as did the Darwinians themselves.   That one exception, however, is extremely significant for an understanding of Mivart as an evolutionist.   To the Darwinian, natural selection was universally valid and competent to account for *all* existent species.   This universality was based upon the assumption of an infinite number of inheritable variations. Thus, Darwin could write shortly after the publication of the *Origin:* "With respect to your question, I think the arguments are valid, showing that all animals have descended from four or five primordial forms; and that analogy and weak reasons go to show that *all have descended from some single prototype*" (italics mine—J.G.).[18] An argument such as this had to be based upon the assumption not only of infinite variations but also of variations all of which were of equal value.

For Mivart, such a uniformitarianism pervading the whole of the natural world was unthinkable on the grounds of reason. For him, the world of nature was compartmentalized into categories or groupings each of which was qualitatively different from every other. A difference of kind existed between inorganic and organic matter, between plant or nonsentient life and animal or sentient life. Within these categories the variations were comparable, but between them, never. Thus, while a process of natural selection could operate upon variations within the plant kingdom to originate new plant species, no process other than a direct creative act could transform one qualitatively distinct category into another. While that creative act can be either direct or derivative, the basic types are expressions "of an intelligence of some kind." It is this intelligence which, in ordering the universe, has provided each basic type with the potentialities to develop in conformity to natural laws, i.e., regular, as opposed to miraculous, principles. Mivart seems never to have made up his mind as to the number of these basic types or "creative ideas"; he vacillated from the few primordial types of Darwin to the many with which Owen peopled his organic world formed through his principle of "Derivation."

Mivart's conception of evolution was essentially a synthesis derived from his own theistic naturalism, which may have been only coincidentally similar to that of his friend and teacher Owen, and from the empirical naturalism of the Darwinians. Assuming on rational grounds the existence of a First Cause, some initiating principle or being which he equated with the ordering intelligence pervading the universe, and that "one harmonious action underlying the whole of Nature, organic and inorganic, cosmical, physical, chemical, terrestial, vital and social," his evolutionism represented the working out of that harmony through natural laws within the organic realm. His is a broader, though much less explicit, system than that of Darwin; for he includes within it an explanation—through unknown laws—of intraspecific as well as interspecific variation. According to his view,

An internal law presides over the actions of every part of every individual, and of every organism as a unit, and of the entire organic world as a whole. It is believed that this conception of an internal innate force will ever remain necessary, however much its subordinate processes and actions may become explicable.

That by such a force, from time to time, new species are manifested by ordinary generation . . . these new forms not being monstrosities but harmonious, self-consistent wholes. That thus, as the specific distinctness is manifested by obscure sexual conditions, so in obscure sexual modifications specific distinctions arise.

That these "jumps" are considerable in comparison with the minute variations of "Natural Selection"—are in fact sensible steps, such as discriminate species from species.

That the latent tendency which exists to these sudden evolutions is determined to action by the stimulus of external conditions.

That "Natural Selection" removes the antecedent species rapidly when the new one evolved is more in harmony with surrounding conditions.

That "Natural Selection" favours and develops useful variations, though it is impotent to originate them or to erect the physiological barrier which seems to exist between species.

By some such conception as this, the difficulties here enumerated, which beset the theory of "Natural Selection" pure and simple, are to be got over.[19]

In this system which attempts to explain both intra- and interspecific variations through the operation of an "internal innate force" there is a glimmering of the genetics to come. Reading Mivart outside the context of his philosophical and theological system, one is tempted to regard him as anticipating the remarkable contributions which the geneticists have made to an understanding of evolutionary processes. One is tempted to interpret his "innate force" which plays so important a role in determining the type and degree of individual variations making the operation of natural selection possible as the genetic constitution of the individual which provides every organism with its unique character.

To make this kind of translation from the past into the present, however, is to distort the essential meaning of Mivart's system. Had he lived into the era of genetics—and he died on its very threshold—it is hardly likely that he would have been satisfied with the transformation of his "innate power" into a bundle of material genes; while accepting their reality, he would have constructed another "natural" power to explain their behavior. For he was convinced, on philosophical grounds, that there was some transcendent power operating in the organic universe which could not be explained in physical terms. Behind all the changing phenomena of the physical universe there was a static reality, an unknowable intelligence, in which the natural laws and the phenomena through which they operated had their origin. There was the First Cause, the final cause, the creative cohesive agent of a harmonious whole. It was through this First Cause that organic types were eventually achieved through a working out—an evolution in an eighteenth-century sense—of their divinely created potentialities in conformance with a changing environment. The environment called forth, at the preordained and appropriate time, those modifications which were already inherent in the type. Thus, species and the more abstract taxonomic groupings were, in effect, eternal, not as physical manifestations, but as ideas; and they "have been evolved through the orderly operation of powers divincly implanted in the material creation." This concept of the reality and permanence of the idea, as opposed to the transitory character of its expression, Mivart used as the basis for much of his work.

Despite Mivart's frequent, often fervent, avowals of allegiance to evolution, one can doubt whether he was really an evolutionist at all. The logical extreme to which his system can be carried—an extreme which he dangerously approached on occasion—is that each and every existing type is the expression of a creative idea, that, in fact, not only the type, but the individual itself, exists as a discrete expression of such an idea.

"Species, genera, families, orders, and classes," he wrote, "as such are ideas; they have an ideal existence in the human mind—have they no other ideal existence? Every Theist must admit that the mind of God contains all that exists in the human mind, and infinitely more. . . . Our ideas are derived from material things, while the Divine ideas are ideas whence the material things have been themselves derived. . . . It is thus that we recognize in all beasts the concrete embodiment of the mammalian idea. . . ." [20] Such a conception implies the acceptance of a doctrine of special creation even more rigid than that of the most devout creationist.

For the natural unity of genetic affinity throughout the organic world, Darwin's most significant contribution to an understanding of nature in natural terms, Mivart would have substituted the philosophical unity of a creative and cohesive intelligence. From the standpoint of Mivart's philosophical faith, that intelligence had to exist; and the necessity of that belief inhibited any real contribution which Mivart, as a biologist, might have made to *natural* science. In the words of one of his obituaries, "His scientific work was . . . limited by his religious creed. Perhaps had he been less dominated by preconceived ideas he would, with his industry, have achieved something more striking than anything that can be claimed for him." [21]

2

Mivart's "preconceived ideas" underlay his conception of man's duality. In this species "two distinct orders of being impinge and mingle," that of the body and that of the soul. Apart from the observations which were adduced to support this duality, its truth was affirmed on a priori grounds. While the corporeal aspect of man was a reality through the facts of observation, his mental and moral aspect derived its reality from reason alone. Man has a body as a matter of observation; he has a soul whose existence is affirmed by revelation which "appeals for its acceptance to 'reason'." Moreover, the distinction between the two aspects is absolute. "To those who accept the belief in God, the soul and moral responsibility. . . .

To them, the placing of non-moral beings in the same scale with moral agents will be utterly unendurable." [22]

With this distinction, Mivart's idea of human evolution and origins becomes a strange attempt to harmonize the empirical data of natural science with the rationally derived data of a revealed philosophy. Since each of man's natures is derived from a different order of reality, both cannot be explained in the same causal terms. For the origin and development of the body, evolution, operating with whatever natural principles it has at its disposal, is a sufficient explanation, as it is for the origin and development of all other corporeal forms; but such an explanation is insufficient to account for the origin of the intellectual aspect of man. That aspect appears *de novo* by creative fiat. No other explanation would be valid, since the appearance of mind represents something absolutely new, a major discontinuity in the evolutionary record.

This preconceived notion of the absolute distinction between the two natures of man always underlies Mivart's treatment of this species. Such an idea was antithetical to the monistic interpretation which was a direct outcome of Darwinism. In an interesting passage which is strangely reminiscent of one in which Huxley had attempted to illustrate the method of an objective classification of man, Mivart emphasizes the significance of his duality:

Let us suppose ourselves to be purely immaterial intelligences, acquainted only with a world peopled like our own, except that man had never lived on it, yet into which the dead body of a man had somehow been introduced.

We should, I think, consider such a body to be that of some latisternal ape, but of one much more widely differing from all the others than such others differ from one another amongst themselves. We should be especially struck with its vast brain, and we should be more impressed by it when we noted how bulky was the body to which the brain belonged. We should be so impressed because we should have previously noted that, as a general rule, in back-boned animals, the larger the bulk of the body the less the relative size of the brain. From our knowledge of the habits and faculties of the various animals in relation to their brain structure, we should be led to infer that the animal man was one possessing great power of co-ordinating movements, and that his emotional sensibility would have been considerable. But above all, his powers of imagination would have been deemed by us to have been prodigious, with a corresponding faculty of collecting, grouping and preserving sensible images of objects in complex and coherent aggregations to a degree much greater than in any other animal with which we were acquainted. Did we know that all the various other kinds of existing animals had been developed from one another by evolution; did we know that the numerous species had been evolved from potential to actual existence by implanted powers in matter, aided by the influence of incident forces; then we might reasonably argue, by analogy, that a similar mode of origin had given rise to the exceptional being, the body of which we were examining.

If, however, it were made clear to us—immaterial intelligences— that the dead body before us had been, in life, animated, not by a merely animal nature, but by an active intelligence like our own, so that the difference between him and all other animals was not a difference of degree but of *kind*—if we could be made to understand that its vast power of collecting and grouping sensible images served but to supply it with the materials made use of by its intelligence to perceive, not merely sensible phenomena, but also abstract qualities of objects—if we became aware that the sounds uttered by it in life were not exclusively emotional expressions, but signs of general conceptions . . . then the aspect of the question would be entirely altered for us.

We should probably decide that if the body before us seemed to us to be so little related to the informing rational soul that its existence anterior to and independent of such rational soul was conceivable and possible, then its origin by a process of natural evolution would, indeed, also be conceivable and indeed *a priori* probable.

But if, on the other hand, we were convinced, from whatever reason, that it was inconceivable and impossible for such a body to be developed or exist without such an informing soul, then we should, with perfect reason and logic, affirm that as no natural process would account for the entirely different kind of soul—one capable of articulately expressing general conceptions—so no merely natural process could account for the origin of the body informed by it—a body to which such an intellectual faculty was so essentially and intimately related.[23]

Thus the soul was absolutely distinct in its nature from the body. The body of man, differing only in degree from those of other animals, could have had its origin in an evolutionary process. But of the intellectual nature of man, his corporeal kin have no germ, rudiment, or vestige whatsoever. There is no transition, but a sharp and distinct break indicative of a creative act. Among no human group, however savage, could there be found any transitional step between the nature of the brute and that of man. From the investigations of a developing anthropology, Mivart concluded that in respect to language, morals, religion—in respect to all those traits which reflect an intellectual as opposed to a mere sentient faculty—

One common fundamental human nature is present in all the tribes and races of men . . . which are scattered over the whole surface of the habitable globe. . . . From the absence of any positive proof as to the brutal condition of mankind, and from the absence of even any transitional stage, a presumption, at least, arises that no such transition ever took place. . . . The religion of Abraham and Chrysostom, the intellect of Aristotle and Newton, the art of Raphael, of Shakespeare, of Mozart, have their claims to be no mere bestial developments, supported by that testimony. Through it these faculties are plainly seen to be different *in kind* from complex entanglements of merely animal instincts and sensible impressions. The claims of man as we know him at his noblest, to be of a fundamentally different nature from the beasts which perish, become reinforced and reinvigorated in our eyes, when we find the very same moral, intellectual, and artistic nature (though disguised, obscured, and often profoundly misunderstood) present even in the rude, uncultured soul of the lowest of our race, the poor savage—*Homo sylvaticus.*[24]

It is this concept of the unique origin of man's moral and mental faculty as soul which led Mivart to question even the genealogical affinities which Huxley had constructed from the mass of corporeal relationships observable among the higher Primates.

Man and Apes, a little book published in 1873, was designed, in fact, to call into question the whole scheme of relationships which Huxley had so patiently constructed a decade earlier and which had laid the foundation in comparative anatomy for Darwin's more recently published *Descent of Man.* "If the Gorilla really possesses that exceptional affinity to man with which it is popularly credited (and which would mark its type as that immediately ancestral to man), it must exhibit a cluster of structural approximations to man such as are not to be found in any other animal." [25] With this assumption as a starting point, Mivart then proceeded, with the consummate skill of a trained lawyer, to marshal his evidences to demonstrate that the "affinities seem rather to radiate from man in various directions than to follow one special route." In fact, "the teaching . . . of the skeleton, as also of the other parts . . . , seems to be that resemblance to man is shared in different and but very unequal degrees by diverse species of the order, rather than that any one kind is plainly and unquestionably much more human than any of the others." [26] So conflicting and ambiguous is the evidence from structural relationships, that it "is manifest that man, the apes, and Half-apes cannot be arranged in a single ascending series of which man is the term and culmination. We may, indeed," he noted,

by selecting one organ, or one set of parts, and confining our attention to it, arrange the different forms in a more or less simple manner. But, if all the organs be taken into account, the cross relations and interdependencies become in the highest degree complex and difficult to unravel.

．　．　．　．

The human structural characters are shared by so many and such diverse forms, that it is impossible to arrange even groups of general type in a single ascending series from the Aye-Aye to man (to say nothing of so arranging the several single genera), if all the structural resemblances are taken into account.

．　．　．　．

If the number of wrist bones be deemed a special mark of affinity between the Gorilla, Chimpanzee, and man, why are we not to consider it also a special mark of affinity between the Indris and man? That it should be so considered, however, would be deemed an absurdity by every evolutionist.

If the proportions of the arms speak in favour of the Chimpanzee, why do not the proportions of the legs serve to promote the rank of the Gibbons?

If the "bridging convolutions" of the Orang go to sustain its claim to supremacy, they also go far to sustain a similar claim on the part of the long-tailed, thumbless Spider monkeys.

If the obliquely-ridged teeth of *Simia* and *Troglodytes* point to a community of origin, how can we deny a similar community of origin, as thus estimated, to the Howling Monkeys and Galagos?

The liver of the Gibbons proclaims them almost human; that of the Gorilla declares him comparatively brutal.

The ear lobe of the Gorilla makes him our cousin; but his tongue is eloquent in his own dispraise.

The slender Loris, from amidst the Half-apes, can put in many a claim to be our shadow refracted, as it were, through a Lemurine prism.

The lower American apes meet us with what seems "the front of Jove himself," compared with the gigantic but low-browed denizens of tropical Western Africa.[27]

Thus, taxonomic confusion still reigns. The Darwinian theory of human origins is built on quicksand. Man is still unique, the product of a divine creative act.

V. BREAKING POINT

The reception of the *Genesis* by the public was heartening both for its author and for the proponents of the view he expressed. The initial sale was excellent, in spite of—perhaps because of—the fact that Darwin's long awaited *Descent of Man* was published almost simultaneously. So well did the *Genesis* sell, in both its English and its American editions, that a second edition "with notes in reference and reply to Darwin's *Descent of Man*" appeared on the last day of August, 1871. It was still being advertised in *Nature* two years later.

It seemed that Mivart had found the formula by which theists, notwithstanding the degree of their devoutness, could accept evolution as a principle of nature. To show that evolution was compatible with even the most extreme of Christian positions, he marshalled as witnesses a host of patristic writers and authorities, in all of whose writings he was able to show sentiments which, although not prophetic of a doctrine of evolution, did not specifically preclude the possibility that such a doctrine might be held. Moreover, Mivart not only made this claim for evolution in general, but also asserted it for the evolution of man's body from some nonhuman progenitor. Only with respect to the origin of man's soul did he speak with the voice of revelation, reaffirming that that most important aspect of the human individual was, in keeping with tradition, infused in the body by a divine creative act.

Despite the extreme liberalism of some of his views, notably that with respect to the origin of the human body, the *Genesis* was received with great favor by the spokesmen—or, at least, those who would venture comment—for the Catholic community in England. The *Tablet,* a weekly organ of the ultramontane party, after reporting with favor the arguments put forth against Darwinism, concluded its commendatory review with a welcome to

the present work as a valuable contribution of an English Catholic man of science to the defense of religion against those materialistic theories of the age which are accounted by many as forming a most serious obstacle to the reception of religious truth. . . . Little has been done as yet to combat this most trying evil of our age [intellectual atheism]; nor can it successfully be combatted, unless Catholics in England will do what their brethren have been doing in France for the last half century. They must add to the gift of faith both extensive metaphysical knowledge and an intimate acquaintance with physical science, based upon natural talent and love for the investigating of nature for its own sake, and not for a mere polemical purpose. The author of the *Genesis of Species* has shown himself to be possessed in no ordinary degree of these qualifications, and we hope that he will continue his useful labours and extend their area.[1]

The Month, in whose pages Mivart's criticism of Darwinism first appeared, confined itself primarily to a reportorial review of the book, the reviewer disclaiming any authority with reference to the facts themselves. However, in restating Mivart's thesis that evolution need not be inconsistent with faith, he commended the author of the *Genesis* as a scientist who had the merit of being "a sound careful reasoner, who will sift arguments, examine for himself into the logical value of received observations, and test theories by applying them to the explanations of all, and not only a part of, the facts which they ought to explain." [2]

The most laudatory review was contained in the *Dublin Review,* then under the editorship of W. G. Ward, lay leader of the then dominant ultramontane party, and its chief exponent and apologist in England. Of this "welcome and masterly book," Ward wrote:

The reception which Mr. Mivart's book on the Darwinian theory of the Origin of Species has received from the most able part of the periodical press cannot but be gratifying to those who, like ourselves, are anxious to defend Revelation and at the same time to do full justice to Science. For apt learning, for clearness of exposition, for force of proof combined with utmost courtesy and good temper, there is no work on the subject that can be compared to the compact volume now before us.[3]

In the writer of this book which "is as full of solid learning as of excellent spirit, Darwinism has no contemptible antagonist," for Mr. Mivart "handles his science with as much ease as efficacy." Concluding with "the hope that it may be extensively used by all who care to have enlightened views on subjects on which views of some kind must be held by all educated men," [4] the reviewer implied that the *Genesis* contained nothing incompatible with Catholic belief.

Despite the enthusiasm of the Catholic press, there were those who were unwilling to follow Mivart on the path which he had struck. There were the fundamentalists, both among the laity and the clergy, who would have no truck with evolution, no matter what its guise; and there were those who saw in Mivart's compromise a simple manipulation of words whose ultimate object would be a denial of one of the fundamental tenets of faith, the spirituality of the soul. Typical of the latter objection was a series of anonymous letters to the *Tablet,* complaining that Mivart, by making a distinction between the origin of the "vitality and intelligence" of animals and of man, must logically reduce the origin of the human soul to the same processes as those which produced the intelligence of lower animals, namely, an evolutionary one. "Mr. Mivart stops short," the writer noted, "being warned off by the clear voice of Revelation; but without reference to Revelation what grounds can he assign for drawing so arbitrary a line between the ape and the savage? . . . I cannot admit," he continued, that such a doctrine "is tenable by a Catholic, leading as it does, apart from revelation, to the conclusion that the brain of the savage may owe all of its intellectual powers to the evolution of matter, as well as that of the ape." [5]

For such criticisms, the scholastic call to authority was invoked. Replying to the above critic, "Sacerdos," in the *Tablet* for March 11, 1871, concluded that the writer *"may* be some 'great unknown' in disguise; until, however, he reveals his true personality, it will be probably sufficient for the pur-

pose of calming the scruples of perplexed readers of his corro-
sive remarks, if I inform them of the following fact—namely,
that several ecclesiastics of undeniable ability have cordially
confirmed the author of the *Genesis of Species* in his conviction
that it contains nothing incompatible with any authoritatively
declared obligations of Catholic Theology or philosophy." [6]

Moreover, from spokesmen more potent than the anonymous
reviewers and correspondents of the lay press Mivart also received praise and encouragement.   Newman, still the spokesman for intellectual Catholicism though his ecclesiastical advancement had been halted by the influence of the hostile
Manning and Ward, gave Mivart his forthright commendation.   Acknowledging the receipt of the *Genesis* which Mivart
had sent upon its publication, Newman wrote: "I thank you
very much for your valuable work.   I have read enough of it
to know that it *is* as valuable as it is interesting, and to make
me eager to read more of it.   And I have to thank you for the
notice you take of me in your last chapter.   And also for your
kind letter." [7]   Further compliments were contained in a later
letter.   On December 9, 1871, he expanded his estimate of the
Genesis and of its influence for good:

> Ever since you wrote to me in October, I have meant to send you
> a line to thank you for the kindness of your letter.   But when I slip
> the first day or two, then difficulties come in the way of my fulfilling
> my intention.
> Let me do so now.   And let me say that I shall be abundantly
> satisfied and pleased if my Essays do a quarter of the good which I
> hear your volume is doing.   Those who have a right to judge speak
> of it as a first rate book—and it is pleasant to find that the first real
> exposition of the logical insufficiency of Mr. Darwin's theory comes
> from a Catholic.
> In saying this, you must not suppose I have personally any great
> dislike or dread of his theory, but many good people are much
> troubled at it—and at all events, without any disrespect to him,
> it is well to show that Catholics may be better reasoners than phi-
> losophers.[8]

Final approval came from Rome.   Five years after the first
appearance of the *Genesis,* which had been succeeded by the
publication of *Man and Apes, Contemporary Evolution,* and

Lessons from Nature, all reiterating the thesis first enunciated in the *Genesis,* Pius IX conferred upon the author the degree of doctor of philosophy, signifying thus to the Catholic world papal sanction of the views which Mivart had been so fervent in expressing.

2

In addition to the acclaim with which the *Genesis* was hailed by the Catholic press, it also received generally favorable reviews in both popular and professional journals whose point of view was secular rather than religious. The *Saturday Review* stated broadly that "In no work in the English language has this great controversy been treated at once with the same broad and vigourous grasp of facts, and the same liberal and candid temper." And the *British Medical Journal* noted that "Mr. Mivart has succeeded in producing a work which will clear the ideas of biologists and theologians, and which treats the most delicate questions in a manner which throws light upon most of them, and clears away the barriers of intolerance on each side."

Even *Nature,* whose columns have since its beginning welcomed the work of scientific pioneers, looked upon the *Genesis* as a valuable work. The lead, and only, review for February 2, 1871, deals with it solidly and generously. Neither the carping criticism nor the bitterness which characterized later reviews is present. In this volume, notes the reviewer, "even those who differ from his conclusions will find a mine of physiological information and ingenious speculation. Nor can we do more than allude to the theological portion of the work, wherein he ably defends the doctrine of Evolution against the *odium theologicum* and the *odium anti-theologicum.*" Referring to Mivart's conclusions themselves, he wrote:

A theory may be true, and yet may not be adequate. . . . Mr. Mivart . . . admit[s] the potency of Natural Selection to have produced the greater number of specific forms and organic structures we see around us; for the production of others [he] believe[s] that it can be proved to be inadequate and that we must look to some other innate prin-

ciple for their formation. Mr. Mivart supports his arguments with
so much cogency of reasoning, so great a knowledge of anatomical
structure, and so complete an acknowledgement of the strength of
his opponent's position, that they cannot be disregarded by anyone
interested in the subject. His objections are the more deserving of
careful consideration, inasmuch as he states that he was himself by
no means disposed originally to dissent from the theory of Natural
Selection, if only its difficulties could be solved, but that he has
found each successive year that deeper considerations and more careful examination have more and more brought home to him the in-
adequacy of Mr. Darwin's theory to account for the preservation
and intensification of incipient specific and generic characters. It
behooves, therefore, every Darwinian to satisfy himself that either
Mr. Mivart's premises or his line of argument is unsound.[9]

The Darwinians, while they took note of the effect produced
by the *Genesis,* were slow to react in print to the most powerful attack levelled against their doctrine in the dozen years
since its presentation. Confessing that "it at first appeared
. . . very formidable, on the principle of aggregation," Darwin
prepared to answer Mivart's critique in the forthcoming sixth
edition of the *Origin,* due to appear early in 1872.[10] Here he
devoted the major part of a new chapter to an even-tempered
but inconclusive discussion of the difficulties raised by Mivart;
and he concluded with the considered opinion that to admit
such views as those held by his critic would be "as it seems to
me, to enter into the realms of miracle, and to leave those of
science." [11]

While the abhorrence of controversy prohibited Darwin
from directly entering the conflict, his case was effectively
argued by Chauncey Wright in America and by Huxley in
England.

Wright's two articles on [12] Evolution in general and Mivart's
position in particular, though, even to Darwin, "not very
clearly written, and poor in parts from want of knowledge," [13]
were, from a philosophical point of view, by far the most significant rebuttal of the *Genesis.*

Paying tribute to the work as "the most effective general
criticism of the theory of Natural Selection which has as yet

appeared, or one which, at least, is likely to exert the greatest influence in overcoming the remaining prejudice against the general doctrine of evolution," Wright regretted that "the work falls far short of what we might have expected from an author of Mr. Mivart's attainments as a naturalist." [14] He admitted, however, that Mivart's "position before the religious world, and his unquestionable familiarity with the theological bearings of the subject, will undoubtedly gain for him and for the doctrine of evolution a hearing and a credit, which the mere student of science might be denied." [15] The major part of the review consists of an able—and justifiable—attempt to show that Mivart's criticism of Darwinism, as distinct from evolution, was based upon an inability to understand fully the specific problems with which Darwin had concerned himself. Fully admitting that while Mivart may have "in a notable degree" a genius for bringing "together in clear connections and contrasts in classification the objects of Nature in their broadest and realest relations of resemblance" and for seeking "with success for reasons and authorities in support of cherished convictions," Wright taxed him with an utter lack of that third genius for pursuing "successfully the researches for unknown causes by the skilful use of hypothesis and experiment." Thus, while granting Mivart's excellence as an observer and dialectician, Wright stripped him of any real ability as a theoretical biologist or "experimental philosopher," an ability which Wright felt was an absolute prerequisite for those who would either understand or justly criticize such a theory as that of natural selection.

Among some other "rods I have in pickle for Mr. St. George Mivart" [16] were some allegations which were less just.

With little or no justification he accused Mivart of dishonesty and distortion in the matter of quotations, a charge which Darwin was to accept and upon which he was to base some of his more bitter personal references toward his antagonist. With Darwin, Wright regarded the *Genesis* as a "conspicuous example of . . . a one-sided treatment of a proper scientific question," a statement with which most other reviewers did not agree. And finally, as did Huxley, he attempted to refute Mivart on his own grounds of theology by maintaining "the theses that the doctrine of Final Causes [one on which Mivart rested a major part of his criticism] in natural science is not Christian, but Platonic; and that the principle of the theory of Natural Selection is taught in the discourse of Jesus with Nicodemus the Pharisee." [17]

In general, however, the initial reaction to the *Genesis* was respectful and impersonal. Even Darwin was tolerant of the criticisms it contained. After a first and hurried reading he wrote to Wallace on January 30, 1871,

I hope to God there will be nothing disagreeable to you in Vol. II [of the *Descent*], and that I have spoken fairly of your views. I feel the more fearful on this head, because I have just read (but not with sufficient care) Mivart's book, and I feel *absolutely certain* that he meant to be fair (but he was stimulated by theological fervour); yet I do not think he has been quite fair: he gives in one place only half of one of my sentences, ignores in many places all that I have said on effects of use, speaks of my dogmatic assertion, "of false belief", whereas the end of the paragraph seems to me to render the sentence by no means dogmatic or arrogant; etc., etc. I have since its publication received some quite charming letters from him.

What an ardent (and most justly) admirer he is of you. His work, I do not doubt, will have a most potent influence versus Natural Selection. The pendulum will now swing against us. . . .

Mivart is savage or contemptuous about my "moral sense", and so probably will you be. I am extremely pleased that he agrees with my position, *as far as animal nature is concerned,* of man in the series; or, if anything, thinks I have erred in making him too distinct.[18]

A few days later, Wallace who, though disagreeing with him often, considered Mivart to be one of his "chief friends," wrote of the *Genesis:*

Have you seen Mivart's book, "Genesis of Species"? It is exceedingly clever, and well worth reading. The arguments against Natural Selection as the exclusive mode of development are some of them exceedingly strong, and very well put, and it is altogether a most readable and interesting book.

Though he uses some weak and bad arguments, and underrates the power of Natural Selection, yet I think I agree with his conclusion in the main, and am inclined to think it is more philosophical than my own. It is a book that I think will please Sir Charles Lyell.[19]

The *Genesis* itself was not lacking in the respect due a scientific hypothesis of such comprehension as natural selection put forth by a scientist of such demonstrated competence as Darwin. On the whole, this was controversy in the best tradition of science, an exposition of divergent points of view to which competent workers had committed themselves. But Mivart's *Genesis,* composed as a rebuttal to Darwin's *Origin,* was only a prelude. As Darwin had not yet published his views on man, Mivart, except for an occasional theological interpolation, did not speak to the subject.

Man, however, was to be included in the evolutionary process. That which had been but a muted theme was to become the major motif. The general theory of evolution, trumpeted in the *Origin,* was being drowned in the dissonant chorus of the "man question." The growing, almost inevitable, tendency to play out the natural symphony on the theme of man's evolution reached its climax, while the *Genesis* was in press, with the publication of *The Descent of Man.*

Here there was no uncertain utterance. To Darwin, an acceptance of his views with respect to evolution in general could lead only to the almost certain conclusion that man in his entirety was, with the whole organic world, an evolutionary product, developed through the same forces of natural selection from some nonhuman ancestor. What Mivart had feared had at last occurred. This was no disciple's voice; this was no speculator, arguing in bias a preconceived point; this was no philosopher, elaborating a universal system on the basis of misinterpreted data. This was Darwin himself, documenting his thesis with the care and caution that were his trademark. And the end result, it seemed to Mivart, was to deprive man of his last shred of security founded on belief in the truth of man's divine nature.

For Mivart, to whom that truth and the security it gave was life itself, the issue was drawn with the publication of the *Descent.* Any further hope of reconciliation on ideological grounds was out of the question. To attempt to find a meeting point on a subject of such overriding importance, now that a positive statement had been made with such assurance in the *Descent,* was fruitless.

3

When the *Origin of Species* had been published in 1859 the conservative *Quarterly Review* had entrusted its review to Bishop Samuel Wilberforce, whose argumentative powers were equaled only by his ignorance of natural science. With the appearance of the *Descent of Man,* the *Quarterly,* although its philosophy had not changed during the intervening twelve years, did not commit the same error. Mivart, whose *Genesis* marked him as the foremost opponent of Darwinism in English science, was engaged to write the review. Entitled simply "Darwin's *Descent of Man,*" it appeared under the customary protection of anonymity in July, 1871.

The tone of this article is different from that of the *Genesis.* Where the latter, even at its most critical, was warm, friendly, and congenial, the former was bitter, overbearing, and condemnatory. While only tinges of the personal appear in the *Genesis,* the review is saturated with personal bias. This difference, both in tone and in argumentative approach, reflects Mivart's decision to combat the false application of Darwinism to man with every weapon at his disposal.

For Mivart, Darwin's statement on man was so patently absurd on both scientific and philosophical grounds that its acceptance could be explained only by the personal regard with which its author was held. It was necessary, then, to attack the position of Darwin as the prophet of evolution and as a scientist of philosophical depth. If successful, such an approach would deprive his opinions of the infallibility with which it was assumed they were so often viewed. It would, in addition, strike a blow at his disciples, notably Haeckel, who were constructing entire philosophical systems upon the quicksand of what could be shown to be nothing more than a series of modifiable hypotheses.

Criticism alone, however, was essentially negativistic. While it might accomplish the immediate objective of demolition, it would provide an intellectual chaos whose total effect would be worse than the conditions it sought to rectify. Positive steps were needed, steps by which the truths of mankind, of which evolution was but one, could be comprehended in an over-all explanatory system valid in the realms of both science and philosophy. To erect such a system was Mivart's next major goal. Since man appeared to be the major point of contention, he set out to demonstrate that, scientifically considered, man's nature was so peculiar as to render him unique from the rest of the animal world and therefore impossible of explanation in terms of the theory of natural selection.

The *Quarterly Review* article pursued this double path for forty closely printed pages. It proclaimed, from almost every page, a qualitative difference between the mind of man and that of his morphological kin so vital as to transcend all other considerations. It was the same difference, dressed in the clothing of science, which an authoritative voice had proclaimed in the *Dublin Review*. "With regard to the soul of man," wrote that spokesman for Catholicism, "no evolutionary theory can be held. Each human individual receives his soul, as Adam did, immediately from the 'breath' of Almighty God." [20]

As both the sole scientific expositor of such a doctrine and the chief critic of a volume which sought to prove, on equally authoritative scientific grounds, its opposite, Mivart used the review as a means of disparaging the authority of Darwin in an attempt to warn off those who would follow in so important an area of belief the blind authority of one venerated for his previous work. Mivart fervently believed that the principles advocated by the Darwinians and implicit in their concept of the origin of man "cannot but tend, by a fatal necessity, in one direction, to produce results socially, politically, and morally, which their purveyors would be the first to deplore. They tend in the intellectual order to the degradation of the mind, by the essential identification of thought with sensation, and in the political order to the evolution of horrors worse than those of the Parisian Commune." [21]

In a species of *argumentum ad hominem,* Mivart, although paying tribute to Darwin's factual and theoretical contributions in the natural sciences, juxtaposed quotations to show that Darwin, far from being convinced of the validity of his own theories, had consistently modified and contradicted earlier statements with respect to his conclusions. "While willingly paying a just tribute of esteem to the candour which dictated these several admissions," he continued,

it would be idle to dissemble, and disingenuous not to declare, the amount of distrust with which such repeated over-hasty conclusions and erroneous calculations inspire us. When their Author comes before us anew, as he now does, with opinions and conclusions still more startling, and calculated in a yet greater degree to disturb convictions reposing upon the general consent of the majority of cultivated minds, we may well pause before we trust ourselves unreservedly to a guidance which thus again and again declares its own reiterated fallibility. Mr. Darwin's conclusions may be correct, but we feel we have now indeed a right to demand that they shall be proved before we assent to them; and that since what Mr. Darwin before declared *"must* be", he now not only admits to be unnecessary but untrue, we may justly regard with extreme distrust the numerous statements and calculations which, in the "Descent of Man," are avowedly recommended by a mere *"may* be". This is the more necessary, as the Author, starting at first with an avowed hypothesis, constantly asserts it as an undoubted fact, and claims for it, somewhat in the spirit of a theologian, that it should be received as an article of faith. Thus the formidable objection to Mr. Darwin's theory, that the great break, in the organic chain between man and his nearest allies, which cannot be bridged over by any extinct or living species, is answered simply by an appeal "to a *belief* in the general principle of evolution" (vol I p 200), or by a confident statement that "we have *every reason to believe* that breaks in the series are simply the result of many forms having become extinct (vol I p 187). So, in like manner, we are assured that "the early progenitors of man were, *no doubt,* once covered with hair, both sexes having beards; their ears were pointed and capable of movement; their bodies were provided with a tail, having the proper muscles" (vol I p 206). And, finally, we are told, with a dogmatism little worthy of a philosopher, that, *"unless we wilfully close our eyes,"* we must recognise our parentage (vol I p 213).

These are hard words; and, even at the risk of being accused of wilful blindness, we shall now proceed, with an unbiassed and unprejudiced mind, to examine carefully the arguments upon which Mr. Darwin's theory rests.[22]

The remainder of this article, although not particularly characterized by the lack of bias and prejudice of which Mivart felt himself capable, is a rather remarkable attempt, on the one hand, to refute Darwin's newly enunciated theory of sexual selection and, on the other, to establish simply and forthrightly the basis upon which he considered man's uniqueness to rest.

Behind the catalogue of scientific inadequacies and hidden by the philosophical verbalizations, there is a more serious theme running through this article. It is the fear that through the translation of hypothesis into fact, science itself will be throttled by dogma. As he viewed the new role science was coming to play, Mivart feared the ease with which hypotheses were being used as firm bases for the construction of more extensive philosophical systems. More specifically, he viewed with alarm the growing faith in a philosophical system based upon a supposedly scientific fact which, since it could not be empirically verified, proved to be nothing more than a philosophical statement itself. That which was to be proved was being used as proof of itself. Certainly a procedure of this sort was opposed to all canons of logic and reason; just as certainly such a procedure must inevitably lead to the acceptance on faith of that which was to be proved. If acceptance on faith was to be permitted in science, then all of philosophy must be confusion and chaos, since it was to science that philosophy must look for the verified facts upon which its systems were built. The circular reasoning to which such a procedure could lead was nothing more than a return to the dogmatic authoritarianism which characterised the philosophy of the Middle Ages and which imprisoned by its very authoritarianism the scientific forces which would free it.

Such, in essence, was Mivart's general position. Seeing the hypothesis of man's descent, as expressed by Darwin, as no more than a philosophical statement, on a par with all others, he feared its acceptance as scientific fact. Nor were his fears altogether unjustified; for the reputation of Darwin and his followers as *scientific* investigators was such as to insure for their pronouncements, even those of a hypothetical sort, a ready acceptance.   Mivart saw a cult arising which would regard almost as revelation the theories of the new science; and it was against the displacement of free investigation by such a cult that his arguments, often not so impersonal as he might wish them, were directed.

VI. FIRST CONFLICT

Appearing within six months of the scientifically critical *Genesis*, the personal remarks of the *Quarterly* review crystallized the incipient antagonisms of the Darwinians toward Mivart. They felt that in reducing scientific inquiry "to a mere controversy in which he holds a brief against the Darwinians," Mivart had permitted theological predispositions to emerge victorious in the struggle with scientific habits for the possession of his mind.[1] And once apostasy had been recognized, all sins could be ascribed to the fallen.

While Darwin was working on a new edition of the *Origin* in which he was to answer the arguments of his critics, he wrote Wallace, on July 9, 1871, without as yet having read the piece in the *Quarterly Review:*

You will think me a bigot when I say, after studying Mivart, I was never before in my life so convinced of the *general* (i.e. not in detail) truth of the views in the "Origin". I grieve to see the omission of the words by Mivart, detected by Wright. I complained to M. that in two cases he quotes only the commencement of sentences by me and thus modifies my meaning; but I never supposed he would have omitted words. There are other cases of what I consider unfair treatment. I conclude with sorrow that though he means to be honourable, he is so bigoted that he cannot act fairly.[2]

In answer, Wallace attempted to mollify Darwin, pointing out, with good humor, the unjustness of his complaints:

I must say . . . I do not see any great reason to complain of the "words" left out by Mivart, as they do not seem to me materially to affect the meaning. Your expression "and tends to depart in a slight degree", I think hardly grammatical; a *tendency* to depart cannot be very well said to be in a slight degree; a departure can, but a tendency must be either a *slight tendency* or a *strong tendency;* the degree to which the departure may reach must depend on favourable or unfavourable causes in addition to the tendency itself. Mivart's words, "and tending to depart from the parental type", seem to be quite unobjectionable as a paraphrase of yours, because the "tending" is kept in; and your own view undoubtedly is that the tendency may lead to an ultimate departure to any extent. . . . I do not see that the expression he uses really favours his view a bit more than if he had quoted your exact words.[3]

With respect to Mivart's general criticism and the spirit in which it was carried on, he continued:

In your chapter on Natural Selection the expressions "extremely slight modifications", "every variation even the slightest", "every grade of constitutional difference", occur, and these have led to errors such as Mivart's. I say all this because I feel sure that Mivart would be the last to intentionally misrepresent you, and he has told me that he was sorry the word "infinitesimal", as applied to variations used by Natural Selection, got into his book, and that he would alter it, as no doubt he has done, in his second edition.

. . . . As to all his minor arguments, I feel with you that they leave Natural Selection stronger than ever, while the two or three main arguments do leave a lingering doubt in my mind of some fundamental organic law of development of which we have as yet no notion.[4]

A few days later, having just read the recently published review of the *Descent* in the *Quarterly,* Darwin again wrote to Wallace. Parts of this letter are of interest in tracing the metamorphosis of Darwin's interpretation of the nature of Mivart's criticisms:

I feel very doubtful how far I shall succeed in answering Mivart; it is so difficult to answer objections to doubtful points and make the discussion readable. I shall make only a selection. The worst of it is that I cannot possibly hunt through my references for isolated points; it would take me three weeks of intolerably hard work. . . .

P.S. There is a most cutting review of me in the *Quarterly.* I have only read a few pages. The skill and style make me think of Mivart. I shall soon be viewed as the most despicable of men. This *Quarterly* review tempts me to republish Ch. Wright, even if not read by anyone, just to show that someone will say a word against Mivart, and that his (i.e. Mivart's) remarks ought not to be swallowed without some reflection.

I quite agree with what you say that Mivart fully intends to be honourable; but he seems to have the mind of a most able lawyer retained to plead against us, and especially against me. God knows whether my strength and spirit will last out to write a chapter versus Mivart and others; I do so hate controversy, and I feel I should do it badly.

He concluded this plaintive note with a second postscript, "I have finished the review; there can be no doubt it is by Mivart, and wonderfully clever." [5] To this Wallace replied, "I don't think Mivart could have written the *Quarterly* article, but I will look at it and shall, I think, be able to tell." [6]

Wallace was, in fact, wrong in his judgment. To the close reader the similarities between the review and the *Genesis* were too numerous and too fine to preserve for long the anonymity of the author of the former. As Huxley pointed out, mockingly, "there are some curious similarities between Mr. Mivart and the Quarterly Reviewer, and these are sometimes so close, that, if Mr. Mivart thought it worth while, I think he might make out a good case of plagiarism against the Reviewer, who studiously abstains from quoting him." [7]

As the summer went by, the bitterness became more acute. On September 16, in a letter to his close friend, J. D. Hooker, Darwin complained:

Every one of his cases, as it seems to me, can be answered in a fairly satisfactory manner. He is very unfair, and never says what he must have known could be said on my side. He ignores the effect of use, and what I have said in all my later books and editions on the direct effects of the conditions of life and so-called spontaneous variation. . . . [8]

The public excoriation of the apostate—and this in the popular press—was reserved for Huxley. Toward the end of the summer of 1871 he began, while at Edinburgh, the review which was to appear as "Mr. Darwin's Critics" in the *Contemporary Review*. In this article, which Huxley's son and biographer regarded as "one of the most deadly in the history of controversy," the most articulate voice of the new science attacked Mivart not only as the author of the *Genesis* but also as the suspected "Quarterly Reviewer" who, he felt, was far too contemptuous of Darwin.

"I have been reading Mivart's book," he wrote Hooker from Scotland on September 11, "and the devil has tempted me to follow up his very cocky capsuling of Catholic theology based as he says upon Father Suarez. So I got some of the old Jesuit's folios out of the Library here and have been revelling in scholastic philosophy and catholic theology with the effect of discovering that Master Mivart either gushes without reading or reads without understanding. Frater Suarez would have damned him forty times over for holding the views he does. I am sorry," he continued, "as Mivart is clever and not a bad fellow but he allows himself to be insolent to Darwin and I mean to pin him out. Only fancy my vindicating Catholic orthodoxy against the Papishes themselves." [9]

Hooker wrote of the forthcoming Huxleyan article to Darwin, who replied:

I am glad to hear about Huxley. You never read such strong letters as Mivart wrote to me about respect towards me, begging that I should call on him, etc., etc; yet in the *Q. Review* he shows the greatest scorn and animosity towards me, and with uncommon cleverness says all that is most disagreeable. He makes me the most arrogant, odious beast that ever lived. I cannot understand him; I suppose that accursed religious bigotry is at the root of it. Of course he is quite at liberty to scorn and hate me, but why take such trouble to express something more than Friendship? It has mortified me a great deal.[10]

And in a letter to Huxley a few days later, complimenting him on his forthcoming critique, he wrote:

Your letter has pleased me in many ways to a wonderful degree. I laughed over Mivart's soul till my stomach contracted into a ball, but that is a horrid sensation which you will not know. What a wonderful man you are to grapple with those old metaphysico-divinity books. It quite delights me that you are going to some extent to answer and attack Mivart. His book, as you say, has produced a great effect: yesterday I perceived the reverberations from it even from Italy. It was this that made me ask Chauncey Wright to publish at my expense his article, which seems to me very clever, though ill-written. He has not knowledge enough to grapple with Mivart in detail. I think that there can be no doubt that he is the author of the article in *Q. Review,* in which he shows such scorn and spite towards me; this has mortified me, as he professed warm friendship towards me. Did you notice how cooly he assumes, with-

out consulting my authorities, that I had mistaken the malar bone
and premaxilla. I sent to Italy and have received a fresh paper on
subject. I am preparing a new Edit. of Origin and shall introduce
a new chapter in answer to miscellaneous criticisms, and shall give
up greater part to answer Mivart's cases of difficulty of incipient
structures being of no use; and I find it can be done easily. He
never states his case fairly and makes wonderful blunders. I have
just had through great kindness of A. Agassiz abstract of his unpublished observations on the pediculariae of Echinodermata, showing
beautifully their gradation and useful development. I shall confine
myself to details and not enter on any general discussion with
Mivart. His Genesis at first appeared to me very formidable, on the
principle of aggregation; but after maturely considering all that he
has said, I never before in my life felt so convinced of the *general*
truth of the Origin. The pendulum is now swinging against our
side, but I feel positive it will soon swing the other way; and no
mortal man will do half as much as you in giving it a start in the
right direction, as you did at the first commencement. God forgive
me for writing so long and egotistical a letter; but it is your fault,
for you have delighted me: I never dreamed that you would have
time to say a word in defense of the cause which you have so often
defended. It will be a long battle, after we are dead and gone, as
we may infer from Malthus even yet not being understood. Great
is the power of misrepresentation. . . . [11]

From another of the Darwinian circle, the physicist Tyndall,
Huxley received the approving remark that "Mivart you have
handled most admirably. The remarks about his 'Guidance'
are excellent and will give satisfaction to all good men." [12]
And Hooker's extensive reply offered strong support:

There is irony in your going in for Suarez in Scotland: Were not
his works burnt by James I? I have just glanced again at Mivart's
last chapter; it is curious for the illustrations it adduces pro and
con his views, which seem to have been sought with zeal and produced without discretion. The pages on the attributes of an Almighty God are hopelessly vague and common place. And I never
had much respect for the God who originates *derivatively*. His
"God inscrutable" is no better or worse for me than Spencer's "God
unknowable" who he won't have! Given a God who can be in two
places at once and can give his whole mind to two things at once—
and it is mighty little odds whether you call him inscrutable or unknowable in reference either to his disposal of events, or to our consideration of him or his attributes!
The whole scheme of "Derivative Creation" in its religious aspects
always seemed to me a poor makeshift—a sweet to the physic of evo-

lution; and I should indeed be astonished if the Jesuit fathers' conceptions of creation squared with this. All they contended for, I assume, was that God made beasts and birds out of solids and not out of vacuum.

I see that as far as possible Mivart gives Providence a wide berth—well for him.

If I understand him aright he believes in an original creation of soul in every man (not a derivative one)—it is a pity that he had not expanded that idea; he could scarce have escaped the pitfalls of Heredity in reference to the attributes of the soul, i.e. of all we know of what we call soul—which I take it is simply a mixed idea.[13]

Nine days later, having read the proof of Huxley's soon-to-be published attack, Darwin wrote in admiration:

It was very good of you to send the proof-sheets, for I was *very* anxious to read your article. I have been delighted with it. How you do smash Mivart's theology; it is almost equal to your article versus Comte,—that never can be transcended. Mivart under his mild and pleasing and modest manners must have a good stick of self-sufficiency, not to say arrogance. Nothing will hurt him so much as this part of your review. But I have been preeminently glad to read your discussion on his metaphysics, especially about reason and his exposition of it. I felt sure he was wrong, but having only common observation and sense to trust to, I did not know what to say in my 2nd Edit. of Descent. Now a footnote and a reference to you will do the work. Good Heavens what a mess he has made of it. For me, this is one of the most important parts of the Review. But for *pleasure*, I have been particularly glad that my words on the distinction if it can be so called, between Mivart's two germs of morality caught your attention. I am so pleased that you take the same view, and give authorities for it; but I searched in vain on this head. How well you argue the whole case. I am mounting climax on climax; for after all there is nothing, I think, better in your whole review than your argument v. Wallace on intellect of savages. I must tell you what Hooker said to me a few years ago—"When I read Huxley, I feel quite infantile in intellect." By Jove I have felt the truth of this throughout your review. What a man you are. There are scores of splendid passages, and vivid flashes of wit.

I have been a good deal more than merely pleased by the concluding part of your Review; and all the more, as I own I felt mortified by Mivart's accusation of bigotry, arrogance, etc. in the *Q. Review*, as he had expressed friendship, and as I liked him. But I spare you, he may write his worst and he will never mortify me again. . . .

P.S. What you say about Mivart writing differently when anonymous and with his name is true. In the Month, which preceded the Genesis, he used coarse abuse about Pangenesis and called it grossly atheistical—the most atheistical production which he had ever read, or something to that effect. In Scientific Opinion the Editor included a footnote to the effect that it must not be supposed that the writer of the article in the Month wished to depreciate me, —a good instance of he who excuses himself assures himself.[14]

The clearest expression of the turn which the dispute had taken can be gained from a brief exchange between Darwin and Hooker, his "best of friends," early in October of 1871, soon after the appearance of Huxley's review. Hooker wrote:

I return Huxley's article which I have read with all the admiration I can express. What a wonderful Essayist he is, and incomparable critic, and defender of the faithful. Well I think you are avenged on your enemy—but are not the happier for that—though you must be for the spirit and body which the avenger has given to the subject, and above all for the grand use he has made of your own arguments for confuting your enemy. What you must feel, and always feel, is that peculiar and quite unreasonable bitter sorrowing which a man excites who praises you to your face and abuses you behind your back. Why should this excite anything but contempt at worst, or pity at best? And yet there is no man with generous emotions but feels more sad and sorry over such treatment than either angry or vindictive.[15]

To which Darwin replied:

I am quite delighted that you think so highly of Huxley's article. I was afraid of saying all I thought about it, as nothing is so likely as to make anything appear flat. I thought of, and quite agreed with, your former saying that Huxley makes one feel quite infantile in intellect. He always thus acts on me. I exactly agree with what you say on the several points in the article and I piled climax on climax of admiration in my letter to him. I am not so good a Christian as you think me, for I did enjoy my revenge on Mivart. He (i.e. Mivart) has just written to me as cool as a cucumber, hoping my health is better, etc. My head, by the way, plagues me terribly and I have it light and rocking half the day.[16]

Thus, in a few short months, the "skillful" and "honourable" opponent had become a bigoted and hypocritical "enemy."

2

Composed in cold anger, Huxley's review was biting, a slashing condemnation not only of Mivart's theological and scientific arguments but of his personal motives as well. It was the public chastisement of the apostate.

But it was more. It was a proclamation that between the new science and theology there was—there could be—no middle way, no reconciliation, no common ground.

This attack stemmed from the fundamental aspect of Huxley's regard for science: his profound belief that science was a province of investigation dealing with the real, the sensible, the knowable, and that, consequently, it could have no truck with religious supernaturalism. To allow the intrusion of religious arguments into scientific discussions was, he felt, to display a basic ignorance of what science really was. In addition he felt strongly the inhibiting force of religious belief and dogma—particularly as it expressed itself in medieval Catholicism. While not expressly intolerant, he was content only to recognize religion in general as perhaps useful or even valuable for others, while rejecting it for himself because its basic propositions were unknown and unknowable. Science must not be fettered with beliefs or prejudices derived from such an unknowable basis. "The student of science," he wrote,

who is satisfied that the evidence upon which the doctrine of evolution rests, is incomparably stronger and better than that upon which the supposed authority of the Book of Genesis rests, will not trouble himself further with . . . theologies, but will confine his attention to such arguments against the view he holds as are based upon purely scientific data—and by scientific data I do not merely mean the truths of physical, mathematical, or logical science, but those of moral and metaphysical science. For by science, I understand all knowledge which rests upon evidence and reasoning of a like character to that which claims our assent to ordinary scientific propositions. For if any one is able to make good the assertion that his theology rests upon valid evidence and sound reasoning, then it appears to me that such theology will take its place as a part of science.

The present antagonism between theology and science does not arise from any assumption by the men of science that all theology must necessarily be excluded from science, but simply because they are unable to allow that reason and morality have two weights and two measures; and that the belief in a proposition, because authority tells you it is true, or because you wish to believe it, which is a high crime and a misdemeanor when the subject matter of reasoning is one kind, becomes under the alias of "faith" the greatest of all virtues when the subject matter of reasoning is of another kind.[17]

Towards Catholicism, however, perhaps sharing the general distrust of its theology which was common in nineteenth-century England, he was much more bitter, feeling that the Catholic Church was the "vigorous and consistent enemy of the highest intellectual, moral, and social life of mankind." [18]　Though Mivart was convinced that the reconciliation of evolution with Catholic theology was possible, and had devoted a portion of the *Genesis* to demonstrating this, much of Huxley's review was an attempt to prove that Mivart's proposition was a snare and a delusion, untenable either under Catholic belief or under the nature of evolution itself.　In fact, Huxley stated with some contempt that "in addition to the truth of the doctrine of evolution, indeed, one of its greatest merits in my eyes, is the fact that it occupies a position of complete and irreconcilable antagonism" to the Catholic Church.[19]　With an attitude such as this, it is not surprising that he should have seized upon the opportunity given him by the publication of the *Genesis* to state his position clearly, particularly since he felt that Mivart, by dragging in the theological position, was muddying the waters of the scientific question.

The point of issue was a simple one, although one by no means easy to adjudicate.　Mivart, through quotations from orthodox Catholic sources, had sought to demonstrate that, contrary to popular belief, nothing in the writings of Church authorities condemned as heresy a belief in organic evolution; he maintained, in fact, that, in so far as the limited data available to these authorities allowed, they expressly considered organic evolution a possible explanation for species variation.

Huxley could not agree; with his knowledge of Catholicism, he was astonished that anyone should even attempt to establish such a position, and, as he wrote,

My astonishment reached its climax when I found Mr. Mivart citing Father Suarez as his chief witness in favour of the scientific freedom enjoyed by Catholics—the popular repute of that learned theologian and subtle casuist not being such as to make his works a likely place of refuge for liberality of thought.　But in these days, when Judas Iscariot and Robespierre, Henry VIII and Catiline, have all been shown to be men of admirable virtue, far in advance of their age, and consequently the victims of vulgar prejudice, it was obviously possible that Jesuit Suarez might be in a like case. And, spurred by Mr. Mivart's unhesitating declaration, I hastened to acquaint myself with such of the works of the great Catholic divine as bore on the question, hoping, not merely to acquaint myself with the true teachings of the infallible Church, and free myself of an unjust prejudice; but, haply, to enable myself, at a pinch, to put some Protestant bibliolater to shame, by the bright example of Catholic freedom from the trammels of verbal inspiration.[20]

To that end, he read up on Suarez while in Scotland and found, according to his reading, that Mivart "either misquoted or misunderstood him"; and through a judicious use of quotations from the original he taxed Mivart with his error, using that error as a means of reiterating his position that "the contradiction between Catholic verity [as expressed by Suarez] and Scientific verity is complete and absolute, quite independently of the truth or falsehood of the doctrine of evolution." [21]

The implications of this Huxleyan attack were obvious. By apparently catching Mivart in an error of interpretation of his sources, he upended one of the most fundamental of his theses, one, in fact, from which much of his philosophico-scientific synthesis was derived.

In using this theological argument as a major one in his refutation of "Mivartism," Huxley was more controversial than objective, and fell, consequently, into the error of overgeneralization. Mivart did not, as an actual fact, cite Suarez as his "chief witness," but merely as one of several Church fathers who, although by no means actually foreseeing evolution as a scientific doctrine, had fully provided for its acceptance in the old philosophy. Reaffirming his argument more strongly, an argument that "in truth, no possible development of physical science (and as to Biology I claim to speak with some slight knowledge) can conflict with Christian dogma, and therefore every attempt to attack from that basis is necessarily futile," [22] Mivart, in his reply to Huxley, refused to admit his interpretation. After throwing additional excerpts from Suarez into the breach, he noted:

These passages are not, let it be recollected, adduced to show that Suarez held the doctrine of evolution, or that he maintained as a fact that species were evolved, except in peculiar cases, or that he took St. Augustin's view as to the fact of creation; but to demonstrate that he distinctly admits *principles compatible* with evolution, and that even where he asserts direct and immediate divine action, yet that even there the exceptions he admits bring out still more clearly how completely I was justified in adducing him as a witness to the compatibility of evolution with the principles of scholastic philosophy.[23]

But even if he were wrong and Huxley right, he continued, this would in no way invalidate his position, since there are many other authorities who could be used—and from these he quotes extensively.

Whatever the merits of either position in this immediate controversy over scholastic sources, it is significant in the interpretation of the motivating forces of the whole dispute between Mivart and the Darwinians. The use of this single argument, and a minor one at that, to prejudice Mivart's position from both a scientific and philosophical point of view is indicative of Huxley's attitude towards the Church. It is not difficult to agree with Mivart in his suggestion that "with the extreme hatred of Catholicity which animates my critic, it is easy to understand the irritation which my demonstration of the harmony which exists between the Church and modern science has caused him." [24]

The importance attached to this particular argument is reflected in the comments of both Darwin and Hooker, who were not displeased to have Mivart so thoroughly demolished on his own grounds. Nearly half of Huxley's review, which was directed against Wallace as well as Mivart, concerns itself with this single aspect of the theological question, while almost the whole of the remainder, where it does not deal with Wallace, attempts to refute Mivart's distinctions between human and animal intellect, a refutation which reads strangely a century later. As for his scientific objections to Darwinism, Mivart could justifiably complain that his critic had, to an important extent, ignored them.

The same fervor with which Huxley attacked the abhorrent theological notions characterizes that portion of the review devoted to Mivart's putative insolence to Darwin.

Mivart's remarks of a personal nature fall into two categories. The first, and less important, is that in which Mivart repeatedly reminds the reader that Darwin was not the sole originator of the theory which had come to carry his name. Mivart was careful, perhaps too careful, to pay tribute to Wallace as the co-discoverer of the hypothesis of natural selection. Such statements Huxley righteously regarded as an "oblique and entirely unjustifiable attempt to depreciate Mr. Darwin." Perhaps they were. To Mivart's mind, however, it was justifiable and, in a sense, honorable, to set the record straight.[25] He felt, perhaps too strongly and with insufficient reason, that too much homage and trust was being tendered Darwin in admiration for a mind which some might regard as superhuman because of its ability to give birth to the evolutionary theory. To counter such hero-worship, that could lead only to a degradation of science, which must be based on the authority of fact alone and not that of a person, he felt it necessary to point out that the theories laid down in the *Origin,* a book ranked by some alongside Newton's *Principia,* were a product of the times and could emerge from the minds of at least two independent investigators. Furthermore, Mivart was extremely careful, in his own writings and in his treatment of those of others, regarding the matter of priority. It is not surprising that, with his regard for and friendship toward Wallace, he should seek to pay his friend the honor due him. When set alongside many other passages in both works, in which lavish praise is paid Darwin for his many contributions to the natural sciences, these alleged depreciations pale into insignificance; and it takes a mind peculiarly sensitive to and perceptive of the nature of personal criticism and invective to regard them in that light.

The same may be said for the more numerous passages of the second category in which Mivart takes Darwin to task for errors of method, of fact, or of philosophical view, in order to demonstrate the fallibility of the prophet. As works of criticism, neither the *Genesis* nor the review lacks statements which are critical of the author of the doctrines under review. Naturally, these critical remarks are not laudatory; nor were they intended to be. But neither can such references as these from the pen of an avowed critic be construed either as "insolent" or as "unjust and unbecoming," as they were both by Huxley and by others of the Darwinian circle. When they are balanced against statements of admiration toward Darwin, contained in the same works, it is difficult to see how such critical remarks could have been interpreted as personal abuse. In actual fact, Mivart set forth his position, and the need for the apparently personal references he used, in his forthright reply to Huxley. His "object," he wrote, "was to show that the Darwinian theory is untenable, and that natural selection is *not the* origin of species. This was and is my conviction purely as a man of science, and I maintain it upon scientific grounds only." [26] Continuing, he replied to the specific charge of indulging in personal remarks as arguments:

> Professor Huxley blames the *Quarterly Reviewer's* treatment of Mr. Darwin as "unjust and unbecoming", because he endeavours to show how Mr. Darwin has changed his ground without (in spite of his generally scrupulous candour) disavowing "natural selection" as *the* origin of species.
> I confess that it seems to me that the reviewer was fully justified in so doing; for Mr. Darwin's reputation as a man of science stands so high, that it was plainly the reviewer's duty to endeavour to prevent the public attaching, in mere deference to Mr. Darwin's authority, a greater weight to his assertions than the evidence adduced warranted. . . . [27]

With respect to Darwin, however, as opposed to Darwinism, he continued:

> In common, I am sure, with all those who have been privileged to know not only Mr. Darwin's works, but Mr. Darwin himself, I have ever entertained, and shall continue to entertain for that amiable gentleman and most accomplished naturalist the warmest sentiments of esteem and regard. Convinced as I am that he is actuated by a pure love of truth, admiring, nay, venerating him for his acute, his unwearied and widely-extended researches, it has been to me a most painful task to stand forth as his avowed and public opponent. The struggle between my inclination to praise and to acquiesce, and my sense of duty which impelled me to dissent, led me to express myself very imperfectly, and I thank Professor Huxley for thus giving me occasion to acknowledge my regret that those sentiments should have led me to give such very inadequate expression to my

dissent from, and reprobation of, Mr. Darwin's views, especially as manifested in their later developments.[28]

Differences over particular points of fact or interpretation could not conceal, however, the underlying theme of the dispute. Huxley was arguing a fundamental point of view; and Mivart knew it. How deeply he felt the point of his teacher's criticism can be seen in the vehemence of his reply. In this he made one last desperate attempt to stop the advance of an error he so much dreaded. The initial paragraphs set the tone for the whole, place it in its proper frame of reference, and make clear that the author understood the meaning of Huxley's review in terms of the personal intimacy which had once existed between them. "On reading the criticism," he began,

> I felt that, as a subaltern in science, I was being severely reprimanded by my superior officer; that I might apprehend a sentence of degradation to the ranks, if not actual expulsion from the service. I found myself taxed, if not with positive desertion to an enemy with whom no truce is allowed, yet, at least, suspected of treasonable communication with a hostile army, and treacherous dalliance with ministers of Baal.
>
> Now, recognising as I do that, in physical science, Professor Huxley is *indeed* my superior officer, having his just claims to respect and deference on the part of all men of science, I also feel that I am under special obligation to him, both many and deep, for knowledge imparted and for ready assistance kindly rendered. No wonder then that the expression of vehement disapproval is painful to me.
>
> It was not however without surprise that I learned that my one unpardonable sin—the one great offence disqualifying me for being "a loyal soldier of science"—was my attempt to show that there is no real antagonism between the Christian revelation and evolution.[29]

Mivart's excommunication from the new science had begun.

3

With this reply in the *Contemporary Review*, the initial phase of the dispute was ended. But although some semblance of his former relations with Darwin and Huxley remained, a rift had unquestionably developed that was not only professional but personal. With respect to Darwin, Mivart later wrote that "for a time, I succeeded in soothing his susceptibility, and friendly visits and pleasant intercourse continued," [30] but it is difficult to imagine that there was any renewal of the former warmth of the relationship, particularly in view of Darwin's expressed attitude toward his critic. The same can be said for Mivart's friendship with Huxley. "By degrees," wrote Mivart, "I became more and more painfully and distinctly aware of the widening of the 'rift within the lute.' Nor did I, nor could I, wonder at it. He was devotedly, chivalrously attached to Charles Darwin. . . . I felt the strain it must be on Professor Huxley to continue friendly with me in the position I had felt bound to assume, and, indeed, he once said to me, 'One cannot go on running with the hare and hunting with the hounds.' " [31] Relations of at least a superficially friendly sort continued. Although Mivart spent little time in London from early in 1872 until the middle of 1874, he still saw Huxley occasionally, even enrolling his son as a student of Huxley's at the School of Mines in South Kensington. [32]

It was not long, however, until circumstances favored a renewal of the controversy, the personal effects of which had been mitigated to some extent by the passage of time. With this renewal the personal estrangement became complete.

The immediate occasion for the final, irreparable breach between Mivart and the Darwinian circle occurred through what Darwin's son George, who in the early 1870s was beginning to write articles for the popular reviews in support of Galtonian eugenics, considered to be a personal and unwarranted attack.

In the July, 1874, number of the *Quarterly Review,* Mivart published anonymously, as was the practice, a review of the recent works of Tylor and Lubbock on primitive man. [33] He took this occasion, and the facts adduced by the developing school of anthropology, to support and reiterate his beliefs in the uniqueness of man in terms of his psychological or mental attributes. In the course of the article for illustrative purposes, he referred to a recently published article [34] of the younger Darwin which dealt, from a eugenics point of view, with the desirability of instituting certain restrictions on marriage in order to inhibit the hereditary transmission of mental illnesses. Endeavoring to show that one of the distinctive characteristics

of human existence is not only progress but also degeneracy,
Mivart used what he considered to be certain views of the
eugenists to illustrate the degenerative trends in modern society. One paragraph read:

Another triumph of the same Christian period has been the establishment of at least a pure theory of sexual relations and the protection of the weaker sex against the selfishness of male concupiscence.
Now, however, marriage is the constant subject of attack, and unre-
strained licentiousness theoretically justified. Mr. George Darwin
proposes that divorce should be made consequent on insanity, and
cooly remarks that, should the patient recover, he would suffer in
no other respect than does *anyone* that is forced by ill-health to
retire from any career he has begun (!); "although, of course, the
necessary isolation of the parent from the children *would be a particularly bitter blow.*" Elsewhere he speaks in an approving strain
of the most oppressive laws, and of the encouragement of vice in
order to check population. There is no hideous sexual criminality
of Pagan days that might not be defended on the principles advocated by the school to which this writer belongs. This repulsive
phenomenon affords a fresh demonstration of what France of the
Regency and Pagan Rome long ago demonstrated; namely, how
easily the most profound moral corruption can co-exist with the
most varied appliances of a complex civilization.[35]

In this reference Mivart made a tremendous blunder—as he
was soon to discover.

His interpretation of George Darwin's remarks is only partially correct; and that which is incorrect is of such a nature as
to constitute real libel, particularly within a social atmosphere
which prided itself on its high level of morality and humanitarianism. It is true that George Darwin, operating under the
illusion that all forms of insanity were hereditary, did advocate
divorce on condition of insanity in order that that defect might
have no chance of being transmitted to the potential offspring.
It is also true that in the body of his article he included a catalogue of marital restrictions among other peoples and at other
times, restrictions which must have been read with horror by
the subscribers to the *Contemporary Review*. So much is true.
The younger Darwin did not, however, speak of such restrictions in "an approving strain"; he used these instances only as
illustrations of the fact that the freedom of the individual to

marry has at all times and in all societies been subject to social restrictions, thus permitting the hope that the particular restrictions he proposed might, at some time in the future, also be sanctioned by an "enlightened public opinion" in the interests of the welfare of the society and the progress of the race. Nor does he speak of vice, either approvingly or disapprovingly, in connection with population checks but merely advocates the granting of divorce on condition of criminality and vice.

One can well imagine the reaction to such a breach of ethics. The error was in reality compounded because it dealt with terms and institutions of such moral force. "Vice," "divorce," "oppressive laws"—these were loaded words; and the unwarranted ascription of support for their extension was, indeed, tantamount to slander at the height of the long Victorian era.

George Darwin, righteously indignant, took the unusual step of replying by letter to the unfounded accusations in the pages of the *Quarterly Review*.[36]   With respect to the charges involving his approval of vice, oppressive laws, and sexual criminality, he declared each to be "absolutely false and groundless." To this letter is appended Mivart's defense which, while seemingly retracting the assertions proved to be false, in no way constituted the apology called for under the circumstances. Beginning with an apparent disclaimer,

Nothing could have been further from our intention than to tax Mr. Darwin personally (as he seems to have supposed) with the advocacy of laws or acts which he saw to be oppressive or vicious. We therefore, most willingly accept his disclaimer, and are glad to find that he does not, in fact, apprehend the full tendency of the doctrines which he helped to propagate. Nevertheless we cannot allow that we have enunciated a single proposition which is either "false" or "groundless," [37]

he concludes with an indictment almost equal to that contained in his original article:

We would further remind Mr. Darwin that the words, "there is no sexual criminality of Pagan days which might not be defended on the principles advocated by the school to which this writer belongs," by no means imply that Mr. Darwin himself has in his essay defended such crimes.   We expressly disown the interpretation which he puts upon our words. We spoke of the school, and not of an individual. But when a writer, according to his own confession, comes before the public "to attack the institution of marriage," even though it be "only in so far as that certain changes therein are required," (such changes being, in our opinion, fatal in their tendency), he must expect searching criticism; and, without implying that Mr. Darwin has in "thought" or "word" approved of anything which he wishes to disclaim, we must still maintain that the doctrines which he advocates are most dangerous and pernicious.[38]

Not unnaturally this attack was construed as a renewal of the old controversy. Charles Darwin took the passage as a direct and slanderous insult upon his son and, through him, upon himself. In a letter to Wallace, he wrote: "I care little about myself; but Mr. Mivart, in an article in the *Quarterly Review* (which I know was written by him), accused my son George of encouraging profligacy, and this without the least foundation. I can assert this positively, as I laid George's article and the *Quarterly Review* before Hooker, Huxley, and others, and all agreed that the accusation was a deliberate falsification. . . . Well, he has gained his object in giving me pain, and, good God, to think of the flattering, almost fawning speeches which he has made to me! I wrote, of course, to him to say that I would never speak to him again. I ought, however, to be contented, as he is the one man who has ever, as far as I know, treated me basely." [39] The letter to Mivart, apparently no longer extant, breaking off personal relations, must have been extremely severe; for Mivart, in an unpublished letter to Huxley, excused himself for not making a direct apology to Charles Darwin by saying "that I never thought of writing Mr. Darwin, Sr. because from his expression in the last letter I received from him I thought he would much rather I should not."

Darwin's friends rallied to his defense and sympathized with the personal hurt caused him by what seemed to be so unwarranted and spiteful an attack. Huxley commiserated with him, writing:

I entirely sympathize with your feeling about the attack on George. If anybody tries that on with my boy L., the wolf will show all the fangs he has left by that time, depend upon it. . . .

You ought to be like one of the blessed gods of Elysium, and let the inferior deities do battle with the infernal powers. Moreover, the severest and most effectual punishment for this sort of moral assassination is quietly to ignore the offender and give him the cold shoulder. He knows why he gets it, and society comes to know why, and though society is more or less of a dunderhead it has honourable instincts, and the man in the cold finds no cloak that will cover him.[40]

Huxley, however, was not content to ignore the offender. He felt too strongly the injustice of Mivart's accusation. "I will not leave a square inch of unwaled skin upon his idolatrous carcass before I have done with him," he wrote Hooker. "On reading the article over again I came upon the passage in which Darwin is accused of concealing his opinions about the 'bestiality of man.' Well you will see truly that I can't be charged with concealing my opinion about the bestiality of Mivart. I am in great form and lead a joyful life between heaps of new work and smiting the Amalekites—the two occupations of all which are most to my taste." [41] In his rage at the most recent Amalekite, he used the occasion of a review of Haeckel's *Anthropogenie* to "call the attention of the public to the most conspicuous lapse from that journalistic honour which has happened within my recollection." Almost forgetting the book under review, Huxley struck out against the author of the anonymous *Quarterly* article:

Possessed by a blind animosity against all things Darwinian, the writer of this paper outrages decency by insinuations against Mr. George Darwin, well-calculated to damage a little-known man with the public, though they sound droll enough to those who are acquainted with my able and excellent friend's somewhat ascetic habits. . . .

The high moral tone assumed by the *Quarterly* reviewer . . . is truly edifying. Joseph Surface could not have done better. Unless I err, he is good enough to include me among the members of that school whose speculations are to bring back among us the gross profligacy of Imperial Rome. This may be doubtful. But what is not doubtful is the fact that misrepresentation and falsification are the favourite weapons of Jesuitical Rome; that anonymous slander is practice and not mere speculation; and that it is a practice, the natural culmination of which is not the profligacy of a Nero or of a Commodus, but the secret poisonings of the Papal Borgias.[42]

Apologizing for the amount of space devoted in the review to Mivart's article, Huxley wrote Haeckel:

I have written a notice of the "Anthropogenie" for the Academy, but I am so busy that I am afraid that I should never have done it— but for being put into a great passion—by an article in the *Quarterly Review* for last July, which I read only a few days ago. My friend, Mr. ——, to whom I had to administer a gentle punishment some time ago, had been at the same tricks again, but much worse than his former performance—you will see that I have dealt with him as you deal with a "Pfaffe." There are "halb-Pfaffen" as well as "halb-Affen." [43]

The month preceding the *Academy* rejoinder had generated too much emotional fervor for any conciliatory move to be successful. No mere apology could now prevent the controversy initiated several years before from reaching its ultimate conclusion. According to Mivart's son, who was then a student of Huxley's, "it was clearly evident that Huxley thought the time had then come to get matters on this basis and make a complete breach. My father was really grieved and much regretted he had used a phrase capable of being distorted in such a way. I remember hearing my father say that nothing was more remote from his mind than to hint at the possibility of suggesting anything against G. Darwin, a young man then, whom he knew slightly and rather admired." [44] Whatever Mivart's intention had been, his words were interpreted differently by Darwin's friends.

From his first acquaintance with the affair, early in December, Huxley, with his friends, had determined that the break must come. A short series of unpublished letters in the Huxley Collection tells the story of its coming.

On December 11, shortly after the appearance of Mivart's "apology" in the *Quarterly*, Huxley wrote to Hooker and, in passing, remarked that

Darwin told me the other day that the July *Quarterly* contained an infamous attack on George Darwin for which he had made them print an apology in the October *Quarterly*.

I have not had time to look at either yet. But if they are as bad as Darwin feels them to be and are the work of that d—d Jesuit

Mivart as there seems to be no doubt they are I shall cut that fellow's acquaintance.

He sticks to me like a leech and thanks me all over—having no doubt ends in view.

I haven't broken out in wholesome indignation for a long time and it would do me good.[45]

The next day Hooker answered with a plan of action consistent with the positions and reputations of those involved:

As to the G. Darwin affair I wanted to talk to you about it. Do not be in a hurry. My impression is that we should drive Mivart into a corner before taking any strong step.

Considering his, your and my official positions, we must take care that our course is clear. If it is as you and Darwin say, and I do not doubt it, the friends of G. D. ought to take united action. Why should not you, I, Busk, Allman, Lubbock, write a joint letter to Mivart telling him that internal evidence points so unequivocally to him that nothing short of his explicit denial, or full apology, can justify us in overlooking it? and take steps accordingly. Considering your previous sparring with him, and his connection with the R. C. College, we must take care that it is not said that we are activated by personal, religious, or other wrong motives, in cutting the man unheard.

I have seen Litchfield and Mr. L. about it. They are not altogether satisfied with George's work and are indisposed to have any further publicity given to the matter. This may be all very well, but it does not help us who must cut or keep on with the fellow.[46]

A week later, before Hooker's cautiously laid plans could be put into effect, Huxley decided that the time had come for him to act. Of that action he wrote Hooker:

I had no opportunity of talking to you about Mivart's affair on Thursday but it came to a catastrophe that evening. I read the July article at the club and [agreed with] Darwin's opinion about it. It is scandalous and the apology is actually insufficient. Smith ought to be ashamed of it and I shall let him know what I think, when opportunity serves.

Mivart was at the meeting in the evening; and while the swell of my indignation was still on—he came and bothered me about the MS of my Linnean paper. I told him I had settled all that with the President, in the dryest of tones, and turned my back on him to talk with someone else. Next morning I reflected that this sort of thing could not go on—and as his ghostly father, Roberts, is attending my lectures I called him aside after my lecture and asked him for a few minutes conversation.

I told him what had happened and asked him to let Mivart know my opinion about the article. I told him that I had neither right nor wish to ask if M. was the writer of the article—still less to influence the expression of his opinion—but that I had a right to regulate my own social relations. That G. Darwin was a friend for whom I had every respect and that I desired Mivart to know that I objected to have anything to do with the writer of an article which had so unjustifiably attacked a friend of mine.

Father Roberts is a gentleman and quite appreciated my views and undertook my commission. He did not tell me in so many words that Mivart wrote the article—but his manner left no doubt of the fact in my mind.

I will let you know what turns up if anything does. In the meantime I think Darwin had better let the matter rest. It is not worth his while to write to Mivart. The explosion will go down to the account of my short temper and all the desirable practical results will be obtained.

The slavery humbug has had one dressing at my hands and he knows better than to provoke another and worse.[47]

Roberts carried out his mission. The following day, Mivart, obviously distressed by the turn of events, attempted to explain his error and thus prevent the loss of a friendship which he valued so highly. Asking that his letter be kept *Private and Confidential,* he wrote Huxley:

I thank you for your consideration in selecting the channel through which to convey the message I have received. I do not write to attempt to justify the passage referred *to* (the writing of which has since caused me more pain and regret than anything I have before written) but for two reasons:

First, because I think, on account of past matters to which I have too lately referred to repeat myself now, that a reply is due from me to you.

Secondly, to make a certain statement of fact, which I ask your patience to consider and leave the results in your hands.

Extracts and notes for the article referred to were written out by me long ago and taken with me abroad for use if the opportunity offered. Amongst them were notes on Mr. Darwin's article which I read before I left England and did not take with me any more than the other works referred to or reviewed. When I wrote out at Dresden my MS for the *Quarterly* I unhappily trusted to my notes which I believed at the time to be fully justified, though I now think they were *not* and that the impression left on my mind by Mr. Darwin's paper was more vivid than a careful consideration of the words warranted.

Of course I need not say that I *never dreamed* of implying anything whatever *against Mr. Darwin personally* as it is most certain that persons of the highest character may advocate principles without in the least degree realizing their consequences, from which, in fact, they would be the first to shrink in horror.

After my return to England I made inquiry as to the article and found it was just going to press. The opportunity was offered me of looking over it which I stupidly declined to avoid trouble.

I had not read it for months and of the particular passages (including the one referred to) I had no distinct recollection. When I read it as published I was startled and vexed fearing it might give rise to misconstruction. I regretted it as I still regret it all the more because the article not appearing as *mine* I was precluded from that sort of apology and reparation which I have especially *since October* felt to be due Mr. Darwin. For when I read his letter in August I certainly felt that he erred and misunderstood me (in saying that I had written what was *"absolutely" false*) as much as *I* had misread *him.*

I have however long determined that an apology and reparation should be made to Mr. Darwin *in my own name* as a simple act of justice at the very first opportunity and if you can suggest to me a mode in which it can be performed I shall be grateful, but if you decline I shall nonetheless seize the first opportunity to perform it.

In brief, I have, through the warmth of feeling engendered by a controversy I deem *most important,* committed a fault I bitterly regret. I frankly acknowledge having done so and am anxious as far as I can to repair it. I do not know what more I can do but whatever the result I have at least the satisfaction of knowing that what I wrote was at least free from every atom of *personal hostility* and that whatever your decision as to the future I can not be deprived of those pleasant memories of the past which will never allow me to be other than yours truly and gratefully.[48]

Huxley's reply of December 23 was as coldly impersonal as his intentions were clear:

I am much obliged for the letter which you have sent me in reply to the message which Mr. Roberts was kind enough to convey from me.

The letter is marked P & C and I shall endeavour to respect your wishes in that matter so far as such a course may be consistent with justice to those concerned in its contents. You tell me that you now regret the publication of the atack on Mr. George Darwin and that the impression made upon your mind by his article and under the influence of which you wrote is not to be justified—and I gather that this regret and conviction that your attack was not justifiable have existed in your mind for some months. In fact ever since the article was published.

Under these circumstances had I been in your position there were two things I should have felt it my duty to do. In the first place I should have written to Mr. G. Darwin or to Mr. Darwin with whom you have been in friendly correspondence and offered him the fullest and frankest apology I could put into words, and in the second place, I should have requested the editors of the *Quarterly Review* to insert a note fully and fairly retracting all that could be considered unjust and therefore offensive to Mr. G. Darwin.

You did neither of these things and when an apology was extorted from the *Quarterly,* what appeared presumably with your sanction, if not from your hand, was a defense rather than a retraction.

Proceedings of this kind are not in accordance with what I understand to be the rules by which men should endeavour to guide their conduct; and as I concur with Mr. George Darwin in thinking that the charges made and insinuated against him are as he says absolutely false, it will be obvious to you that our views on those questions which *I* hold to be the most important of all mankind are too hopelessly divergent to make familiar intercourse between us pleasant and advisable.[49]

Although the finality of Huxley's answer was unmistakable, Mivart made one last effort to placate his friend. On the following day he wrote in amplification of his previous remarks:

I thank you for your letter of yesterday's date as also for your promise to respect the P & C character of these communications— a distinction which is merely temporary, namely till I have the liberty to speak openly in my own name. The way however in which you take my letter makes it necessary for me in justice to myself, to reply and define more exactly what my meaning is. You say that you gather that this regret and conviction that the attack was not justifiable was in my mind ever since the article was published —this impression of yours is not accurate. On seeing the passage as published I had a feeling of vexation lest my meaning should be misunderstood and a consequent wish that I had written in my own name and it was only since October that careful reconsideration of what Mr. Darwin wrote led me to deem that the expression I used was not in fact justified and that I found the determination to make all the reparation I could. This intention was not a mere vague one but I had a definite plan before me, the execution of which has been to my great annoyance delayed through no fault of mine.

Thus as I said in my letter I did not feel in August as I have felt since October and when the apology was made for which I take to myself the *entire responsibility* I felt it was sufficient because it seemed to me to make sufficiently plain that I did not intend to attribute to Mr. Darwin any personal slur but only an advocacy of principles leading to the consequences named without in the least meaning that he would admit the legitimacy of the inference. However I had to consider the dignity of the Review and not merely my own.

Even now I must in justice declare that bitter as is my regret and deep as is the pain I have experienced for having written as I did, that regret does not extend to the whole passage but refers to two special matters.

(1) The first of these is my having used the words "speaks in an approving strain" because a careful consideration of Mr. G. Darwin's paper has convinced me that the expression is unjustifiable except as regards the "most oppressive laws" of which it still seems to me he does speak with approval. Accordingly as to this expression I am not only willing but anxious as a simple matter of justice to retract and to apologize to Mr. Darwin expressing my very deep regret although, as was said in the apology, Mr. Darwin's tone seemed to me such as to render such a mistake "excusable" though not "justifiable."

(2) The second matter I regret is having referred to sexual matters in a passage in which an author's name was mentioned. I regretted it and I regret it very much because there are so many people stupid enough to fancy or malicious enough to represent that the Reviewer meant to imply some personal blame as to the author referred to instead of understanding, as was the fact, that the reviewer simply selected an example likely to bring out his point most forcibly and one coming naturally apropos of marriage laws. This was the misunderstanding I dreaded and to which my last letter referred.

As to the course of conduct you say you would have followed, I must in reply say that I never thought of writing to Mr. Darwin Senior, because, from his expression in the last letter I received from him, I thought he would much rather I should not. Neither did I think of writing to Mr. Darwin junior because I thought he would deem my doing so an impertinence.

The suggestion you make is new and welcome to me. Nevertheless in spite of my great regret as to the points referred to I must maintain my opinion as to the tendency of Mr. Darwin's article generally.

With respect to "hideous sexual criminality" I may say that I know a most highly cultured and intellectual man, of the school I intended to oppose, who deliberately maintains that the propagation of the criminality referred to would be most useful and beneficial to society as tending to limit population without requiring what he calls the "immorality" of ascetic self-denial.

Widely divergent as are our views as to what is most important for the welfare of mankind, I shall never, while we both live, cease to hope that that divergence may cease and even while it still exists it does not *on my side* in the least obstruct "familiar intercourse" or render it "unpleasant" *to me* because it does not on my side produce the least personal ill feeling. Of course I can only submit to your wishes in this respect but I do so with regret and with a hearty wish for many happy New Years for you and yours.[50]

It was to no avail; there was no answer.

Nor had Huxley acted for himself alone. After reading this final correspondence, both Darwin and Hooker expressed their pleasure and satisfaction with the manner in which the affair had been handled. Darwin wrote with unusual feeling:

Your letter to Mivart is a tremendous reproof to him. (I have read it again, it is tremendous.) As he now owns that he has thought himself for some time in the wrong, it makes his miserable shabby equivocating rejoinder worse. I have forwarded your note to me and a copy of the note to Mivart to Hooker, and told him to return the letter to you. As you think it best I will not write to Mivart at present, but I do not feel inclined to allow such conduct to pass without telling the author what I think of him in plain language. As for Mivart, now that he's afraid of you, saying he is sorry, it goes for nothing. He practiced a similar dodge with me about some passages in the *Genesis of Species*. Nor would a private apology to George in my opinion be at all sufficient. To my knowledge one person has been disgusted and horrified at George, from believing in the *Quarterly*. I will wait and do nothing at present, but if George receives a mere simple expression of regret, or if we do not hear, I do not think I shall resist telling him how base a man I think him. You have been, my dear Huxley, most generous in this whole affair.[51]

And Hooker, anticipating similar action on his own, wrote only that "Your action in re Mivart has been most successful. Your

letter to him of which D. sent copy to me put the screw into
the right worm and I could not help admiring the way the
turns disappeared till all but the head was sunk in his vitals.
I am most anxious to learn the result, as I shall have to write to
him whichever way he takes your discrimination and acts
upon it." [52]

The final act was Darwin's. He could not, at last, refrain
from personally severing his relationship with the friend who
he thought had so wronged him. Although his letter to
Mivart is apparently not extant, he wrote to Huxley of his
action soon after the latter's outburst in the *Academy* early
in January. "I have just received the Academy," he began,

and read with delight your article. What a man you are. I am
convinced that all the writers in England could not have written
such an article. How greatly you have defended me from the
charges of duplicity. You have also greatly honoured George. You
have indeed been a true friend to me.

Though contrary to your advice, I cannot make up my mind not
to write to Mr. Mivart and tell him with the most plainness what
I think of his conduct. There will then be no doubt, if we ever
meet, that I shall cut him dead.

What will his feelings be when he reads your article! I wish the
Bishop was alive.

P.S. As I thought it to be most disagreeable to meet Mr. Mivart
in London, without a clear understanding of the terms on which
we are to stand, I have written him a formal letter, stating his grave
offences, and saying that I should never hold any communication
with him for the future, and signing "Your obedient servant." [53]

4

And thus friendships founded upon a mutual love for and
dedication to an objective science of nature ended on the bitter
notes of personal vituperation and vain regret. The rancor
distilled in the controversies of the '70s permeated the lives of
the antagonists and made impossible any but the most formal
relationships between Mivart and his opponents. Although
after Darwin's death a semblance of the old relationship with
Huxley returned, Mivart's letters of this period reveal how
tenuous and cold the new friendship was, a pale reflection of
the warmth that had been.[54]

Others of the Darwinians were even less forgiving. The wounds opened by Mivart's attack upon Darwin and through him upon his friends and disciples were never healed; they continued to fester throughout the lifetimes of the participants. Until the day of his death Mivart was haunted by the hostility, latent and overt, of the small circle which had surrounded Darwin.

Nor was this a powerless group: Huxley and Hooker dominated the natural sciences of the latter part of the nineteenth century and were primarily responsible for the reorientation of biology about the Darwinian axis; Spencer, for all his personal unpopularity, stood for the developing social sciences; Lubbock, the anthropologist, introduced Darwinism to the study of man; and Tyndall, chemist and physicist, spoke for "materialism" in the physical sciences. Within this small group post-Darwinian science matured. Collectively, these five, with Busk the anatomist, Frankland the chemist, Hirst, a mathematician, and Spottiswoode, queen's printer, mathematician, and later president of the Royal Society, formed the "x Club," informally organized in 1864, "to afford a certain meeting ground for a few friends who were bound together by personal regard and community of scientific interests." This club, a most exclusive one, was a core of Darwinism in the immediate post-Darwinian period. The influence of its members in nineteenth-century science may be measured by the fact that, small as their numbers were, "five of them received the Royal Medal; three the Copley; one the Rumford; six were Presidents of the British Association; three Associates of the Institute of France; and from amongst them the Royal Society chose a Secretary, a Foreign Secretary, a Treasurer, and three successive Presidents." [55]

Aside, however, from their influence in the fields of science directly, they exerted strong pressures in other areas only indirectly related to their fields of competence.

It was because of this influence that Mivart's election to the Athenaeum Club—an election which was one of his lifelong desires—was thwarted. Founded in 1824 "for the association of individuals known for their literary or scientific attainments, artists in any class of the Fine Arts, noblemen and gentlemen distinguished as liberal patrons of science, Literature or the Arts," and with a membership restricted to 1200, the Athenaeum, aside from the material advantages it provided, existed as a goal of social attainment. To be elected a member was a badge of social acceptance in the upper middle class society which dominated the social and intellectual life of London during the Victorian era.

During the 1880s Mivart appears to have made several attempts to gain membership.

A first attempt at election failed even before it began, despite the fact that he had the support of such important figures as Lord Acton and Gladstone. A letter from Lord Acton to Gladstone's daughter Mary refers to this initial attempt and a later maneuver: "As Mr. Gladstone has had various correspondence with Mivart, it may interest him to know that that very distinguished philosopher, the most eminent man of science our Church has in England, was constrained to decline election at the Athenaeum, being certain of blackballs, by reason of his quarrel with the Darwinians. In the hope that the Committee may elect him, he wishes to be put down in the books again; and he asks me to propose him.[56] As I have never spoken to him in my life, it is against the rule; but I have agreed to do it, in acknowledgment of his unquestioned eminence and because of Mr. Gladstone's weakness for him, which I, otherwise, do not share. The wicked Sclater,[57] vendor of Jumbo, is the Seconder." [58]

Acton's support may have been partially gained by Mivart's own hopes and, as it turned out, wishful thinking regarding the endeavors of others within the club to aid him. To Acton he wrote in a grateful though plaintive vein:

I thank you very much for your most kind letter (received yesterday) and for your cordial promise to *propose* me which is what I so much desire. As to my chances of election by the Committee, I am fully aware how difficult a matter it is to get chosen one of the select fifteen especially when it is known that there is an influential opponent. I am therefore prepared to wait but if it is known that the opposition is small numerically and does not even include all the Darwinian set I venture to hope I may eventually succeed.

That I am not opposed by all Darwin's school is shown by the promise I received from Sir John Lubbock (before I withdrew my name) not only of his vote but also that he would exert his influence to obtain votes for me. Sir Joseph Hooker is also I think friendly towards me and Mr. Frank Balfour (now I am sorry to say ill with Typhoid fever) would—though so enthusiastic a Darwinian —also I believe support me. My seconder will (with your approval) be Dr. Sclater, the secretary of the Zoological Society and I think it better that my seconder should be a zoologist. Mr. Frederick Harrison volunteered his services on my behalf and I think I can count on men of very different views willing to say they would be glad to see me a member. My opponents, besides Huxley, would probably be Herbert Spencer and perhaps Francis Galton. I am also about to publish a small book—a dialogue on philosophy—which I trust may help me. I may say that Mr. Kegan Paul is of the opinion it will do so. I am not surprised at what you tell me of Lord Arthur Russell, for he has shown me an unvarying kindness for which I shall ever be deeply grateful to him.

Once more thanking you, my dear Lord, not only for your much valued compliance with my request but also for the exceedingly kind way in which you have expressed it.[59]

Mivart, however, underestimated the strength of the feeling against him, particularly on the part of the Darwinians. His bid, despite the sponsorship of so respected an individual as Acton, failed. The antipathy toward him is vividly revealed in a letter from Hooker to Huxley, dated November 28, 1888, in which the writer could not conceal the contempt which still persisted after so many years.

A few years ago Lord Acton asked me to second his proposal of Mivart for the Athenaeum which I incontinently refused to do.

Now I hear he is to be brought before the Committee as a fit and proper person (though not nominated for immediate election), and I am again asked (not by Lord A.) what I think of it, and whether time has not condoned his offences. I answer that the Committee has no business to elect as a member "honora causa" a man who would be blackballed otherwise, except on special grounds —as when official spite, jealousy or other unworthy motives have interfered with or would interfere with a general election and in such cases the good of the Club should be the standard for the Committee.

No one can say that the Club would benefit by Mivart's election even were he whitewashed. On the contrary it would introduce a member to be cut dead by some others.

But I have added that I doubt if Mivart's claim as a scientific man was up to the mark of a Committee Election; and upon this matter I want your confidential opinion. Can you suggest better names? I can. . . .

Acton and Mivart are brother Jesuits to the backbone. . . .

P. S. Stokes has seconded Mivart's proposer in the books.[60]

Whatever the "better names" suggested by Huxley at a meeting between the two old friends later in the week at the Royal Society, Mivart did not become a member as a result of this, apparently his last, attempt. His application was, perhaps, ill-timed; for it was submitted at the very time when, on the occasion of the publication of Darwin's *Life and Letters,* Mivart again entered the lists against the perennial specter of Darwinism.

The continuing, if not growing, antipathy toward Mivart as both man and scientist, expressed by those who were becoming the leaders of post-Darwinian science, virtually excluded him from the mainstream of science for which Darwinism was the source. This antipathy, gradually establishing the caricature of Mivart as a dogmatic and biassed opponent of Darwinism, led for all practical purposes to the negation of his more pregnant observations. As an apostate he was forgotten, relegated to the ash heap upon which lay the remains of all those who, for one reason or another, selfish or unselfish, good or bad, sought to check the wholesale acceptance of all things Darwinian. Only after his final refusal to compromise principle with authority, only after his excommunication from his Church, was he invited to return to the scientific fold. Then, it was too late.

VII. INTERLUDE

The publication of the *Genesis,* the review of the *Descent* which supplemented it, and the subsequent controversy with the Darwinians set the pattern of Mivart's future intellectual life. He was forty-three in 1871, and the point of view which these publications so pointedly expressed was to dominate his thinking in and out of science for the rest of his life. It was in the *Genesis* that he found himself as an intellectual being; rather, it was in the writing of the *Genesis* that he discovered the system in terms of which all phenomena became intelligible with little risk to the security he hoped to maintain between the sometimes contradictory pressures of a changing science and a changing theology. The appearance of the *Genesis* marked the end of the purely descriptive emphasis which had characterised Mivart's activities during the 1860s, as it marks the beginnings of his intense preoccupation with matters of a more metaphysical and interpretive nature.

To his descriptive work, he added popularization and propaganda—not only on behalf of natural science, as Huxley was to do in his later years, but for the purpose of effecting that harmonious reconciliation between the intellect and faith, that synthesis of truths from both nature and revelation, which continued to be the major goal of his life until his death. "In spite of my love of science," he confessed, "which is the deepest seated and most rooted feeling I possess . . . I have ever deemed it my highest privilege to be allowed to point out the essential harmony which exists between the truths of science and the dictates of religion." [1]

The events of the early 1870s gave Mivart a name, a reputation, and a notoriety upon which he could trade both within and without his intellectual community. He stood for the scientific opposition to the supposed materialism of the new biology and for the maintenance of Christian orthodoxy. And in the controversies between science and religion during the latter part of the nineteenth century, during which what were to be accepted as the truths of the twentieth century were being revealed, the *Genesis* marked him as an antagonist and protagonist whose name—and pen—were to be reckoned with. "I care a *very great deal*," he once wrote to Meynell, "about the cause of truth—a cause I have ever tried to serve for its own sake."[2] There is no evidence that he ever failed to serve the truth as he knew it, even at the risk of personal derogation and tragedy.

2

The crisis of 1874 and the regrets which Mivart entertained at the personal turn taken by the controversy did not abate his antagonism toward the doctrine he considered so pernicious. Nor did he lessen his efforts to combat actively and at every opportunity those who continued to set their investigations within the now-accepted Darwinian frame of reference.[3] Mivart viewed with optimism the newer developments in the natural sciences as they swiftly succeeded one another during the latter decades of the century; and in each he sought—and thought he found—additional evidence to confirm his original criticisms of Darwinism. So confident was he of the essential correctness of his view that he omitted no opportunity to restate his opposition.

Much of his later writing is devoted to the reinforcement of his original position on grounds of biology, psychology, and philosophy. In his later years, making of his wish a reality, he could maintain that not only was Darwinism scientifically dead, but that even Huxley, its most ardent supporter and defender, had turned against it.[4] Thus, though disagreeing with their approach he seized upon the work of the younger naturalists as proofs that the path to truth plotted by the earlier

Darwinians was, in reality, a blind alley.[5] He had, for instance, an ambivalent attitude to the revolutionary work of Weismann, hailing him, on the one hand, for his disproof of natural selection as the origin of species; yet, with equal vehemence, he condemned that "prolific Professor at Freiburg" for not recognizing the divine element directing the internal force upon which Mivart based his theory of species change. As he accepted uncritically, in 1871, the "proofs" of spontaneous generation adduced by Bastian,[6] since they were consistent with his own thinking, so did he view uncritically the conclusions of others when they supported his own convictions. Typical of this approach is a comment in a letter to Poulton, whose whole-hearted support of Weismann's theory of inheritance led some to consider him an anti-Darwinian. "I have," wrote Mivart in an amiable mood, "always been disposed to attribute an amphibian origin to the mammalia but the shoulder girdle of the Monotremes stuck in my gullet and I could never swallow it. Then Caldwell's discovery accentuated the affinity of the Monotremes with the Reptiles while yours showed they had been able to provide themselves with a Mammalian tooth—apparently on 'their own hook.' All this with Gegenbauer's discovery of the abnormal nature of the monotremata mammary gland seems to me to make a dual origin possible. I have always held that things may grow alike and I have believed, e.g. that the old and new world apes had quite different origins and now Cope tells us that the horse of America and the horse of Europe differed widely in phylogeny! Yet they are now no less both *Equus*. If these views prevail what becomes of the genealogical tree as the type of classification? It seems to me to be cut down root and branch. . . ."[7]

Even without the polemics occasioned by his position as chief defender of Christian orthodoxy against the assaults of Darwinian heresy, these would have been busy years for Mivart.

The years prior to his retirement from the Chair of Comparative Anatomy at St. Mary's in 1884 were full and active ones. He found himself constantly occupied in his research, in his writing, and in the various functions he was called upon to perform in the professional societies of which he was a member. Asked for an opinion of a paper submitted for publication in the Proceedings of the Zoological Society, he could but scribble a hasty note to the secretary: "Coming home at night, I found your note and the paper—I am very tired have several letters to write and start tomorrow morning *early* for Oxford— I can therefore do no more than glance at this paper. . . ." [8]

In the various societies of which he was a member he took an active part, frequently chairing the meetings of the Linnean and Zoological Societies. In 1869 he was for the first time elected vice-president of the latter society, an office which he held on several other occasions during the next thirty years. Similarly he was elected, at different times, a member of the council which administered the affairs of the Linnean Society; and at the annual meeting on June 4, 1891, he was nominated its vice-president. "His ready help in all that concerned its welfare was always conspicuous," and during the last years of his life "he was . . . its social head as Hon. Treasurer of the Linnaean Society Club."

In 1879 he served as president of the Biological Section of the British Association; and in that capacity publicly gave expression to the debt he owed—the debt all naturalists owed— to Buffon who, in his *Natural History,* had introduced him to the exciting realms of science.

Indicative, too, of his prominence as both scientist and Catholic during the 1870s was his admission to the Metaphysical Society whose membership included the intellectual elite of London. This society was organized in 1869 by James Knowles, then editor of the *Contemporary Review,* to "discuss speculative subjects." Essentially it was an attempt to attain some *rapprochement* among the diverse views consequent upon the impingement of the new science upon an older theology and philosophy. The society's membership, therefore, included men of note differing in their religious, scientific, and philosophical views. Huxley, Martineau the Unitarian, Ward and Manning the Catholics, Gladstone, Tennyson—all were among the select group who during the twelve years of the Society's existence met monthly to discuss, on the basis of prepared papers, those problems which were so vital to all of them. Mivart did not become a member until 1874; and his formal participation consisted of three papers, about average for the total of fifty-nine members.[9]

3

He also made numerous appearances before the lay public. In relatively frequent addresses, both in and out of London, he followed the lead of Huxley in an attempt to popularize not only the details of the science to which his life was dedicated but also his particular approach to the biological problems of evolution. His was a receptive audience; for his theistic approach appealed to the many to whom a concept of nature without a God was abhorrent. His appearances and his appeal as a popular lecturer on zoological subjects were enhanced by his ability to inject both enthusiasm and interest into the subjects with which he dealt. As the writer of his obituary in *Nature* noted, "he had that charm of manner and intonation which could surround with a halo of interest even the driest and apparently most unpromising subjects of zoological research, a charm of manner largely due to a suave and old-fashioned courtliness. . . ." [10]

His interest in popular science was too great to permit his efforts on its behalf to be limited to the spoken word. As deeply conscious as he was of the importance of scientific research, he recognized as well the necessity of communicating the conclusions of the specialist to the layman. For this recognition of the necessary relationship between the scientist and his community and, more particularly, the methods by which he sought to effect it, Mivart was, as in so much else, indebted to Huxley. Like Huxley, he was not content in the restricted role of the investigator; he was a teacher as well—and his class, the public at large. Deeply conscious of "the calm pleasure afforded by the intelligent contemplation of Nature," as contrasted with the "feverish pursuit of gain or the heartburnings of social competition," Mivart wished, by universal instruction in science, to afford everyone that pleasure.

To the fulfillment of this wish he devoted an increasing part of his energies from the late 1860s until the end of his life. In 1868 he had initiated a popular biological series with an article on the lobster in the *Popular Science Review*. This, together with its successors describing the cuttlefish, the echinus, man and apes, the kangaroo, and bats, sought to lay out for the untutored reader the principles of classification in particular and biology in general through the description of certain type specimens, each of which represented a much larger related category. Such an approach, the introduction to the general through a minute investigation of the particular, had been initiated by Huxley in his popular lectures; and it was upon that approach that much of his success as a teacher depended. The earlier of Mivart's articles reveal not only in their approach but in their content as well the strong influence and the rigid scientific discipline of Huxley, an influence which the student was not loath to acknowledge. "Professor Huxley," he remarked in a footnote to the initial article, "in his lectures at the School of Mines . . . selects the Lobster as his type of the annulose division of the animal kingdom. The present writer *in limine* wishes to express his obligations to the Professor not only for many of the facts here stated, but in great part for the mode of presenting them also." [11]

The significance of the early articles in this series as a device for popular education is problematical. They are, in the main, straightforward descriptive anatomies, listing pedantically, much in the fashion of the classroom lecturer of the day, all the anatomical characteristics which mark the specimen under study as a member of the category of which it has been selected as the representative. Here is descriptive anatomy at its dullest. Huxleyan though these articles may have been in inspiration, they lack the blackboard technique for which Huxley was justly famous; nor do they possess the verve springing from Huxley's mastery of the English language, which drew layman and specialist alike to the lectures of the most successful expositor of biology in the nineteenth century. These articles, furthermore, possess none of the philosophical breadth, none of the zest, none of the real understanding of what the author was about which permeate the later articles of the series and, in an even greater degree, that truly charming group of biological essays written for the *Contemporary Review* a decade later.

While part of the dullness of his early articles may be ascribed to a lack of suitable technique for the new medium of communication, much of it is in all probability due to the fact that Mivart himself at their writing was not certain of his own approach, his own point of view. In these articles he aped Huxley, transferring the notes of the lecture hall to the pages of the magazine. He was reportorial and didactic, failing to understand that his readers wished those very answers for which he himself was groping during these years. The articles which follow the *Genesis,* however, and the *Genesis* itself, are not open to such criticism. In the *Genesis* he had crystallized a point of view; and it was within its limits that his future scientific articles for popular consumption were framed. It was against the backdrop of his holistic view of the world in which, through man, the natural and spiritual are fused into a harmonious whole, that his later popular articles were written; and it is by virtue of this view that they possess their charm and their persuasion.

This approach to the subject of biology is essentially anthropocentric. Its most eloquent expression occurs in "On the Study of Natural History," the first of a series of articles in the *Contemporary Review* at the end of the 1870s, a series which represents Mivart at his best as a writer of popularized science. In answer to the question "Why study Natural History?" he wrote:

Apart, however, from such interest in it as may be due to controversies of the day, the love of this study is one which must grow upon men as they advance in the knowledge of their own organisation, owing to the very conditions of their existence. For man is so related to other living creatures, that fully to understand himself, he must, more or less thoroughly, understand them also.

Every increase in the knowledge of the organic world has its effect upon the study of man, and helps him not only towards a better knowledge of his own organisation, but also helps in the pursuit of his own happiness and in the fulfilment of his duty.

Thus man plainly shares in the most diverse powers and faculties of his material fellow-creatures, and he sees also reflected by such creatures, in varying degrees, those different kinds of existence which unite in him . . . . Unlike even the highest of the brutes however he not only feels the Cosmos, but thinks it. He is not only involved in it in an infinity of relations, but he recognizes and reflects upon many such relations, their nature, and their reciprocal bearings. "The proper study of mankind is man'; but to follow out that study completely we must have a certain knowledge of the various orders of creatures in the natures of which man, in varying degrees, participates. Man's intellect is indeed supreme, nevertheless it cannot be called into activity unless first evoked by sense impressions which he shares with lowly animals; nor can his intellect, even after it has been aroused into activity, continue to act save by constant renewal of sense impressions—real or imagined. Such impressions give rise, in him, to imaginations, reminiscences, anticipations, and emotions, which serve as the materials for the exercise of intellect and will; and as these imaginations, reminiscences, anticipations, and emotions are possessed also by brutes, it is to the study of creatures that we must have recourse to obtain one of the keys needed to unlock the mystery of man's existence.[12]

Writing of this sort was essentially controversial. It expressed a view of nature with man at the center, man the unique animal related on one side to the brute and on the other to God. Always there was man's divinity whose expressions were as clear in man's behavior as the evidences of his brutish past. In the exposition of such a world-view, Mivart sought to combat the rising tide of materialistic agnosticism which was so evident in the works of many of his contemporaries. Thus, referring to a collection of his essays which had been published in book form in 1876, he wrote, in 1883, to Wilfrid Meynell, the editor of a Catholic literary review, the *Weekly Register:* "Your correspondent . . . asks for books with satisfying answers to Spencer, Bain, etc. I wish you would say that in *Lessons from Nature* published by John Murray there are such answers. That book was written expressly to combat the whole agnostic school—Huxley, Tyndall, Bain, Mill. . . . Ward's reply is addressed to Mill's special school. Newman does not directly and expressly answer any of them. This I have tried to do and hope before many months are over to bring out a book to do so yet more fully and more popularly." [13]

It was in this spirit and with this purpose that he embarked

upon an extended series of articles critical of Spencer, a series
which appeared in the *Dublin Review* between 1874 and 1880.
These articles, coupled with a critical review written in 1873
for the *Quarterly Review,* are more than a specific attack upon
a single author and his work; they represent an ambitious attempt to combat a whole school of philosophical thought of
which Spencer was rapidly becoming the oracle.

The effect of Mivart's criticisms upon Spencer was hardly
noticeable. In replying to the review in the *Quarterly,* he
considered it "respectful, though antagonistic"; and the series
in the *Dublin Review* he thought more helpful than damaging.
To Youmans, his American editor and friend, Spencer wrote in
1874 "that Mivart is commencing in the *Dublin Review* a most
elaborate examination of the *Principles of Psychology.* He is
actually taking it chapter by chapter, and proposes, in successive
articles, to go thus through the whole of it! So far as I have
seen, his criticisms are the merest quibblings; which, besides
being baseless, do not in the least touch the general issues. But
I am quite content; he will doubtless aid in the further diffu-
sion of the work." [14]

The application of *his* view as to man's place in nature and
the pertinence of *his* philosophical frame of reference for the
progress of man and society Mivart described in two articles
which appeared in the *Nineteenth Century* in 1879. Both
were expanded versions of papers read before the Metaphysical
Society.[15] In them Mivart pitted the optimism for man's
future inherent in his divinely guided universe against that
pessimism which he considered a necessary consequence of the
degradation of man implicit in the philosophy of his opponents.
He was confident of the worthiness of his efforts to elevate man
through the facts of science and their application; and to
some extent his confidence was justified by the response from
some of his readers, a response which led him to write, charac-
teristically, to John Murray, his publisher:

Have you by chance read my two papers in the *Nineteenth Century* for March and April?
From letters I have received, from strangers, about them I am
inclined to think they might sell if reprinted as a thin book, with a

rather larger type, good paper and cut margins. One gentleman
(whose name I must of course keep secret) has written to me to say
I have converted him from advocating Euthanasia and the murder
of deformed children.

And preachers have recommended my articles from the pulpit to
their congregations.

Would you be disposed to republish the articles in the way I
suggest? [16]

Although—or perhaps because—Mivart's series on *Contemporary Evolution,* written in a similar vein and with a similar
purpose, had been so republished three years earlier, Murray
respectfully declined the invitation so temptingly offered.

More ambitious than his popular science articles in the various reviews was a series of books designed to instruct not only
the layman but also the student of the whole of zoology.

Like popular science itself, science education and the consequent production of adequate texts was a product of the
renascence in the natural sciences which was epitomized in
Darwin's *Origin.* Prior to the middle of the nineteenth century, natural science was not usually a subject looked upon with
favor as a part of the university curriculum except when it had
a direct bearing upon such of the practical arts as medicine.

With the growth of scientific interest around the middle of
the nineteenth century, however, and the gradual inclusion of
courses in natural science as independent elements within the
universities and public schools, textbooks, manuals, and hand-
books in the various fields of biology became a necessity.

While he could say that he preferred the student not to dis-
tract his mind by reading such texts, it was Huxley who pioneered in the development of this contemporary biology text.
Those which were produced either by his pen or under his
supervision bore the stamp of his own successful teaching technique which "in plain and concise language" separated "the
well-established and essential from the doubtful and the unimportant portions of the vast mass of knowledge and opinion"
in biology.

As in so much else, Mivart followed Huxley's lead. In Macmillan's valuable and pioneering biological series of "Elementary Lessons," of which Huxley's *Elementary Lessons in Physi-*

ology was the first to be published in 1866, Mivart wrote the second. His *Lessons in Elementary Anatomy* was published in 1873 and met with an immediate success as a worthy companion to its counterpart in physiology. Flushed with the success of his first textbook, Mivart attempted two more: *The Common Frog* in 1874, based upon an extended series of articles in *Nature;* and *The Cat* in 1881. Although neither of these received the laudatory notices earned by the *Lessons,* each was regarded in its own way, as "tinged throughout with the author's individuality and . . . the outcome of his best and most earnest labour for the advancement of sound learning." [17]

4

Despite the continuing demands upon his time and energies made by his concentration on the field of popular science, Mivart was still able, in the years following the publication of the *Genesis,* to produce a respectable number of the works upon which the reputation of a man of science depends. Although forming the smaller portion of his total output, his technical articles continue to show the promise exhibited by his first series on the Primates. These papers, however, as well as those which spotted the last years of his life, represent a plateau of achievement: they herald that elusive promise of greatness which was never realized. Except in a few rare instances, Mivart seems never to have been able to move beyond the restricted pattern of investigative research within which all his early work lies.

As his technical productions increased in number year after year, his grasp of the essential meaning of biology, an understanding of the fundamental relatedness of all organic phenomena through a network of causal relationships rooted in nature, appears to have decreased. His problems seem to have become more and more limited as he moved further and further in time and association from the spring of knowledge from which he had drunk so liberally in the 1860s. Such an impression may be illusory. It may be illusory in the sense that while Mivart's later works, excepting those accomplished in haste toward the end of his life, are not actually inferior to his early works, they compare less favorably with those of his contemporaries. For biology was not static in the post-Darwinian years. Darwinism provided an impetus which not only attracted scholars of excellence to a science that had been growing moribund but also instilled within the fraternity of naturalists the enthusiasm without which real advance could not occur. The fault of Mivart's later work is not so much in the work itself as in the inability of the worker to keep ahead—or even abreast—of the developments, philosophical and otherwise, in the field in which he was working. In a sense, his later writings display Mivart as a vestige in scientific investigation; and just as organic vestiges have their value and function, so did Mivart have his. But his value and function became more and more limited as he lost contact with the investigative organism of which he was a part.

The difficulties which inhibited Mivart's development as a biologist centered around the problem of the evaluation of particular traits in the establishment of organic relations either in time or in space. For the Darwinians and their followers, such difficulties had either been minimized or ignored through the acceptance of an evolutionary frame of reference. But for Mivart, for whom evolution through natural selection was a secondary or derivative process, such a view seemed either to beg the question or to lead to circular reasoning.

What Mivart sought as a solution to his classificatory difficulties was a reference point, some standard of judgment which might serve as an objective criterion for the comparison of diversity. The inability to objectify the criteria of comparison, to standardize differences so as to recognize their relative importance, produced a taxonomic mire which inevitably rendered any comparisons directionless and, within a generalized universe, meaningless. *Man and Apes* appears to have been written expressly to demonstrate the utter confusion to which such trait comparisons lead in the absence of a central point of reference. One could compare gorilla with man, man with chimpanzee, chimpanzee with orang, orang with gorilla, and so on through the order; but the end result was nothing more than a mass of comparative detail without meaning or significance in the classification of the order as a whole unless some basis of comparison was assumed to serve as a single standard against which *all* forms in their modified state could be related and evaluated. It was this lack of an objective standard which the evolutionist sought to satisfy by his use of genetic traits as *the* criteria of classification.

On the basis of his own researches, however, Mivart could not accept such criteria either as practicable or as completely valid.

His solution was the construction of a type, recognizably ideal on empirical grounds, but one which could be regarded as if it were real. In constructing such a basis for his systematics Mivart was drawing heavily upon the philosophy of Owen; but in borrowing Owen's archetype, he attempted to make it compatible with the more inductive and less philosophical approach to biology which he had derived from his intimate intellectual association with Huxley. Thus, with some show of righteous indignation, he felt it necessary to "protest . . . against the notion . . . that the acceptance of the theory of evolution, even of the special Darwinian form of it, is any bar to the reception of that view which represents all organic forms as having been created according to certain fixed ideal types. The two beliefs, far from being reciprocally exclusive, can and do co-exist in perfect harmony in one and the same individual mind." [18] For Mivart, of course, there was no inconsistency, since to him evolution was but the unfolding of an already existent plan with the aid of "the exigencies of life."

Following the spate of papers on the Primates, he plunged, with characteristic vigor and enthusiasm, into the growing mass of data relating to the Amphibians, a class which was then assumed to represent the transitional form from fish to mammal. From this research there flowed a stream of articles dealing with the descriptive osteology of the various orders of that class and their classification. It was these investigations of the Amphibian skeleton—admittedly representing a relatively early and "primitive" form of the vertebrates—which inspired him to construct, as a guide for an understanding of affinities within that phylum as a whole, that generalized vertebrate skeleton from which all members of that unit could be considered as modified forms.

This skeletal archetype was not, nor had it ever been, an observable or existing reality. It was an abstraction, "the simplest possible generalized expression of observed facts," which could be used as a tool of research, a means by which the relationships of organic types one to the other could be better understood through a proper understanding of the relationship between their constituent parts. These intertype relationships of the parts, the only relationships Mivart thought proper for the systematist, were embodied in the concept of homology which Owen himself had developed through his own interests in the construction of ideal archetypes. And for Mivart, operating within an Owenian frame of reference, homology could not be defined without reference to an archetype. "With regard to the question," he wrote,

"What . . . is covered by the term homology . . . ?", it may be replied that it is a complex correspondence between parts as to their relative positions, according to a certain line of thought, and independently of their mode of origin; in other words conformity to type. . . . It is true that types have none but an ideal existence, that types, *as types,* are not real objective entities but that is no more reason for refusing to recognize their ideal existence and their objective realization in individuals than is the non-existence objectively of species, *as species,* a reason to recognize their individual realization or to make use of zoological specific names.[19]

By such a construction of an ideal type which had practical utility Mivart provided himself with that reference point, that perspective, which gave order to the chaos of a systematics based only upon reciprocal comparisons derived from that which alone was objectively real—the structural traits of the individual. The vertebrate archetype, defined skeletally because of the limitation of the data, was for him the unifying force which bound together into a coherent whole a host of diverse forms; and through its application to immediate problems of classification, degrees of differences could be objectively measured and evaluated by the degree of their diversity from the ideal type. The goal of Mivart's classification was a system constructed not in terms of development but rather with reference to the ideal type which itself was perhaps a more basic expression of "an intellect of a higher order than that of man," a "creative idea," to which existing forms could be related as timeless modifications. His system of classification would represent, diagrammatically, an irregular wheel whose hub symbolized the ideal type and whose spokes led to the individually modified forms observable in real experience. The wheel itself—like the philosophy which underlay its conception—was essentially two- rather than three-dimensional; and the type which lay at its center had only an incidental origin-value since one could not, should not, assume its sense reality.

Within a conceptual system based upon the idea of archetypes, each animal is viewed as a distinct and separate individual, constantly striving to express itself in terms of the ideal plan of which it was a part and seeking to reestablish the pure form of its origin-type. Such strivings, however, were constantly inhibited by altered conditions which necessarily resulted in variously modified forms. The degree of difference between the individuals and the ancestral type did not result, as in the Darwinian view, from hereditary separation but rather from the differences in the conditions of life with which they were forced to cope. There was no continuous line of descent from some ancestral line but rather a complex of affinity lines which related each type, each individual, in fact, to the ancestral ideal, the archetype.

Any system which has as its base the construction of an idealized archetype is necessarily a philosophical one. It represents not only a philosophical approach to the problems of nature but particularly one which assumes the preexistence of some plan apart from and beyond the shifting design derived from the happenstance of a continuous, fortuitous, and unpredictable process of adaptation. Such an attribute was a basic aspect of Mivart's biological outlook; and it is most pointedly illustrated in his approving quotation from a fellow philosophical anatomist, Jeffries Wyman, to the effect that:

Such a conception as an archetype involves is necessary in our attempts to study the creative idea which underlies all animal structures, apart from their adaptation to the modes of existence in each species; and just in proportion as such conception is based upon a more and more complete knowledge of the plan of structure and of development, anatomy will, in the same degree, become philosophical.[20]

The acceptance and use of the archetype concept in the treatment of taxonomic problems mark Mivart's ultimate divergence from the point of view upon which the evolutionists based their systems of classification. As the latter constructed their systems in terms of genetic relationships—real or assumed—which a revivified comparative anatomy, a newborn physiology, and a maturing palaeontology were beginning to demonstrate, Mivart erected his systematics in a limited universe governed by the archetype—presumably of divine origin. Aside from any theistic aura which pervaded such archetype-systems, the use of the archetype made inevitable a distinct separation of the various classes of life for which each archetype had been erected; and in so doing it negated the basic assumption of the evolutionists that all life was connected by a web of natural relationships. For their natural ties within the organic universe, the archetypist supplanted the all-enfolding mind of the Creator.

Whatever the strength of the opposition, he never lost his faith in the existence of an ideal plan of nature, the expression of some superhuman intellect, within the framework of which the real entities of the natural world must be interpreted. He seemed, however, in his later years, to have been content with the illumination of the more restricted and more specific details of that plan. He continued to publish articles, books, and memoirs. These later works—some more comprehensive than others, but all descriptive and static—were, however, generally unsuccessful. The reason for their lack of success must be sought in Mivart's failure to understand the new biology, whose uniqueness and value lay in the dynamism with which it infused the systems of nature. To the end of his life, Mivart remained an excellent osteologist and a more than competent comparative anatomist; but a generation's expansion of an integrated biology laid bare his deficiencies as a biologist.

And thus the scientific life which had begun with such promise in the detailed researches and the Huxleyan enthusiasms of the 1860s ground slowly to an end thirty years later, its abilities dissipated in the desperate search for and the superficial demonstration of that harmony which underlay the world of nature.

VIII. REASON

Mivart's philosophical approach, his emphasis on the extra-empirical aspects of science has already been demonstrated in much of his work. Nowhere, however, is this approach so apparent—and so fruitful—as in his treatment of man. His universe was anthropocentric. All of his views he tested in the light of their relevance to an understanding of man. Because it was through human reason alone that truth could be approached and because it was through man alone that the harmony of nature could be established, man became the focus of his thought, the axis upon which the world of nature revolved.

To the biologists and the growing number of philosophers who derived their inspiration from Huxley and Darwin, and through them from the common-sense empiricism of Mill, man could be studied and understood, interpreted and defined within the monistic frame of reference which the new biology was constructing. To them man's morality was a morality of nature, his values the values of survival. For the most enthusiastic of them, biology in general and zoology in particular became the root sciences from which all else derived. Thus, Lankester wrote of zoology in the *Encyclopaedia Britannica:*

Darwin . . . completed the doctrine of evolution, and gave it that unity and authority which was necessary in order that it should reform the whole range of philosophy. The detailed consequences of that new departure in philosophy have yet to be worked out. Its most important initial conception is the derivation of man by natural processes from ape-like ancestors, and the consequent derivation of his mental and moral qualities by the operation of the struggle for existence and natural selection from the mental and moral qualities of animals. Not the least important of the studies thus initiated is that of the evolution of philosophy itself. Zoology thus finally arrives, through Darwin, at its crowning development; it teaches, and may be said even to comprise, the history of man, sociology, and psychology.[1]

It was a monistic view such as this, rooted in the new biology, which in Mivart's mind was leading to

the besetting sin of our day—the sin which leads to the degradation of art and science alike— . . . "sensationalism." This it is that would reduce painting and sculpture to an exclusive reproduction of what the mere eye sees, neglecting what the refined and cultivated intellect may apprehend. This it is again which has made possible novels like those of Zola, or poems like those of Richepin—not to refer to yet more nefarious productions. In physical science, also, we again encounter this besetting tendency to exaggerate the value of the sensuous imagination at the expense of the intellect; resulting in an avidity for mechanical explanations, because those are the explanations most welcome to our lower faculties. . . .[2]

With vehemence Mivart rejected in its entirety the view that man as a totality could be explained in such simple biological terms. For man, while an animal susceptible to investigation on an animal level, was yet more. And as his supra-animal, uniquely human characteristics could not be biologically explained, so man himself as a unity could not be completely comprehended in such terms. "Man being," he wrote in the most concise and pregnant expression of his point of view, "as the mind of each man may tell him, an existence not only conscious, but conscious of his own consciousness; one not only acting on inference, but capable of analysing the *process* of inference; a creature not only capable of acting well or ill, but of understanding the ideas 'virtue' and 'moral obligation,' with their correlatives freedom of choice and responsibility—man being all this, it is at once obvious that the principal part of his being is his mental power. . . . We must entirely dismiss, then, the conception that mere anatomy by itself can have any decisive bearing on the question as to man's nature and being as a whole. To solve this question, recourse must be had to other studies; that is to say, to philosophy, and especially to that branch of it which occupies itself with mental phenomena —psychology."[3]

There were few who would have disagreed with Mivart in his emphasis upon the mind as the distinguishing feature of man; but there were few biologists who, immersed in researches of an anatomy capable of observation and sensible perception, would have agreed with him that that mind was anything more than an extension of the observable body. Where Mivart differed most radically from his fellow biologists was in his erection of the human mind as an entity distinct, and absolutely distinct, from the body it inspired. Consequently no relationship between the corporeal aspects of man and other animals had significance for psychological relations or origins. Since, to him, the intellect was uniquely human, it lacked comparable phenomena within the rest of the organic universe. The nature of man was thus composed of a corporeal aspect which it held in common with the rest of the animal world and a mental aspect which was man's alone.

In maintaining the uniqueness of the human mind, Mivart was doing little more than reiterating the reality of the human soul whose unique creation had so often been proved by the early philosophers of the Church and whose rationality was a heritage from Descartes. But Mivart was not content to argue by dogma alone. Fully convinced of the correctness of his own position through the application of reason, he, as both scientist and philosopher, sought to demonstrate that correctness, a demonstration which led him into the strange new world of psychological investigation.

Psychology itself, of course, was no novelty in the latter part of the nineteenth century. What was new was its rigid empirical approach which led to the development of an experimental, laboratory science whose method and point of view were derived from the dominant biology of the day. Mivart was contemptuous of the psychophysics of the empiricists and of their attempts to circumscribe the phenomena of the mind with the laws applicable to matter. He regarded as incomplete, and pertinent only to the animal nature of man, the minor conclusions resulting from the strictly delimited investigative problems. His psychology and its problems had little place for the meaning of sensations or the timing of reflexes; these were but the extensions of corporeal existence. He was concerned with the more challenging of psychological problems—language and thought, morality and virtue, consciousness and self-consciousness, the intellect and the rational process. These were mental processes; these were the traits of man whose origins and explanations were required. And, for him, no mechanical conception, no biological approach was sufficient to provide those explanations.

Whatever the source of his bias, whatever the roots of his "psychological profession of faith," it was in this insistence on the distinctness of the human mind as contrasted with the body that Mivart showed his greatest divergence from the school of thought which had played so great a part in his early career as a scientist.[4]

Mivart's opposition to the inclusion of the human mind within the Darwinian system began with his review of Darwin's *Descent of Man* in 1871. From that time until his death he never wavered in his position. As the years went by, his arguments became more sophisticated and more telling; but, as the new biology swept everything before it, each decade saw these same arguments tossed before a smaller and smaller audience.

The basis of Mivart's psychological system was laid in the earliest of his articles dealing with the processes of the mind. Recognizing that mental activity was a function of the nervous system, he distinguished "at least six kinds of action to which the nervous system ministers:

I. That in which impressions received result in approximate movements without the intervention of sensation or thought. . . . (This is the reflex action of the nervous system)

II. That in which stimuli from without result in sensations through the agency of which their due effects are wrought out. (Sensation)

III. That in which impressions received result in sensations which give rise to the observation of sensible objects. (Sensible perception)

IV. That in which sensations and perceptions continue to coalesce, agglutinate, and combine in more or less complex aggregations, according to the laws of the association of sensible perception. (Association)

V. That in which sensations and sensible perceptions are reflected on by thought and recognized as our own and we ourselves recognized by ourselves as affected and perceiving. (Self-consciousness)

VI. That in which we reflect upon our sensations and perceptions, and ask what they are and why they are. (Reason) [5]

This listing was much more than a simple hierarchy of mental function. For Mivart, a significant qualitative distinction separated the first four types of activity from the last two. The former actions "minister to and form *Instinct*" for they are "only indeliberate operations, consisting, as they do, at best, but of mere *presentative* sensible ideas in no way implying any reflective or *representative* faculty." The latter classes of operation, however, are distinguished by the fact that they "are deliberate operations, performed, as they are, by means of representative ideas implying the use of a *reflective representative* faculty . . . [which] distinguish the *intellect* or rational faculty."

The qualitative distinction between these two groups of mental functioning was more highly refined and more explicitly elaborated in later works, particularly in *On Truth,* which he wrote in 1889 as the ultimate expression not only of his psychological but also of his entire cosmological system. Contrasting the "lower mental powers" with man's "higher mental powers," he noted that the former, directly related to and derived from the biological organization of the individual, consists of the following attributes:

1. Powers of growth, repair and reproduction; 2. A power of motion; 3. A power of being impressed by unfelt stimuli; 4. A power of responding to such impressions by appropriate movements (reflex action); 5. A power of persistently reproducing a modification once induced by the environment (organic reminiscence); 6. A power of correspondence with new conditions (adaptation); 7. A power of feeling; 8. A power of special sensation in appropriate sense organs; 9. A power of synthesizing feelings (consentience); 10. A power of responding automatically to felt stimuli (excito-motor actions); 11. A power of forming habits; 12. A power of performing instinctive actions; 13. A power of experiencing pleasure and pain; 14. A power of sensuous memory; 15. A power of reproducing past feelings, and so forming phantasmata or mental images; 16. A power of associ-

ating such mental images in groups, and groups of groups (imagination); 17. Passions and desires; 18. Sensuous emotions; 19. A power of associating past feelings, imaginations, and emotions (sensuous association); 20. A power of grouping clusters of present sensations and associating imaginations therewith (sense perceptions or sensuous knowledge, and automatic classification); 21. A power, with an expectant feeling, of reviving past imaginations on the occurrence of sense perceptions (organic inference); 22. Feelings related to causation; 23. Feelings of activity and passivity, of self and not-self, and of difference; 24. Feelings related to succession, extension, position, shape, size, number and motions; 25. Feelings relating to surprise, doubt, agreement and disagreement, pleasurable satisfaction from conduct; 26. A tendency to imitation; 27. A feeling of preferential taste; 28. Emotional language; 29. Sensuous attention; 30. Feelings of means and ends; 31. A power of synthesizing impulses into one dominant impulse (organic volition); 32. A power of synthesizing motions into one complex general action to carry out an organic volition.[6]

With the behavioral traits contained in such an analytical catalogue most biologists and psychologists felt competent to construct those mental processes which were a priori considered to be distinctly human. In these various powers and attributes which Mivart considered a part of man's animal nature, they could see the germs from which had sprung, through evolutionary development, the higher intellectual faculties of man. Mivart's concept, however, of both the lower and the higher mental powers forced him to regard as "probably the most fundamental and the most important of all the distinctions to be made in the study of mind" that "fundamental difference which exists between . . . our higher, reflective, self-conscious mental acts (the acts of our intellectual faculty) and our lower, direct, merely felt acts (those of our sensitive faculty)." So important is this distinction, moreover, and so long neglected by the student of the human mind that

when its truth becomes generally recognized, that recognition will occasion nothing less than a revolution in mental science. The failure to appreciate this distinction is not so much due to an exaggeration of our lower faculties, as to a want of apprehension of what is really implied in our higher mental powers. Perhaps the most remarkable circumstance connected with popular modern writers on this subject, is the conspicuous absence in them of any manifest comprehension of those very intellectual powers they continually exercise, and their apparent non-appreciation of that reason to which they so often appeal.[7]

But what lies at the base of this reason, this intellectual faculty of man, which is so distinct from the mechanical operation of his sentient nature?

As he had done with the lower mental powers so Mivart analyzed those traits which together constitute the higher:

1. A power of apprehending objects as they are in themselves, through the impressions they make on us (intellectual perception); 2. A power of directly perceiving our own activity (self-consciousness); 3. A power of turning the mind back upon what has before been directly apprehended (reflection); 4. A power of actively seeking to recall things to mind, or of recognizing spontaneously arising reminiscences as pertaining to the past (intellectual memory); 5. A power of forming abstract ideas, or "true universals," such as those of being, substance, cause, activity, passivity, self, not-self, difference, succession, extension, position, shape, size, number, motion, novelty, dubiousness, agreement, disagreement, truth, goodness, beauty, etc. (abstraction); 6. A power of uniting our intellectual apprehensions into an explicit affirmation or negation (judgment); 7. A power of combining ideas and observations, and so giving rise to the perception of new truths (intellectual synthesis and induction); 8. A power of dissecting ideas, and so gaining new truths, apprehending truths as being necessarily involved in judgments previously made (intellectual analysis and deduction, or ratiocination); 9. A power, which, though mentioned almost last, is indeed primary by nature—namely, a power of apprehending self-evident truths as such, and as absolutely, positively, and universally necessary (intellectual intuition); 10. A power of pleasurable or painful excitement on the occurrence of certain intellectual apprehensions (higher, i.e. intellectual, emotions or sentiments); 11. A power of apprehending highly abstract ideas, such as being, power, beauty, goodness, and truth; 12. A power of giving expression to our ideas by external bodily signs (rational language); 13. A true power of will; that is a power of, on certain occasions, deliberately electing to act (or to abstain from acting) either with, or in opposition to, the resultant or voluntary attractions and repulsions (rational volition).[8]

When these traits are compared with those of the lower mental faculty, the basis of the distinction between the sentient and the intellectual nature of man becomes clear. This characterization of the intellectual faculty of man consists of a series of propositions all of which are based upon the primary philosophical assumption of a real world, apart from and existing independently of the sentient, experiencing organism. This, to Mivart, was the world of God, knowable completely only by the divine intelligence and only incompletely manifested in the rationality of the human mind. "My own conclusion was and is," he wrote in defense of his metaphysics, "that in the action of an all-pervading but inscrutable and unimaginable intelligence, of which the self-conscious human rationality is the *utterly inadequate* image, though the *only image attainable by us,* is to be sought the sole possible explanation of the mysteries of the world about us," [9] i.e., the complete understanding of that real and absolute world in whose knowledge lies truth. The animal mind differs from that of man— and differs absolutely—in that it exists in a subjective world of immediate experience, never able to comprehend the higher reality from which those experiences are derived. The distinction of the human mind lies in its ability to transcend that world of immediate experience and perceive by its rational, divine nature the eternal reality which is the world of God and from which stem those higher virtues, those absolute goals, toward which man was created to strive.

The real world of reason and the experiential world of sense —these signify Mivart's dualism. And as each was a separable and distinct entity, qualitatively different from the other, so were the behavioral manifestations in the individual qualitatively distinct and separate. As sentient nature was a manifestation of the experiential world, subjective and immediate, it was illogical and irrational to assume that it could ever be converted to the intellectual nature which was derived from and dependent upon the objective world of reality. With this affirmation of the qualitative distinction between the two natures of man, both of which must be considered in his definition, Mivart could confidently aver the evolution of his animal self from antecedent nonhuman forms while maintaining with equal confidence the original creation of his uniquely human intellectual nature.

Much of the positiveness with which he espoused his position resulted from the jaundiced view with which he regarded the pronouncements of the empiricists. Mivart saw in the developing popularity—and success—of empirical science with its relativistic approach a threat to the absolute truths in whose propagation alone lay the promise of man's salvation. And in opposing this too-real threat, he sought to emphasize that reality from which all knowledge and all empirical phenomena flow. In this he was like many others who, dismayed at the successes of the new relativism, disparaged empiricism. In doing so they snatched at traditional idealism, in one form or another, because it

seemed the sole intellectual weapon whereby to prove that science does not tell the whole story, and that somewhere, somehow, the world is like man, is working for what man is working for and cares for the objects of his care. Men unwilling to give up what was dear to them, yet also unwilling to appeal to blind faith or authority, eagerly grasped at idealism as a prop and a stay. . . . He could freely admit that everything the scientist discovers is true in its own realm, while at the same time he possessed in addition a method of proving that that world of science is a mere show world, and that behind it, underneath it, permeating it, lies the real world, a very different kind of thing. The real world is not mechanical, not a blind and aimless process; it is spiritual and moral, and guarantees the outcome of man's endeavours.[10]

This view to Mivart, as to so many others, was a comforting one. It was, moreover, the only one that was compatible with both his deeply rooted theism and his fervent love of science.

IX. DIFFICULTIES

As Mivart's biological interests reached their peak in the metaphysical constructions of the latter 1870s they reawakened the enthusiasm which had characterized the Catholicism of his adolescence. *Contemporary Evolution* and *Lessons from Nature* mark the point at which he moved easily from the area of science to that of the Church and its affairs. For the last third of his life he immersed himself with an increasing fervor in the movements—both lay and clerical, both mundane and philosophical—of his second kingdom, whose authority was the Roman Catholic Church. And with the same commitment and zeal which characterized his activities and controversies in biology, he fought for a theology tempered in science and modernism; a theology eternally true by grace of God's word but whose truth was to be constantly tested through its adaptability to a changing world.

In 1884 the *Tablet,* perhaps the most influential and widely read Catholic paper in England, referred to Mivart as "one of the most distinguished physicists of his age, [who] is not less remarkable for his scientific eminence than for his devotion to the cause of Christianity and Catholicity. . . . for years [he has been] one of the foremost members of the Catholic Union, and an active and energetic member of its governing body." [1] Sixteen years later the same weekly, speaking as the unofficial voice of the powerful diocese of Westminster, regarded the same Mivart more harshly. "Dr. St. George Mivart has written in the current number of the *Nineteenth Century,*" commented the *Tablet's* editor, an article which unhappily leaves no room for doubt as to his position. Hitherto in dealing with his doctrinal errors and eccentricities, we have endeavoured, even by straining the possibilities of charitable interpretation, to regard the differences between him and his fellow Catholics as lying within the fold of theological opinion or fact, or as due to misconception, or at most to a regrettable divergence from the spirit of the Church. In the face of his latest utterance such an attitude is no longer possible. Dr. Mivart has carried the issues far beyond the due limits of the domain of domestic Catholic controversy, and as long as he adheres to his actual views, we have no alternative but to regard him as an outsider and an opponent of the Catholic faith.[2]

In 1888 Mivart himself wrote, in the fullness and confidence of his Catholicity: "A great day for the Church is, I am persuaded, fast approaching. Its sunshine I shall probably not live to see, but the glimmer of its dawn is already visible. The period of heresies is over and past. The attacks of physical and historical science on the Church have demonstrated their futility, and the social and economic problems which more than aught else stir the hearts of men, will find no solution save in the teaching of our Lord. . . ."[3] Twelve years later, already condemned as a heretic, he wrote with a confidence hardly dimmed: "It is now evident that a vast and impassable abyss yawns between Catholic dogma and science, and no man with ordinary knowledge can henceforth join the communion of the Roman Catholic Church if he correctly understands what its principles and its teachings really are, unless they are radically changed."[4] He also wrote, "I have no more leaning to atheism or agnosticism now than I ever had; but the inscrutable, incomprehensible energy pervading the universe and (as it seems to me) disclosed by science, differs profoundly, as I read nature, from the God worshipped by Christians [i. e., Catholics]."[5]

2

The radical shift in Mivart's attitudes vis à vis the Church, so vividly expressed in the antitheses above, is rivaled, both in the rapidity with which it occurred and the violence of the expression, only by Mivart's apostasy from the evolutionary teaching of Darwin and Huxley. The similarity in the two events is not coincidental. Both have at their roots the conflict with which Mivart continually lived and which he so valiantly—and so vainly—sought to resolve. Both symbolize the emergence of Mivart as an individual from the ideological community to which he was bound. Both mark the intellectual deviant as he proclaimed his right to—and with it, the inevitable superiority of—his private judgment.

Had he not rebelled against the authority of the Church, the meaning of Mivart's life would not have been fulfilled. Had he died without explicitly rejecting the profoundest of the external authorities to which he was subject, the succession of controversies which marked his life would have had only a limited significance. His final rejection of the authority of the Church was the climax to the striving for an intellectual autonomy, an independence of the intellect from all but itself, which had begun thirty years earlier with the *Genesis,* but was rooted in the character of the adolescent who forsook the secure present of a successful father for the uncertain future of his own selection.

It is, perhaps, a fitting denouement that, having achieved autonomy by discarding the second of the authorities which had ruled him, he died free, independent, and lost in a wilderness of his own making. He who had devoted a lifetime to the reconciliation of the new science and Catholicism died rejected by both. Following the tortuous paths of his own loyalties, he arrived finally at the lonely kingdom of the free intellect.

3

To Catholics firm in their faith and free from the conflicts which haunted Mivart his apostasy was all but inexplicable. To his family, to his friends, to all those in whose minds reason and faith occupied separate and isolated compartments, his rejection of that which, admittedly, had been most dear to him from his youthful conversion, could be explained—more properly, excused—solely as a pathological manifestation of the body grown old. To his apologists and to the apologists of the Church which he so rationally attacked his act was an irrational one, the act of a madman whose mind was corroded by disease.

Physiological corruption was the only explanation that could be found by those who would not—or could not—follow Mivart on the path he charted to the end he finally reached.

So inconceivable was Mivart's apostasy on rational grounds that there is no Catholic source which does not regard it, explain it, and excuse it on physical grounds. For such a reconciliation of the seemingly irreconcilable, diabetes, from which he suffered for several years prior to his death, furnished a convenient scapegoat upon which to cast all his sins.

Upon his death, wrote Francis Aveling in the *Catholic Encyclopedia,* "Sir William Broadbent gave medical testimony as to the nature of his malady amply sufficient to free his late patient from the responsibility of the heterodox opinions which he had put forward and the attitude he had taken with regard to his superiors. His disease, not his will, was the cause of his aberration." [6]   Snead-Cox, editor of the *Tablet,* with whom Mivart had had a running battle for almost a decade, was more positive. In his brief treatment of the Mivart affair in the official biography of Cardinal Vaughan, he wrote:

Then, suddenly, Death came to put a close to the fantastic chapter which was a contradiction to all the life history that had preceded it; and this passing away was also an explanation. For one of the portents of the disease from which St. George Mivart died is in fact a very reversal of a man's veritable self; so that the miser beneath its thrall becomes a spendthrift, the spendthrift a miser, and the man of faith, faithless, as if, indeed, the valve of self-control most in use in health was the very one to give out when illness came.[7]

Nor could his family and friends, those to whom his views had become familiar through repeated discussion and correspondence, believe otherwise. His son, his protégé, Bertram Windle, his close friend, Wilfrid Meynell, and Tyrrell, one of his theological advisers who was later to encounter a similar crisis—all blamed the final break with Church authority and teaching on the ravages of disease; and Father Barry, like Mivart a liberal in matters of Catholic theology, a man who had been intimately acquainted with his views since the early 1880s when he was "in full vigour of body and mind, quite orthodox and strongly opposed to the Agnostic superstitions prevailing in the high places of the Royal Society," could write only that "after a severe illness he became an utterly changed man; and when last we walked together his intellect had altogether given way." [8]

Only Baron von Hugel, with the security of cool reason planted in the firmness of a birthright Catholicism, could see Mivart's apostasy for what it was—the final position of a philosophical trend which excluded from faith the appurtenances of mysticism and superstition, a faith which was founded upon the bedrock of reason.

The bewilderment and shock which marked the attitudes of Catholics and non-Catholics alike toward Mivart's apostasy is the more surprising in that the direction of his writing and his thinking—he never thought without writing—was hardly mistakable to anyone who could read with understanding.[9] The inevitability of his final conflict with Church authority was implicit in almost everything he wrote from the time he first entered the arena of controversy in the interests of reconciliation with the *Genesis* in 1871. What is surprising is not that Mivart ended his life a heretic, but that the always uneasy alliance between him and the Church should have lasted so long. Many of his contemporaries, both in and out of the Church, recognized quite early the dangers to his Catholicism inherent in his attempt to reconcile the miraculous universe of a developing science with that described by traditional theology. There were, in fact, few of his articles, wherever published and for whatever public, which did not elicit from both the clergy and the laity highly critical comments in the columns of the *Tablet.* "Many of us," wrote one such critic in 1887 of a recent attempt to modernize the faith,

had serious misgivings when he sallied forth two years ago in similar fashion . . . gaily armed . . . in the panoply of modern science, and yet bearing aloft the pennon of Catholic Christianity, and having blazoned on his shield the arms of faith. . . . In strange ignorance of what was really thought of him, and boasting that "up to the present time" he has "not received even a private hint of disapprobation from any ecclesiastical authority," he enters again into the lists. . . . Mr. Mivart was allowed to imagine, when he wrote his article in July 1885, [on Catholics and scientific freedom] that he had the consent and approbation of the majority of educated Catholics at his back; and now he has put himself into such a position that he must . . . acknowledge, *and that publicly,* that he has seriously misrepresented Catholic principles. . . . It has really been our fault that he has gone on all this time under the delusion that he was making admissions which one day the Church would acquiesce in. . . . [10]

Later, in the disillusionment of Mivart's final assault upon Catholic orthodoxy, another writer could say what must have been in the minds of many as criticism followed criticism over the years. "We cannot allow," the *Tablet's* correspondent remarked with pent-up bitterness, "a small clique of men to arrogate to themselves the representation of the educated laity of this country. We have been silent when young men with little wisdom aired their strange fancies before the world, but silence must not be misinterpreted; it often means, as in this case, something very far removed from consent." [11]

The most incisive analysis of the untenability of Mivart's position as "peacemaker" between science and Catholic theology or as the spokesman for a "modernized" Catholicism was provided by a non-Catholic. Anticipating, in a critical article in the *Nineteenth Century* for 1887, the inevitability of Mivart's eventual rejection of Catholicism on grounds of intellectual honesty, the writer posed the problem with which Mivart himself, in his more pessimistic moments, must have wrestled. "The temper of mind in which a man believes in a scientific conclusion," wrote Stephen,

and the temper in which he believes in any conclusion without qualification, upon evidence known to be perfect, are so different that I doubt greatly whether they can possibly coexist. A man like Mr. Mivart, who is continually looking out for ingenious reasons why he may be allowed to believe in this, that, and the other, which contradict the opinions usual in the religious body to which he belongs, who wants to be free to explain away creation, to reject the flood, to show as much error in the Bible as he can, may be very ingenious, but he is not in his right place. His position in the Church of Rome is in every respect as false—though its falseness is not of the same sort of importance—as was the position of Dr. Newman in the Church of England. He is playing fast and loose with reason, he is trying to explain away what he acknowledges to be obligations. . . . He takes up all on faith and tries all by reason. Every part of his belief rests upon two conflicting principles. . . . It . . . appears to me to be absolutely fatal to common sense, to common honesty, and to all simplicity and directness of mind. This is the habit of having a double standard of truth. . . .[12]

Mivart's inability, despite the inspiration of his language, to answer successfully the criticisms of Stephen illustrated, thirteen years before his excommunication, the difficulties of his position within the Catholic Church. "I have passed through a very trying and narrow strait but thank God I am *through* it and in open smooth waters where I do not see rocks or breakers ahead," he wrote at this time to Edmund Bishop, his confidant.[13] The smoothness was illusory. The currents of his intellectual life, the sweep of his doubts, were too strong to withstand. The rocks and breakers of a reasoned scepticism lay but slightly submerged.

4

At no time were Mivart's difficulties with his co-religionists ever completely dissipated. His positions were always those calculated to irritate those to whom truth had already been given.

Even during the early 1870s, when his strong and fervent pleas for the Catholic position in the controversies raging over evolution had won for him the esteem and rewards of the hierarchy, he was subjected to a great deal of abuse for the then radical position he espoused. Despite the fact that his novel theory as to the evolution of corporeal man was "somewhat precipately and overconfidently advocated . . . by certain able theological writers who were much impressed by the rapid advance of the Darwinian theory,"[14] he was the recipient of severe and caustic criticism both in England and on the Continent. There were many who denounced the *Genesis* as heretical and sought to have it placed upon the Index. Although there was an occasional cleric, like Bishop Hedley[15] who, while considering Mivart's hypothesis of man's origin to be "rash," thought the work on the whole to be a valuable contribution to Catholic philosophy, it was "the almost universal opinion of theologians of the time that the work would be condemned, and the author obliged to retract or modify his views." [16] Confounding his critics, however, Mivart received the sanction of the pope and the expected condemnation was delayed for over twenty years.

Under the protection he felt he had been given by the liberalism of the newly installed Pope Leo XIII, Mivart expanded his area of reconciliation and modernization during the 1870s in a manner and with an approach which, while justifying the fears of his more orthodox critics, set the tone for all his later utterances with reference to matters of Catholic theology and the course by which its compatability with intellectual evolution could alone be effected.

The essence of his new vision of a reconstituted Catholicism reconciled with reason, the adumbration of the neo-Catholicism which he so fervently championed, is contained in a curious little book, *Contemporary Evolution,* published in 1876. It is significant that it was in this very year that he received the Doctor's Hat from Pius IX. Composed of articles originally published in the *Contemporary Review* and *Dublin Review,* this loosely connected series of essays proclaimed the eventual glory of the Catholic Church—not through the opportunistic adjustments dictated by expediency, not through the imposition of force or the eruption of violence, but voluntarily and peacefully as the end result of the slow, progressive process of evolution naturally inherent in a related and harmonious universe under the aegis of an all-knowing and end-seeing God. "As the process of evolution has gone on from the inorganic world to the organic," he began his prophecy, "from the vegetable to the animal, and from the simplest form of sentient life, through constantly increasing complexity, till the hour struck for the introduction of a rational animal into the world, so the evolution of humanity has proceeded, and is proceeding, from direct and simple conscious apprehensions to more and more reflex, self-conscious, and complex apprehensions. And this applies fully to the acceptance of the Christian Church. As it has been, so it will be. Of time there is no stint. The next glacial epoch is sufficiently remote. By the continuance, then, of this evolutionary process there is to be plainly discerned in the distant future a triumph of the Church compared with which that of medieval Christendom was but a transient adumbration. A triumph brought about by moral means alone—by the slow process of exhortation, example, and individual conviction, after error has been freely propagated, every denial freely made, and every rival system provided with a free field for its display. A triumph infinitely more glorious than any brought about by the sword, and fulfilling at last the old pre-Christian prophecies of the kingdom of God upon earth." [17] Here was nineteenth-century liberalism in full flower.

Mivart spread before his public an evolutionary panorama culminating in that perfectability of man which had eluded the eighteenth-century philosophers who preceded him. Following Newman, and with his assent, he maintained the naturalness of a religious evolution whose only result could be the re-emergence of the Church of Rome, once more truly catholic and paramount. And with the liberalism and rationalism which were so characteristic of him, he recognized that, inevitable though that reemergence might be, it must be based upon a recognition of the absolute right, the "divine right," to the free exercise of one's conscience, the right of each man "freely to perform all such actions as God through his conscience has enjoined him to perform, provided they do not deprive other men of similar freedom to fulfill what they believe to be their duty." [18]

In *Contemporary Evolution* Mivart makes much of this right to behavior in accordance with the dictates of one's conscience. While this emphasis constitutes a minor theme in his disputes with the Darwinians earlier in the decade, it is this series of essays which first established it as a dominant note in Mivart's thinking. Part of this emphasis may be ascribed to the stimulation provided by the writings of Newman who, both in his *Apologia* and in his *Letter to the Duke of Norfolk*, had virtually enunciated freedom of conscience as a fundamental tenet of Catholic faith. Part of it too may have been derived from

Mivart's own difficulties with authority in the early 1870s. But the greatest part had its source in Mivart's somewhat novel interpretation of the concept of the human soul.

For Mivart the soul could only mean man's rational faculties, his intellect. One of the most significant aspects of his divergence from the Darwinians was his construction of the rational intellect as the sole qualitative distinction existing between man and the rest of the animal world. Though he could, with the rest of the Darwinian circle, accept the differences of man as differences of degree, he stopped short—with Wallace—when it came to the human mind. For him, the only explanation for such a qualitative break in the evolutionary series was the interruption of the evolutionary process through the immediate intercession of the Creator. Since revelation taught that it was the soul that was infused by the creative act, soul and intellect must be synonymous. On such a basis, Catholic dogma must maintain the individuality of the individual intellect as it maintains the individuality, the "free will," of the individual soul. As the soul of every man was inviolate, whether for good or for evil, so must the intellect be. As the soul of no man could be trammelled under the heels of authority without sin, so must the intellect be allowed free rein to find truth and right in its own way and in its own time. Allowed such freedom as a grant from the Creator, the intellects of man would eventually find that absolute truth which lay, for Mivart, in the bosom of the Church.

Contemporary Evolution is Mivart, always the optimist, at his most optimistic. There is charm, there is enthusiasm—and there is the naïveté of the dreamer whose eyes are half-blinded by the brightness of his own dream—in this paean of hope for that new and better world toward which man was not blindly groping but firmly marching.

These essays were not meant to be controversial. Like *Lessons from Nature,* published a year earlier, *Contemporary Evolution* was more a thank offering to the Church in which Mivart had found so much satisfaction and from which he derived so much hope. Nevertheless, the evolutionary process through which man must go to reach the millenium seemed too slow and too full of the dangers of heresy to those who reckoned the reestablishment of the Church in human generations rather than in glacial epochs.

More important, however, to the ultramontanists than the postponement of the Church's ultimate victory were the dangers inherent in Mivart's doctrine of freedom of conscience. W. G. Ward, to whom in part Mivart owed his conversion, took up the defense of Catholic orthodoxy in the pages of the *Dublin Review,* whose editor he was. Shocked and filled with regret that "an author, who has done such important intellectual work in the Church's cause, should mar the completeness and symmetry of that work, by treating this momentous theme in a manner so grievously out of harmony with her teaching," [19] the most influential lay Catholic in England castigated that author in terms which left no doubt as to the significance he attached to Mivart's latest attempt to recast the image of the Church. Far from allowing the freedom which Mivart felt so necessary to the eventual supremacy of the Church, Ward maintained that "not only is it consistent with justice, but it is essential to the well-being of a State, that legislation shall exist, which imposes comparative disadvantage on those who sincerely hold this or that erroneous tenet on religion or morality." [20] What of atheists? What of those who, in their degradation and immorality, would do away with marriage, with the family, with all the cherished institutions which have demonstrated their absolute worth through their contributions to the well-being of moral man? Are such persons to be allowed to propagate their views unmolested? Are they to be permitted not only freedom but protection in their attempts to corrupt the ignorant, the untutored, the young? Should they not be extirpated from the social organism as a diseased limb is amputated from the body whose life it threatens? Surely one must recognize, continued Ward, the necessity of repression, by force if necessary, of anything or anyone which threatens through opposition the absolute ideal which the state has taken as its own. To do otherwise would be to risk the loss of truth and the triumph of error.[21]

As he was aware of the dangers to the continuance of Catholicism in the return of the intellectual repression fostered by the medieval Church, so Mivart could see the dangerous path toward totalitarianism and persecution which Ward was urging English Catholics to follow. Familiar through his own experience with the vestiges of the Middle Ages still remaining in Spain, he knew the intellectual stagnation to which Ward's course of counsel must inevitably lead. Religion, to Mivart the religion of Catholics, cannot be separated from the world in which man lives and acts. It is a part of man's life; and it must stand or fall on its ability to meet the tests of an ever more perfect reason. "I am myself persuaded," he wrote, in full confidence that *his* Catholicism could withstand any assault of reason, "that in the concrete, as men now live and move, and in the conditions of modern times, it is only in the bracing air of free religious opposition and controversy that religious life can generally attain its full vigour. Where religion is but a hot house plant, the clergy are apt to become idle, corrupt, and intellectually contemptible. What need would they have to acquire any knowledge of the science of the day were the State always ready to muzzle any scientific teacher whose doctrine they may think proper to declare dangerous to faith?" [22] And more generally he affirmed in the strongest of language his faith in the eventual triumph of truth through the necessary and natural trial of error. In a paragraph which, though it applies to a particular instance of controversy, expressed his attitude toward controversy in whatever intellectual field it may erupt, he wrote: "I am convinced that in the open air of liberty and free discussion there is safety; it is by closing down and shutting in of noxious exhalations from free access to atmospheric influences that those malignant fevers are generated which may decimate our citizens. . . . Peace and safety are alone to be found in giving the fullest and widest scope to Liberty of Conscience." [23]

Unlike Ward who was, perhaps, less certain of the religious truths which he professed, Mivart welcomed controversy as a necessary process for the elucidation of truth, the goal of every intellectual pursuit; for only through controversy could truth be propagated and error eliminated through the searching exercise of human reason.

The heart of Ward's objection to Mivart's thesis was not, however, the abstract questions of discussion or freedom of judgment. It was from their practical application within the particular framework of nineteenth-century English Catholicism that difficulties arose. The year 1870 had seen the culmination of a centuries-long process of centralization of authority within the Church. Weakened by the secessions of the Reformation, the Church had once again unified itself under the aegis of the pope and through the instrument of the dogma of papal infallibility. Once again there was a single voice, the authoritative voice of the pope in Rome, to speak for the Church and its communicants everywhere. With such a voice, where lay the need for freedom of conscience? With such an authority, where was the value in freedom of discussion? Would not, must not, these weaken rather than strengthen the authoritative voice of God on Earth?

"We must . . . express our regret," complained Ward, "that he [Mivart] has not entered on the question of *authority*. His opinions have certainly (to say the very least) much superficial resemblance to the 'Liberal Catholicism' against which the Holy Father has of late been speaking with such singular energy." [24]

It was for answering such pious calls to authority that Mivart usually reserved his strongest language. And to Ward's invocation of the ever-present ogre of authority he replied with his characteristic rational piety:

Reason . . . possesses no freedom of choice, but is compelled to follow evidence. No authority can be accepted in defiance of Reason. Authority can be justified only by Reason, and cannot therefore be justified if it opposes Reason. . . . If, *par impossible,* or *par absurdum,* authority was ever to require me to affirm that no poisonous animal existed before Adam, it would be simply impossible for me, in the face of the carboniferous scorpion, to make such affirmation. If authority and intuitive truth could and did come into collision, if ever an authoritative declaration made it necessary to assert that the whole is equal to its part, or that a thing can both be and not be at the same time, and in the same sense, then authority would simply stultify itself.[25]

These words, this declaration of the overriding authority of reason, are strangely prophetic. It was just such an affirmation required by ecclesiastical authority which, a quarter of a century later, provided the formal circumstance for Mivart's excommunication. But even in this preliminary skirmish authority had its victory, for, despite the fervencies of his belief and the enthusiasm of its expression, Mivart was permitted only a limited reply to the strictures of his critics.[26]

Two factors favored him in this public espousal of his humanitarian liberalism. In the first instance, he occupied, as he engaged in this verbal duel with Ward, a unique position among English Catholics. Not only was he an active and prominent member of the lay community, not only was he the only scientist of recognized merit of his faith in England, not only was he the spokesman for Catholic liberalism, but in addition—and most significantly—he had only recently received the favor of the pope himself. In essence, what he had spoken and written to 1876—including the articles from which *Contemporary Evolution* was drawn—was of such a nature as to warrant papal sanction. In view of the apparent approval of the most authoritative of the voices of the Church it is little wonder that he could be so confident of the correctness of his position in his exchanges with his more orthodox critic. Furthermore, in writing as he did, Mivart was not yet, as so often happened in later years, acting as the representative of a small minority within the Church community. In the 1870s there were many still who, despite the defeats of the previous decade, hoped for and worked for the restoration of a liberal Catholicism fitted to the English temper. These gave Mivart support.

Typical of such support and sympathy are two letters from Newman, regarded by many as the saint of the rejuvenated Catholic Church on English soil. The first, dated May 28, 1876, concerns the immediate reception of the book itself:

You must not be surprised at finding yourself the object of criticism in consequence of passages of your book. No one but will incur the jealous narrowness of those, who think no latitude of opinion, reasoning or thought is allowable on theological questions.

Those who would not allow Galileo to reason 300 years ago will not allow any one else now. The past is no lesson for them for the present and the future; and their notion of stability in faith is ever to be repeating errors and then repeating retractions of them.

I don't know what are the passages which have given offence, but those about persecution were of a character to do so. Montalembert was attacked on this ground. As far as I recollect, he was incautious enough to say that the acts of the Spanish Inquisition, the Bartholomew massacre etc. were against justice—had he said that they were exhibitions of cruelty or of craft; or again damaging to the Catholic cause; or suicidal, (because "two can play at" persecution—and Elizabeth may follow the lead of France and Spain,) I don't see how he could have been found fault with. In other words the abstract principle of inflicting civil punishment on religious offences is sanctioned in Scripture—but not the particular acts, as found in Church history from Constantine to William the 3rd.[27]

The second contains advice with reference to Ward's criticism, advice which Mivart did not follow:

I have seen with great concern the way in which Dr Ward has treated you. Controversy is his meat and drink—and he seems to consider it his mission to pick as many holes in others as he can, and to destroy to the uttermost the adhesive qualities of Catholic brotherhood.

I have suffered from him quite as much as you. He has before now written to Rome against me—but I have never answered him, and doubt whether it is worth while for any one to do so. A Review goes on forever—and thus he is sure of having the last word.

At the same time I can quite understand your feeling that you must put your protest on record against his perverse ingenuity.[28]

It is not surprising that Newman should have so strongly sympathized with Mivart in his disputes with the conservatives within the Church; for Mivart was but applying in secular terms the liberalism with which Newman had sought to imbue Catholic theology.

Contemporary Evolution, with its forthright rejection of authority in all but the highly restricted area of faith and morals, set the tone for a host of future articles, each one designed to add one more plank to the rational platform upon which Mivart felt Catholicism must be built if it were to survive. These essays represent Mivart's first attempt to move out of the limited confines of biological science, in which his competence was recognized and respected by his fellow Catholics, into the larger, more complex, and more rigidly defined area of Catholic systematics and theology, fields in which he felt superbly confident. In such areas, however, he was always regarded by the formally trained as an alien and as an interloper, for in his treatment of problems of faith he sought to use the tools of reason. He was the scientist among the unscientific, the rationalist among the irrational, the man of the world in the kingdom of heaven. Whatever his suggestion, whether it be for the scientific training of the clergy or the amelioration of the horrors of hell, whether it concerned the Catholic in politics or the mode of burial, whether it led to a modernization of ritual or to an increase in the aesthetic appreciation of the services, that suggestion was immediately tainted in the minds of the orthodox by its implicit rejection of traditional authority and the subordination of both tradition and authority to the test of rational inquiry. It made little difference that reason always proclaimed the ultimate strength, truth, and promise of Catholicism; to Mivart's opponents the mere application of reason was indicative of doubt—and doubt led to scepticism, scepticism to heresy.

5

Mivart's deviationism, a deviationism so constant in his writings, and the distrust with which it was regarded are clearly foreshadowed in his controversy with Ward. Here Mivart could see the real distinction between *his* Catholicism and that of the conservatives. As the years passed, he became increasingly aware of that distinction.

With the zeal of the crusader, however, he plunged himself into the lay activities of the Church. Prominent in and an initiator of various charitable activities, he became, in the early 1880s, a member of the governing council of the Catholic Union, the most powerful lay organization in England. In these activities he sought what he hoped to find: a congeniality of opinion, an intellectual base among the laity from which to oppose the conservative and dogmatic preachments of the hierarchy. His search, except for a few personal associations, ended only in an increasing disillusionment. What he found among the laity was sophistication masking as intelligence. Almost everywhere he found a condemnation of evolution, if not of science, based upon ignorance and prejudice. To Ward he had answered that "I am confident that my reviewer makes an exceedingly mistaken statement, when he says that English Catholics for the most part keenly sympathize with the efforts made in Spain to forbid the opening of non-Catholic places of worship and the formation of non-Catholic schools. . . . Englishmen generally, whether Catholic or not, would, I am sure, most heartily concur in asserting that justice requires that such Deists should have freedom to erect schools for their children, and to worship in their own way, provided they respect the rights of the rest of the community." [29]   But as he became more and more acquainted with the English lay body, apart from the small circle of his own friends and supporters, he became increasingly aware of the fact that it was he—not Ward—who was "exceedingly mistaken." The disillusionment of his discovery led not only to a bitterness which was never dissipated but also to a series of attempts to remedy the sad state of the English laity and to reform his fellow communicants.

His despair and his anger he confessed to Newman in a fragmentary correspondence during 1884, just prior to his first general assault upon the fortress of Catholic orthodoxy. Although the measures taken to protect the confidential nature of their contents has led to the loss of the most significant and revealing of Mivart's letters to Newman, one can still detect in the few that remain and in Newman's replies the mental turmoil which was already, in this crucial period, initiating his future attitudes and activities. Newman was to Mivart, as he was to so many during the later years of his life, a confessor on a level far removed from that of the ordinary confessional of the parish church. It was a role that Newman had willingly assumed in his old age and upon the receipt of his cardinalate. Few could forget the sincerity and honest feeling born of frustration in the *Apologia* or the frank liberalism of his *Letter to the Duke of Norfolk*. To those who felt with him, he was the living symbol of the revival of an English Catholicism consistent with the ever-changing ideals and values of the community of which it was a part and which it served. And it was to him, particularly as cardinal and as elder, that the waning number of liberals brought their own frustrations for resolution.

The particular correspondence for 1884 begins abruptly with

a letter from Mivart whose first pages are lost. What is left reveals a man who is bitter to the point of hostility and crusading reform toward the lay body, one of whose leaders he professed to be. Already he had publicly chastised the Catholic community for its self-imposed intellectual isolation manifested in the refusal of the hierarchy to sanction the attendance of Catholics at the universities; and he was privately horrified at the expression of social provincialism in the refusal of Manning to permit the attendance of non-Catholics at the earlier Catholic university. Concerned about the relationship which exists between the Catholic and non-Catholic communities, he wrote Newman of his own ideas of the responsibilities of Catholics:

I confess I regret that in our Church services we have not more prayers for *the State* than we have. Erastianism believe me was *never* my temptation but when I look abroad and consider how blessed has been for so many years our political civilization compared with that of other nations, I sometimes ask myself whether the numerous prayers—no doubt often beautiful prayers—which have for so many years ascended from every parish Church and Cathedral in England, begging blessings on the various orders and degrees of our social Hierarchy, may not have been the cause of the exceptional social blessings we have received.[30]

Even if the Erastian heresy were not his aim, his proposal for the support in Catholic prayers of a social order in which Catholicism played but a minor role would have fared badly at the hands of such militants as Ward and Manning.

To Mivart's criticisms, both public and confidential, of the laity, Newman replied with some understanding but more temper:

Thank you for the confidence you show me in your letter; I wish that I could suitably answer it.

For myself, I think the social interests of Catholics in England have been mismanaged the last 25 years, and they are now in such a tangle that it is difficult to understand where we are, much more where we ought to be. Hence it is easy to deny any alleged grievance such as yours as to State Prayers, Trusteeship, etc., while allowing there *are* grievances, and thus I sympathise with your dissatisfaction while I cannot follow you in your proposed reforms and remedies.

And first I think we ought to realize what a small body we are.

You compare or contrast us with the Church of England; but think of the numbers, the wealth, the prestige, the popularity, the political weight of that communion; the knowledge of the world, the learning, the traditions of three centuries. Think of its place in English history, its biographies, ecclesiastical and lay, its noble buildings, memorials of the Catholic past but in the occupation of Protestants—what have we to show per contra? the Gunpowder plot, and the blundering Stuarts! "Sumi superbiam quasitam meritis."

Catholics then in England have been cowed, and beaten down by centuries of misfortune. I don't pretend to be able to put out a consistent view on this point but, in a fight of life and death, that party that lost the day must have been flung beyond imagination. Can any but a tradition of the gravest danger and consequent terror account for the abstinence of our Peers from the exercise of their rights in the House of Lords? Recollect, too, it is but 20 years before my time that Dr. Chalmer [?] died of fright in the Gordon riots. Your complaint virtually in your letter to me is the incapacity of our laity, and does not their past history account for it?

While then I feel as keenly as you do the state of English Catholics socially and think it our duty to improve it, I doubt whether insisting on small grievances is the way to raise it. I more than fear that little can be done in our (or rather your) day, but suffer me to say, while I keenly sympathise with yourself and others, you must go deeper than you do in your letter to me.

This is not written to hinder your writing again.[31]

The next week saw an almost daily exchange between the two correspondents. Unable, or more likely unwilling, to understand the counsel of patience implied in Newman's first reply, Mivart wrote again, the following day:

I am very grateful for your kindness in writing to me as you have done but I crave something yet more. My desire is to be useful, and therefore to be well guided and no one could guide me so well as Your Eminence.

I am not at all clever at understanding hints. I require to be told plainly what I ought or ought not to do. Your Eminence says: "You must go deeper than you do in your letter to me."

This I can well believe and therefore I most anxiously beg you to tell me fully *how* "deeper"—the direction and the depth.

At the same time I know I am asking a delicate and difficult thing. I half fear I am asking what I ought not to ask and yet my intention is most simple and direct. I want to be put right about "going deeper" which I am well prepared to do.

. . . .

Trusting you will consent to enlighten me as to what I cannot at present at all understand and assuring Your Eminence that I am most ready to act in a docile manner under your direction, I remain. . . . [32]

To which Newman replied:

My brain and fingers get so tired by letter writing that I am as short as I *can* be. Perhaps if I had taken up a second sheet of paper, I should not have seemed mysterious, and I beg you to pardon the appearance.

I will plunge in medias res. Twenty years ago I was desirous that Catholic youths should be allowed to continue at Protestant Colleges, the Bishop of Birmingham wishing, as he did, an Oratory to be established in Oxford. Now the peril of infidelity is so great that I dare not undertake the responsibility of recommending it.

However the Jesuits who have the mission are bound by the Apostolic precept Praedica verbum, insta res, but their mission is large and they have not hands enough. Would they allow a Guild to be set up under their patronage in Oxford, with members all over England, with some blessing or indulgence of the Pope with the express object and duty of opposing the infidelity of the day, Oxford being taken as being a focus, and a special focus, of the evil?

It would be something more than an Academia, but it would involve lectures, and I think would succeed at Rome when other plans would not. Protestants (if they are what is called orthodox), Anglicans, Ritualists, might be eligible as members. Unattached houses of converts might grow out of it.

The great difficulty would be how to find able and well informed men for the purpose of starting.[33]

Newman's "going deeper" had apparently not referred, as Mivart had feared, to his inability to understand the factors which contributed to the failures of the laity. Having escaped the censure which he felt Newman's first letter implied, he could afford to be conciliatory. "I am ashamed," he wrote

of having troubled Your Eminence so much. As I had said in my previous letter that my main object in writing to the C[atholic] U[nion] Gazette was to promote University education, I thought the "going deeper" must refer to something I was blind to or to which I was, and am, much desirous to have light and guidance.

I have heard from F. Parkinson [re Newman's new plan for an Academia at Oxford] and he has, of course, my thorough sympathy and good will but I doubt if we have got the men and I do not want to join in a second fiasco.

I was one of those who signed the memorial, or petition, to Rome twenty years ago and I recollect the ignorance of our condition in England which was then shown by Authority at Rome to our Agent.

Referring to my C.U. Gazette letter I must plead guilty to having been too hard on the Catholic laity—apparently so at least. I did not venture to say that the laity has done as well as might be expected considering the mistakes of those in authority over them. The outlook to me is intensely black and threatening not only in England but all over Europe also.[34]

Newman's reply was short and indicated an end to the discussion:

Had I recollected that you had been one of those who did all that could be done to support the Kensington University,[35] I should not have recommended a new scheme to your notice, which promises so little.

Therefore I comply with your suggestion, and should be pleased to have my letters back, (or else burn them).

I shall not forget what you have told me, but whether I can be of any use in respect to it is another question.[36]

But Mivart could not let it end there. The last of the exchange extant, a letter from Mivart dated March 12th, indicated his desire, as always and under whatever criticism, to justify his opinions and to retain them unchanged.

I herewith return the letters with very sincere thanks to Your Eminence for writing them.

I should be much distressed if I thought I had forfeited Your Eminence's approval by anything I have written or published. The letter in the C. U. G. was written at the suggestion of a common friend and submitted to the judgment of more than one person known to and esteemed by Your Eminence.

I can assure you I have long exercised, do exercise, and will exercise great restraint in my utterances.

There is a very great deal I desire to say and to say strongly and I am not perfectly sure that it is not my duty to speak but as long as I *can* doubt about that duty I will not speak.

The outlook seems to me profoundly gloomy and threatening all over Europe and the Pontificate of Pius IX to have been the most calamitous in its action of any Pontificate for centuries past.

One word in conclusion: I should be sorry for Your Eminence to think that my connexion with the College at Kensington arose from any wavering in my views about the need of University education. I accepted the post there very reluctantly and only in obedience to the express desire of the Archbishop of Westminster.

I remain, my dear Lord Cardinal, ever devotedly yours. . . .[37]

Thus ends the first phase of the 1884 correspondence. Lacking Mivart's earlier dignity as a Catholic critic of his Catholicism, it ends on an unedifying note. The defiance which is always the part of the rebel and the reformer is there; but it is a defiance different from that which ennobled his rejoinder to Ward eight years earlier. Then the defiance had a sincerity which sprang from the convictions of the rebel himself. In this last letter to Newman, however, there is a different quality in the attack upon authority, a quality which more and more intrudes itself into Mivart's public criticisms and which finally drew forth savage personal attacks by the editor of the *Tablet* at the time of Mivart's excommunication. At first a spokesman for his own rationalism, Mivart changes to become a spokesman for others who, it is hinted, are less willing to examine publicly the shortcomings of their faith. Faced with Newman's disapproval of the views he expressed, Mivart shifts the responsibility for his criticisms to the shoulders of "a common friend," eternally nameless. Thus the writer appears to seek whatever praise may be forthcoming while safely hedging in case of blame. This technique, while it may have had great practical value, is allied to the use of anonymous self-praise to which Mivart was also addicted.

Two months later the point of discussion had shifted from the intellectual level of the laity back to the nature of the relations between science and Catholicism. Whereas in his earlier exchanges with the Darwinians he argued as a scientist who was also a Catholic, now he posed as a Catholic who was also a scientist. Nothing so well illustrates the essential difficulty of Mivart's position between the two extremes of science and theology as his attempts to communicate his conciliatory views to these two separate publics. In the end he was ignored by both.

Of this exchange only Newman's letters, unfortunately, have

been preserved; but they leave little doubt as to Mivart's dilemma. The first letter, dated May 9th, reads:

I return the rest of your letter, having to apologize for the difficulty I find in reading running hand.

I can fancy a really Catholic, really scientific article doing much good, but it strikes me that the first step which an author ought to take, before he asks for information from the Church on additional points, is to show that he believes what is propounded already. Most writers ignore the question whether miracles are possible, or admissible in argument. What is the good of the Church breaking silence on the question of the Deluge, if it only leads to men of science questioning the fact of the Resurrection? The primary point is does the writer believe that the Resurrection is a fact? and the second, is therefore the Deluge possible? He may have many good reasons for thinking so strange an event improbable, or not to be taken literally—but if he begins with the avowal that it is too great a matter to accept on faith, I don't see how good can come of arguing.[38]

Later in the same day, in a letter expressive of those difficulties emanating from the Church which faced Mivart in his self-assumed task of reconciler of science and theology, he was still more cautious:

The weakness and stiffness of my fingers reacts upon my brain. I have thoughts and forget them, and lose my thread of argument and any vivid impression, before I can write it down. I never could think, never profitably meditate, without my pen, and now that I cannot use it freely, I cannot use my mind.

I pity and sympathize with the poor priests whom you animadvert on.[39] Three centuries ago they would hear about the earth going around the sun, an idea so simple, so beautiful, so antecedently probable, but so utterly opposed to tradition, to the word of Scripture, and to the apparent necessity of Christian doctrine. What a threatening difficulty to faith and to catechetical teaching! but what evidence, what scientific proof had they that the new doctrine was true?

Far more difficult is the position of priests and confessors now. They are in the front of a battle with unbelief, not merely against a school here or there of scientific research, and they have no time to get up a knowledge of physics, of biology so broad, so deep, as to have a right to judge of the strength and cogency of the views which at first sight are so difficult to harmonize with Scripture. How can they give up what is received by Catholic tradition without some better grounds for surrendering it than they have?

What increases their difficulty, and what supports them in their scepticism, their dislike, of the whole scientific movement is the sudden disappearance perhaps of supposed facts, which have been completely urged against Scripture, and which at length are found by scientific men not to hold water, after some Catholic has elaborated an answer to them;—and they are naturally led to think that, as in other cases, error will eat up error, if they are but patient, without their trouble.

For myself, I confess, I share these views to a great extent, and the more so because I am impressed especially by a fact which I have not yet noticed. What is the good of argument unless opponents can join issue on some certain general principle? how can a priest combat a man of science when the latter virtually denies the possibility of miracles and the former holds that the most stupendous have actually occurred? The man of science ought to know that he has not proved that miracles are not possible, yet he uses that assumption as confidently against the Catholics, as if it was the most necessary of truths. Why am I to deny that the Lord rose again the third day because Professor A or B says it is impossible? He brings no facts.

Before I can fairly be called upon to enter upon difficult questions which involve great study and research for the answering, I have a right to make two conditions before I have that responsibility: first, does the inquirer allow the possibility of a miraculous revelation, and next, what are the facts, and what the *proof* of the alleged facts, which are supposed to interfere with the belief that such revelation is to be found in Scripture.[40]

At the time when these letters were written, the position of the Catholic in science was becoming increasingly more difficult. The principle of consistency of science and theology, which Mivart had so hopefully set forth in the *Genesis,* was beginning to meet difficulties on a level of detail which could not be foreseen on the more abstract level of theory. While one could with some justification, find both in Scripture and in careful selection of its patristic interpreters half-concealed support for the broad generalizations of modern science, the disparity between statements of scientific fact and theological fact was less equivocal. Even with the use of the argument of allegory as applied to certain passages in Scripture, it was difficult to conceal the contradictory nature of those facts which the laboratories of the scientist were beginning to produce in an ever increasing mass and with a dangerously broadened scope. Adam's creation, the Deluge, the Virgin Birth, the Resurrection—these were not only events of theological pertinence but could be submitted to scientific judgment as well. And if these events—even if they be admitted in themselves as acts external to the operation of natural law—should be generalized to include other events of similar nature, i.e., the divine creation of every man, what then becomes of the system of universal causation erected by the scientist in his explanation of nature? Man was either created or he was not. If theology maintains creation and science does not, this is a conflict between the two which no verbalizing can resolve.

It was relatively easy for one such as Newman, unversed either in the methods or in the detailed achievements of modern science, to circumvent the conflict with the dictum "not proved." But to Mivart scientific proof lay not alone in verification through the observation of specific items; proof through analogy was a necessary and invaluable method of science and one which achieved results comparable to proofs from observation. Thus, while the origin of Adam was incapable of observable proof, to the scientist and, more particularly, to the evolutionist, analogy made his origin by fiat highly improbable.

Although his belief in the oneness of the truths of science and religion was still undimmed, Mivart, during these years, must have felt the increasing necessity of resolving the disparity between scientific fact and theological fact. The task was the more urgent since the 1880s saw the reemergence in Catholicism, as in Protestantism, of a fundamentalist approach. The initial blow of Darwinism had been assumed to be so damaging that theologians had been tempted to reconstruct their theologies along the path of the new science. However, as theology found itself relatively unscathed by what had been considered its death blow, it emerged more confident in its powers of preservation. And in this confidence it tended to become not only more conservative, but also more aggressive in its propagation of scriptural truth.

6

The problems of science-theology relationships were soon made explicit by the eruption of the whole controversy in the popular Catholic press. With evolution as the central issue, the combatants waged a violent war of words over the orthodoxy of current scientific notions. In a typical article in the *Irish Ecclesiastical Record*,[41] which Mivart with some justification took to be a personal attack, the Reverend Jeremiah Murphy, writing with the confidence of one who had more powerful support than that of his own convictions, bitterly attacked as heretical the compromises of the 1870s; and he stated in the strongest of terms that it was impossible for an orthodox Catholic to believe in the evolution of man—corporeal or otherwise—since such a belief contradicted both the statements of Genesis and the teachings of the Church Fathers.

Although Murphy's attack was answered on the clerical level and in theological terms by the Rev. Robert F. Clarke, Mivart's erstwhile colleague and collaborator at Kensington, Mivart himself seized the opportunity to state the "relations in which revelation and science stand to each other." [42] It is a bold statement, the boldest he had yet made.

If the Church has as its major function the enunciation of truth, he wrote in "Modern Catholics and Scientific Freedom," it is necessary that Catholics be made aware of the fact that they can be good Catholics and still believe in the discoveries of science. If this were not so and if Catholics were to be guided in matters of science by the dictates of traditional authority, then certainly a large segment of the population would still continue to believe that the sun revolves about the earth, since it was precisely that position which theologians had universally held in the face of scientific evidence to the contrary. Under such conditions truth itself, as derived from the observation of nature, can never prevail. Without the aid of the scientist, the Church acts as the propagator of error rather than the enunciator of truth. Comparing the ecclesiastical attacks against Galileo with those currently being made against the theory of evolution, Mivart pointed the lesson to be learned by all Catholics, by the Church itself.

What is the upshot of these twin condemnations of the seventeenth and of the nineteenth centuries, and these parallel repudiations by ecclesiastical authorities of the teachings of science? What is their bearing on the duties of Catholic men of science generally—whether they be students of astronomy, geology, biology, history, or Biblical criticism? Significant, indeed, is that upshot, and most important that bearing.

.　　.　　.

It has often been audaciously affirmed that Galileo was condemned for proposing an unorthodox interpretation of Scripture, and that authority made no judgment concerning physics, and took no action which impeded the development of science.

But the exact contrary to this is the truth. Ecclesiastical authority *did* give a judgment directly affecting physics, and which impeded scientific progress. It went, therefore, *ultra vires,* but it did much more than that. It founded its erroneous decree affecting physical science, which was *not* its own province, upon an erroneous judgment about the meaning of Scripture, which was universally supposed *to be* its own province. In this important matter it was the man of science that was right and ecclesiastical authority that was wrong. The latter sought to impose, and more or less succeeded in imposing, an erroneous belief as to God's word, from which erroneous belief science has delivered us.[43]

And in order that no one mistake him, he continued with an even more incisive indictment of the fallibility of ecclesiastical authority, past and present:

The proceedings which occurred with respect to Galileo afford us an actual demonstration of two noteworthy facts. One is that what is declared by authoritative congregations to be at once against the teaching of Scripture, of the Holy Fathers, and of antecedent ecclesiastical tribunals concerning a matter touching science, may none the less be true. The second noteworthy fact is, that men of science may have a truer perception of what Scripture must be held (since it is inspired) to teach, than may be granted to ecclesiastical authorities. That is demonstrated by the fact that those who held the very Catholic truth in the seventeenth century were not the inquisitors, but those whom they so rashly condemned.

Pious Catholics have then great cause for thankfulness, for it has thus been made absolutely and unanswerably plain and clear to them by the voice of history . . . what are their duties in the pursuit of science. God has taught us that it is not to ecclesiastical congregations but to men of science that He has committed the elucidation of scientific questions, whether such questions are or are not treated of by Holy Scripture, by the writings of the Fathers and Doctors of the Church, and by ecclesiastical assemblages and tribunals. Moreover, the freedom thus so happily gained for astronomical science has, of course, been gained for all science . . . for whatever comes within the reach of human inductive research, and is capable of verification. . . . [44]

Mivart's meaning could not be clearer. The throne of St. Peter was to be a dual throne. Science and theology were at last to be equals in the search for truth. The scientist and the priest, each keeping to his own half, were to walk the path of knowledge with only an uneasy handclasp to join them.

In view of the certainty which marked Mivart's disavowal of ecclesiastical authority in matters of science, it is surprising that some form of official censure was not forthcoming. Although his statement was no more than a logical extension, to a particular area of intellectual inquiry, of his more general claim to the freedom of conscience in 1876, it must certainly have been clear in 1885 that to carry Mivart's point of view to its conclusion was to deny the Church ultimate authority in all but a rigidly defined area of "faith and morals." Such a restriction was in utter opposition to the then current and dominant moves to extend the limits of papal authority to ever more inclusive regions of thought and action.

No official action was taken, however. Lack of official notice did not mean, though, that Mivart was to go unrebuked. After a delay of several months Murphy's emphatic rebuttal appeared in the *Nineteenth Century;* [45] and the Catholic press was unanimous in its opposition to Mivart's attempt to abrogate the age-old authority vested in the Sacred Congregations at Rome. Reluctantly, the *Tablet* pointed out the errors in his interpretation of the Galileo affair and placed its faith in the wisdom of Rome. [46] The clearest expression of the opposition appeared in an article in *The Month*. Although attempting to be conciliatory, the writer, a Jesuit, was clear in his opposition to the freedom from Church authority which Mivart had so positively granted the man of science. Addressing himself to the immediate concern with the problem of evolution and its relations with Catholic doctrine, Father L. M. Klein wrote:

As for the great biological questions that agitate to-day the scientific world, we believe that the true man of science will find little time to devote to mere controversy about them, so many are the points still requiring our undivided attention and study. For instance, why should a Catholic biologist trouble himself at present with what the Church will do should Evolution become a matter of scientific certainty. He knows already, from the unequivocal definitions of faith, that certain forms of evolution can never be proved, such as, for instance, the evolution of mind from matter. Again, he knows that if some form of evolution be true, it can never be declared authentically, *by the Church,* to be false. Is it not then his plain duty to relinquish mere controversial disputes to "paper philosophers" . . . in order to devote himself peacefully and humbly to the study of nature; to try by personal research to penetrate deeper into her secrets, and to decipher, as far as it is permitted to man to do, that book of nature, which contains the thoughts of God written without and within? . . . . In that great question of evolution . . . what is required is not discussion of the theory so much as a closer examination of the facts before us. In the domain of facts we yield to none in freedom; let us see that we yield to none also in industry and devotion to study.[47]

But what is a fact devoid of its relations to other facts? Of what value is a fact unless it be related to others in order to construct an ever more complex network of relationships out of which those broad generalizations are born which form the basis for an understanding of nature itself? The primary difference between the scientist as scientist and the scientist as Catholic—a difference which Mivart himself was never quite able to grasp, so closely intertwined were science and Catholicism in his being—is that to the former facts of observation must give rise of themselves to the generalizations he seeks; to the latter, such generalizations are already given, presumed in the very existence of God whose thoughts are indelibly written "without and within" the book of nature. For the scientist as Catholic, his duty lies in etching more sharply the details of the already graven divine plan. For the consummation of that goal, revelation must ever be the dominant guide, since in revelation alone lay the gross outlines of nature.

Mivart was caught—increasingly after 1885—between these two positions, unable, until shortly before his death, to choose between them. On the one hand, he was unable to deny revelation as a truth; on the other, he could not deny the truths of science despite their occasional contradiction of verbalized revelation. The result was an equivocal and essentially insecure position in both religion and science, from which he presumed to pick and choose from each source of truth that which his reason demanded. The antipathy of the Church and its representatives to such a position is understandable. No institutionalized structure can exist if it freely permits such an approach. And, particularly, no institutionalized structure which depends for its unity and its strength upon a system of values it recognizes as absolute can maintain itself if it permits the freedom of belief which Mivart was advocating.

With the publication of "Modern Catholics and Scientific Freedom" in 1885, Mivart had begun his long, long journey away from the Church.

X. SECOND CONFLICT

Mivart was apparently unperturbed by the furor which he had created within the lower echelons of the ecclesiastical body. He took the silence of authority to mean acquiescence. Pausing only long enough to reassert the compatibility of science, reason, and Catholicism in an interesting debate with George Jean Romanes,[1] the protégé of Darwin, he proceeded with renewed vigor to cut away the choking underbrush from the forest of his faith.

He chose as the next subject for analysis the developing impingement of Biblical criticism upon scriptural details, some of which were assumed to be the prerequisites of faith; and again the *Nineteenth Century,* with its intellectual audience, was the arena.[2] Satisfied that he had laid the bugaboo of evolution as a heresy to rest, proud that he had created a seat for science in the cathedral, he examined the findings of scientific exegesis, then still in its infancy as a historical discipline, to discover, if possible, whether it, like evolution two decades before, offered any threats to the faith of Catholics. "From the evidence which I have now obtained," he wrote, "it is abundantly clear to me that all danger of conflict between the Church and biology is forever at an end. But if so, is all danger of conflict between science and ecclesiastical authorities also at an end? I am far from thinking that such is the case. If biological science is, as regards Catholic controversy, now an affair of the past, controversy respecting historical science, in the department of Biblical criticism, is, unless I am strangely mistaken and misinformed, an affair of the near future." [3]

Biblical criticism, as it was being developed into a scientific discipline on the Continent, was a field which had begun to intrigue Mivart. It appealed to both his historical and his theological interests; and he saw in the unprejudiced findings of the new school of exegesis the same apparent difficulties to faith which the doctrine of evolution had raised a quarter of a century earlier. He sought once more to allay the fears of the orthodox that religion was in danger. He was deeply aware of the significance of the stand he was taking; and he tried to impress upon his fellow-Catholics the importance of understanding the new movement. Six months before the publication of "The Catholic Church and Biblical Criticism," he had, in seeking the support of the laity, suggested the seriousness of the problem, to the Catholic Union. But although he had used all the persuasion at his command, he felt that he had neither mustered support nor induced understanding. It seemed to him, in fact, that his efforts in so important a matter were being surreptitiously sabotaged. "I took a good deal of trouble," he complained to Meynell, "over my address to the Catholic Union, my object being to rouse Catholic interest about that most important subject 'Biblical Criticism' which will now take the place of Darwinism in the field of Catholic controversy. I did not expressly say this, but, I thought, sufficiently indicated my meaning by the data I gave for the period likely to be of consequence—namely from B.C. 1000 to A.D. 300. It seemed that Mr. Cox is disposed, for some reason, to let this address *fall flat*. Perhaps *you* can make this otherwise." [4]

Such a topic, however, he could not permit to waste away, for, as he commented to Meynell in the midst of the furor evoked by the article itself, "I am becoming more and more convinced that nothing I have yet been permitted to write in support of the Church will be so useful to the Catholic cause as my last 19th Century article." And, noting the adverse comment with which it was greeted, he added sadly, "I am also convinced it was very *much* wasted." [5]

In his reinterpretation and modernization of Catholicism, Mivart set himself before the non-Catholic audience. He sought not only to bring his fellow communicants into the future but also to convince the non-Catholic that Catholicism *was* the religion of the future. He could not see his views as destructive to faith; his own faith was too firm for him to feel that any criticism, any self-examination, based upon reason could be anything but constructive. Even as he struck at the roots of Catholic belief, he could be certain that the Catholic Church was the most highly evolved, the only, church for the theist. "Beneath the abuses and superstitions which . . . must attend every popular religion of many races persisting through many centuries," he sang of his Church, "there lies a profound Theism. It is a Theism which is the deepest, the most completely developed, the most logical and heart-satisfying which the world has ever known. It is the priceless inheritance of the monotheism of the Hebrews, transfigured by the intellect of Hellas, and enriched and perfected by the devout thoughtfulness of the acutest and holiest minds of Western Europe." [6] What need had such a religion to fear the amputation of outworn and unneeded superstitions by the sure scalpel of science? If Scripture is shown to be in error, how can this affect the religion which it supports but whose truths transcend and are prior to Scripture itself? Regardless of its errors, wrote Mivart, in the course of the evolution of man, Scripture had already served its purposes, "to promote the religious education of the world, to encourage belief in the Fatherhood of God and . . . make for righteousness." Moreover, Catholics need not fear that the demonstration of scriptural error will impugn the authority of the infallible spokesmen of the Church, for—and here Mivart repeats in specific context the thesis of his earlier article on scientific freedom—history has already shown that in matters which are not of faith and morals such spokesmen are not, can not, be infallible. And it is in this vein that he defiantly concluded that the numerous historical instances of fallibility

have an especial value since they appear to give (as regards questions of science) the *coup de grace* to those two bugbears of timid Catholics which are known as a "consensus of theologians" and "the ordinary teaching." Nothing will one day appear more strange and unreasonable than the opinion that a body of men, admittedly fallible, could not by any possibility have fallen into a common error, due to common ignorance about matters of which it was impossible for them without a miracle to have any knowledge whatever; or that the ordinary teaching of such men need not have been limited by their very limited knowledge.[7]

"The Catholic Church and Biblical Criticism," published two years after his first indictment of authority, was an attack that could not easily go unnoticed. With impunity Mivart had maintained the abstract right of private judgment in secular affairs; with equal impunity he had rejected the doctrine of infallibility in questions of science; and now he sought to subject to reason and change the whole structure of Church authority, as given not only by the enshrined philosophers and the traditional teachings of the Church but by Scripture as well.

"Very much wasted" his efforts may have been; but their meaning did not escape Mivart's critics either within or without the Church. From Paris, where he had attended the Catholic Congress, Wilfrid Ward, moderate in his liberalism, wrote to Newman that "Dr. Mivart's article appears to have startled them [members of the French ecclesiastical circle] a good deal, and I was pleased to find that there is a strong sense of the difficulty and importance of the question of Scripture Inspiration, and that the abler men (so far as I could hear) are opposed to anything like a narrow view of the subject; though they are shocked at the wholesale surrender of Dr. Mivart and at his language. . . ."[8] In England, Mivart and his article were the subjects of a severely condemnatory and semiofficial pronouncement by Bishop Hedley in the pages of the *Dublin Review*.[9] From the time when he had placed approval on Mivart's *Genesis* in the same review in 1871, Hedley had been recognized as the semiofficial spokesman for the Church in matters of controversy. In his article, which was extensively abstracted in the *Tablet* prior to publication, the bishop, in words consistent with his role of disciplinarian, characterized some of Mivart's views and proposed principles as "theologically wrong, erroneous and mischievous, censurable, if the right authority chooses to take notice of them." He called upon the author to retract those views so characterized and felt that as an obedient Catholic Mivart would do so. Mivart, however, had gone too far to turn back. In his answer to Hedley,[10] he was respectful; but beneath the respect there lay the defiance which he seemed always to feel was necessary in such rebuttals. Far from retracting anything, he reasserted his point of view, using all the verbal ingenuity of which he was capable to mollify his ecclesiastically important critic. Hedley was not to be mollified nor was he to be taken in by apparent contriteness, as he demonstrated in his rejoinder appended to Mivart's reply. To Bishop, pursuing the monastic life at Downside, Mivart wrote that "the Bishop's Rejoinder . . . is not at all conciliatory. I shall try to say no more. Indeed, having now said my say— what I felt I must say—I have no intention of ever writing one line more on the subjects discussed. I wish to consider that a chapter closed." [11]

And closed it was. Although there was no word of censure from Rome, Mivart had placed himself in a difficult position. "I have," he wrote Bishop in the midst of the secular and religious attacks upon him, "passed through a very trying and narrow strait but thank God I am *through* it and in open smooth waters where I do not see rocks or breakers ahead. I could not have rested without publishing that July article. I felt the difficulties connected with its subject so acutely. I have been greatly helped to a satisfactory mental state by a worthy Franciscan Father and I am glad a priest was my aid as it was to priests that my difficulties were due." [12] The risks he had taken, the rebukes that were his, and the inevitable disillusionment which came from the recognition that his efforts were in vain caused him to hesitate in—if not to retreat from—his attempts to convert the medievalism of a Roman Catholicism into the modernism of an English Catholicism.

The half dozen years following his short, but sharp, controversy with Hedley were years of relative inactivity as crusader and reformer. He retreated to philosophy and to detailed descriptive work in zoology. It would appear that these years were devoted to the reestablishment of his position as a Catholic scientist within the Catholic community, a position which had been badly shaken by his outspoken views of 1885 and 1887.

He wrote occasionally for the Catholic press, each time taking great pains to make his opposition to Darwinism clear while at the same time reiterating his devotion to Catholicism and revelation as the repository and source of final truth. To a great extent his efforts, combined with a restraint that was rare for him, were successful. In 1890,, at the urgent request of the rector, he assumed a professorship at the newly created Institute of Higher Studies at the University of Louvain, one of the foremost Catholic universities in Europe. In a program which was designed to "furnish to young men of talent and good-will the means of initiating themselves in the rigourous methods which characterize contemporary science" and to cultivate truth for its own sake, Mivart commenced a course of lectures which he entitled "A General Introduction to the Science of Nature," a course through which he hoped to propagate his system of a universal science. The self-imposed restraint was, however, beginning to trouble him; and he found that the freedom which the lofty aims of the newly organized institute had led him to expect was ephemeral. Although he gave "at least two courses which were greatly liked," he was forced to resign his position, "the invitation to *retire* . . . even still more pressing," than the earnest solicitations which had led him to resume teaching.[13]

2

Mivart's inability to keep the uneasy peace which had been established between him and clerical authority following his pronouncements during the 1880s showed itself most strikingly in the latter part of 1892 and in 1893, years which were the pivotal ones of his later life. The issue upon which all of the difficulties of the last years of his life were founded was a relatively minor one, particularly when compared with the basic cleavage between his belief and that of the clergy so clearly expressed in 1887.

This time it was not Scripture, it was not evolution, it was not science that bothered the critic. It was, rather, a subject of much more practical importance and, apparently, spiritual relevance. It was the subject of hell.

In the development of the Christian epic, hell and its horrors have been of tremendous importance. Armed with the weapon of eternal damnation and the promise of the tortures of hell, the leaders of Christianity have through the ages been able to instill in their followers a rigid obedience to the particular behavioral code which they prescribed. Post-mortem punishment, of which hell was the symbol, has been a major force for social control. In few branches of Christianity is the nature of hell and its universal application so graphically elaborated as in the dicta of the Catholic Church. The threat of an eternally unalleviated punishment beyond comprehension —and, of course, beyond verification—has been sufficient to cause empires to crumble and to bring the most obstinate of men to submit to clerical pronouncements.

To Mivart, in his humanitarianism, the often crude, ever barbaric, conceptions of hell which assailed the Catholic on all sides were abhorrent. What kind of a god could be the source of such horrors? What sort of mercy could be ascribed to a god who, having once condemned, provided no possibility of eventual clemency? Could Catholicism really claim to be modern, to be true, if it condoned such obviously outdated vestiges from a prior stage of barbarism and savagery? To the rationality of Mivart the answers were most obvious and emphatic. If hell there is, if hell there must be, it is a hell in which there is promise of redemption; it is a hell in which, for some at least, there is hope for some happiness.

In December, 1892, Mivart published in the *Nineteenth Century*, the vehicle for his most significant articles vis-à-vis the Church, his "Happiness in Hell." Superficially innocuous and professedly Catholic, these few pages in a secular magazine in which the author attempted to humanize, even within the limits of Catholic teaching, the current conceptions of hell, brought upon Mivart a hail of criticism and invective which, in its violence, surpassed the most virulent judgments levied against his previous writings. When one considers the extent to which

he had been permitted to go without censure on previous occasions, the vehement denunciations which greeted his somewhat restrained views on hell are surprising. His technique of
argument was no different from that which he had used—apparently with some success—over a quarter of a century. And
although the position which he supported was derived from
reason, he placed it upon a supposedly firm foundation of traditional teaching.

Commenting upon the accepted notion of hell as a place of
eternal punishment, he attempted, in conformity with progressive reason, to demonstrate that while hell is certainly not a
good place, it is, by the same token, not the barbarous paradise
of a sadistic deity that it had been painted for so long and so
convincingly. "The modern mind," he wrote, "has come to
feel an abhorrence for beliefs which were viewed with com-
placeny or accepted without difficulty for so many ages. And
not only the sentiment of our day, but what we take to be its
more highly evolved moral perceptions, are shocked beyond
expression at the doctrine that countless multitudes of mankind
will burn forever in hell fire, out of which there is no redemption." [14]   And, in order to give his article more than a personal
purpose, more than a simple expression of individual revulsion,
he continued: "Our experience shows that not a few persons
have abandoned Christianity on account of this dogma, which
also constitutes the very greatest difficulty for many who desire
to obtain a rational religious belief and to accept the Church's
teaching." [15]   In the development of his thesis there is no bitterness, no carping. He felt himself accomplishing a service for
the Church, his deep affection for which he frankly avowed:
"As we have done before . . . so here also we take the teaching
of the Catholic Church as our standard. We do this not only
because it is our inestimable privilege and unspeakable happiness to belong to it, but also because no other test could be so
useful to Christians of all denominations. For if it should
turn out that the oldest, the most authoritative and dogmatic
Christian body should not have committed itself to any dogma
about hell inevitably conflicting with reason and conscience, the
members of more recent and less dogmatic bodies may . . . be

relieved from uneasiness as to their own obligations in such respect." [16]   He then, with the skill of a trained casuist, proceeded to prove his contention of a redemptive and reformatory hell through the juxtaposition of arguments from reason and from an evolved or progressive interpretation of the teachings of the Church Fathers.

Mivart was proud of this article. He considered it, in fact, even in retrospect, as the most important he had yet been permitted to write in the service of the Church. Commenting upon his difficulties, he briefly noted just before his death the reasons which had prompted his essay on hell and the significance he attached to it:

I argued [in previous articles] since it has now become universally acknowledged that both the Holy Office and the Index had erred in their interpretation of Scripture [in the case of Galileo], Catholics had become forever free from such trammels, since one error sufficed to destroy all confidence in the absolute certainty of their future decisions.

Fairly satisfied with my success—and especially since my article, though provocative, elicited no censure—I next attempted to meet a much more serious difficulty—the question of hell.

Well might any Catholic desire to free his Church from the incubus of such teaching, could it be possible for him to do so. This I endeavoured to effect. . . .   Of course, I could not pretend to know anything more about the next world than other men. My task was limited to such a criticism of Catholic doctrine and such a statement of its terms and propositions as might show that the Church's teaching about hell, rightly understood, contains nothing which cannot be seen to accord with right reason, the highest morality and the greatest benevolence.[17]

"Would my interpretation," he wondered, "(brought forward to remove the most fatal of all objections against the Roman Catholic Church) meet with acceptance or even toleration?"

Mivart, was, indeed, eager to get the reaction of his public. He was not under any illusions that his modernization of hell would be accepted without argument. His awareness of the controversial nature of his treatment and of the delicacy of the problem and his eagerness to learn the immediate reaction of his readers are clear in a letter to Meynell written several days after the article's appearance:

Thanks for the Spectator extract. I suppose you have not kept the Pall Mall? Of course you saw the Catholic Times.

Father Nugent appears to be in a great way about my article. But a curious thing has happened. Dr. Barry (my friend!) has written to tell me he has been pressed into the service to oppose me. Can you explain this? Is there any side hostile current—hostile not on theological but *mundane* grounds? Is there any sort of friction between Dr. B. and the Tablet?

On the whole how do you find things going from the gossip you hear? I have had favourable letters from two priests—one (a comparative stranger) telling me he'd never had such a desire for Heaven as since he had read my article about Hell! He thinks, and so does my other priestly correspondent, that the article will do great good.

Of course a great many people will feel vexed and sore at the possibility suggested that their enemies will not be roasted to the extent they had taken as a matter of course they would be—not "done to a turn," bad turn—as they expected.

And in a postscript: "I am very anxious that no one should know I have written to you confidentially as I have." [18]

He did not have long to wait for the reaction to set in; and it was what he must have expected. "By many priests," he wrote, "it was gladly accepted. It was declared tenable by the most learned theologian I have ever known. . . ." [19] But these relatively minor expressions of approval were rapidly engulfed by the ever increasing wave of criticism and damnation which many of Mivart's friends, more cautious and more knowing, had anticipated.[20] The editor of the *Nineteenth Century,* upon receipt of the article, had told Mivart that "they will never allow that whip to be taken out of their hands." [21] And the tone of the subsequent attacks amply justified his warning.

The *Tablet,* already under the control of Herbert Vaughan, the successor of Manning to the archbishopric of Westminster, was extremely bitter in its personal denunciation of the author; and the feeling of the English hierarchy was early expressed in a scathing pastoral from the Bishop of Nottingham to his priests. Officialdom, it seemed, was unable to admit the persuasive power implicit in Catholicism itself; it felt apparently that the maintenance of faith was valuable only as it acted to protect the individual from the tortures of hell. It was said by some, in fact, as a criticism of Mivart's liberalizing tendency that "If there is no hell-fire, what can be the use of being good?" It was of these early criticisms that Mivart wrote, again to Meynell, in the middle of December:

Since Cox [then the editor of the *Tablet*] took to himself a wife his relations to Space are I presume changed and I do not know where to address a letter to him.

You are great friends so I hope I can do it through you. At p. 970 of the Tablet some one (he?) has written: "We do not pretend to know what object Dr. Mivart may have had in publishing such an article, etc."

Since I made my object very plain on the first page when I speak of my experience of persons leaving and refusing to enter the Church on account of what they deem its teaching about torments in Hell, a *very* little charity might surely have aided this writer to know what he says he does not pretend to.

Do you congratulate me on being the subject of the Bishop of Nottingham's pastoral? [22]

The tone of this letter and, more particularly, that of his published rejoinders to his critics indicate the irrevocable nature of the step which Mivart had taken.

He had hoped for some sympathy. He had sought some indication that the Church had not really become subject to the rigid superstitions of which it was accused by its critics and against which Mivart had fought for most of his life. He had provided authority with the opportunity of demonstrating that Catholicism was alive and responsive to an evolving morality. And yet, in the face of his hopes, the spokesmen of his Church, both clerical and lay, seemed inclined to reject as heretical his apologetics, to insist on petrified superstition in preference to living faith.

He hoped, however, that, as in the case of his former articles, Rome would withhold judgment and thus leave in abeyance the matter in question. Even in the face of the most damaging criticism he had ever received, he held to such a hope.

It was reserved for a Jesuit, with whose order Mivart had always been especially linked, to issue the ultimate reproof. Quickly following the appearance of "Happiness in Hell," the *Nineteenth Century* opened its pages to the Rev. R. F. Clarke, S. J. for a rejoinder. [23] Clarke spared no words. Accusing

Mivart of falsely quoting his patristic authorities when he was not maintaining errors of theirs that had already been authoritatively condemned, Clarke pronounced the new propositions "at variance with the teaching of the Church, and calculated to do immeasurable mischief to the souls of men." In a tone of conciliating condescension, he reflected the attitude of the majority of the clergy to the intrusion of the layman into the realms of theology:

Now I thoroughly recognize in Professor Mivart the best of intentions and a laudable anxiety to make "the crooked ways straight, and the rough places smooth" for the Agnostic and the Rationalist. But he forgets that to minimise is, if possible, more dangerous than to exaggerate, and is ruinous if it has no sound basis of fact. It alienates instead of attracting, and lowers the high estimate of the consistency and harmony of Catholic doctrine that exists in the minds of most thoughtful Englishmen. He forgets, too, that there is another class, not less worthy of his consideration, to whom such propositions . . . may do very great harm. The fear of hell is a powerful deterrent to many, educated as well as uneducated, and many a sin would be committed were it not for the wholesome dread of eternal misery before the sinner's eyes. For this reason I cannot help regarding Professor Mivart's teaching as very mischievous as well as false.[24]

Mivart's attempted justification in a lengthy reply was necessarily unsuccessful.[25] In theology he had little hope of besting one whose statements had the ring of intimate knowledge combined with the most necessary ingredient of authority. He could but reiterate his right to speak as he did; he could but strike out once more at the unwarranted aggrandizement of ecclesiastical authority on personal conviction. "I feel it necessary," he argued,

to guard my non-Catholic readers against the mistake of supposing that the fact of my opponent in the *Nineteenth Century* being a priest and a Jesuit gives him any power to bind the Catholic conscience. Not only does no single priest or bishop (save the Bishop of Rome) possess such authority, but not even an entire religious order can claim it. . . . Thank God, the liberty of Catholics, both clergy and laity, is very much greater than it is commonly supposed by outsiders to be, as I hope to make manifest in the following pages.[26]

And, finally, against the official overtones of theological censure which he rightly detected in the attacks of his clerical critics, he could muster only the utilitarian argument of expediency, of the practical value which his views had for the Church. Noting that he had convinced several fellow Catholics not to leave the Church by the very same arguments with reference to hell and that he had been assured by an American priest "that the one great obstacle to conversion in America was the moral disapproval so generally felt to the doctrine of Hell as commonly understood," he felt it was his duty "to try to clear the road in that direction as I had done in others." [27] Obviously pleased with his success in these other fields, he could write "it is with much satisfaction and deep thankfulness that I look back on the destruction of superstitions (as to the origin of species and of man, the age of the world, the universality of the Deluge, the authorship and date of various canonical books, and last, not least, the nature of the torments in Hell) in which I, though unworthy, have been permitted to bear a modest part." [28]

But for all his confidence in the universality of evolution and change in the institutions of man as well as in the totality of the natural world, Mivart was unable to assess the nature of the changes which were occurring then in the Catholic Church. To repeat at this time his previous attempts at liberalization in order to justify his latest was to rub more raw the wound which his hell had opened. The Church as the expositor of the faith had indeed changed; but it was a change toward conservatism unknown since the conversions of the Oxford Movement. Manning and Ward and the ultramontanism whose leaders they were for thirty years had been conservative; but they had been intellectual conservatives who attempted to justify their orthodoxy on intellectual grounds. These were worldly men with extensive associations in the non-Catholic community from which they had come. With the death of the converts, however, and the loss of their leadership to English Catholicism, the Church in England began its retreat to the provincialism of a half century before; the continuity of its system of belief with the world of England was broken.

"With the deaths of Cardinal Newman in 1890 and Cardinal Manning in 1892," writes a historian of English Catholicism, "a change came over the situation.   Many contacts with the literary, scientific and intellectual worlds were snapped when Manning's brougham drove away for the last time from the Athenaeum. . . .   There was manifestly no association between the Vaughan regime and the literary activities of the 'nineties. After 1892 the lines of connection of the see of Westminster with the general English life were primarily administrative and philanthropic, concerned with war and peace, the relations between England and the Vatican and national questions." [29] The dream of the Oxford converts which Manning had almost achieved was ended.   The new orientation was symbolized by Manning's successor, the first of the old-line English Catholics to assume dominance since the Reformation.   "To Vaughan," wrote Wilfrid Ward, commerce "was the most congenial subject next to religion.   Few people I ever met had a stronger sense of the value of money than Cardinal Vaughan—though he devoted it to the highest objects.   On the other hand the training of the intellect which was so much in my father's eyes hardly counted for Vaughan as anything at all apart from its market value—which for a Catholic was *nil.*" [30]

Until after he had become aware of the reaction to his articles on hell, Mivart seems not to have realized, while he was dreaming of the changes to come, the changes that had already been effected.   Within a year he was to feel their full effect.

By a decree of the Holy Office at Rome, approved by the pope, on July 19th, 1893,

The Sacred Congregation of the most eminent and reverend cardinals of the holy Roman Church, appointed and delegated by our most holy Lord Leo the Thirteenth and the Holy Apostolic See, for the drawing up of a list of books of evil doctrine, and for proscribing, correcting, and giving leave for the same, in the whole Christian commonwealth, has condemned and condemns, has proscribed and proscribes, has ordered and orders that the following works shall be entered upon the list of prohibited books: Mivart, St. George, "Happiness in Hell" (*Nineteenth Century*) London, December, 1892, and "The Happiness in Hell", *ib.* February, 1893, and "Last Words on the Happiness in Hell," *ib.* April, 1893. . . .

Wherefore, let no one henceforth, of whatever rank or condition, venture to publish in any place or language, or to read if published, or to keep in his possession, the aforesaid works thus condemned and proscribed, but let him be bound to hand them over to the Ordinaries of the place, or to the Inquisitors of heresy, under the penalties laid down in the Index of forbidden books.[31]

"You see I am just 'indexed'," Mivart wrote Bishop three weeks later,

and I want to know what you think I should do. I have just received the following private but most authentic piece of news: "The *doctrine* of your articles has not been condemned. You may hold those views, but it is not opportune to disseminate them in existing circumstances, on account of the misapprehensions to which they have given rise. I do not remember a case in which there has been such widespread misapprehension. Practically the meaning of the condemnation is to prevent you from publishing those articles apart in book form. There was a very strong *animus* against you in England on the part of some priests and laymen." I think the men of the Civilita Catolica had a great deal to do with it. You see feeling sure that my doctrines have not (the bulk of them *at the least*) been condemned, . . . I think I can honestly submit to the decree as a matter of obedience to the ecclesiastical court and governing authority and not in the least as a matter of faith. But I want to know what you say? [32]

Later, in retrospect, he was to maintain again that "the decree did not censure a single proposition I had put forward. As far as I knew, the act . . . might merely mean that Authority thought the moment inopportune for such a publication, or that I had perhaps handled some dignitaries too roughly." [33]

In answer to his request, Bishop outlined the manner in which Mivart should submit to the decree. "I thank you warmly," Mivart wrote in response, "for your admirable letter which treats the subject (to me very important) in such an exhaustive manner. I read it twice and then sat down and wrote my submission and sent it to the Cardinal who, by the way, has been personally very kind in his way of writing to me about the matter. I am sure you are right and I have acted rightly." [34]

Thus, with Bishop's reasoning and the advice of his "most sympathetic friends," he submitted—but without "unsaying a single word of what I had advanced." His submission is a strange document.[35] It shows a man torn between the conflicting pressures of his reason and of his faith to whose authority he felt himself bound. It shows, too, a man about to break under the strain. It was Mivart's last attempt to synthesize reason and religion into a system in which he could find, in his last years, a hope of mental peace; it was his last attempt to point out—and this time through a demonstration of the reasonableness of his own condemnation—"the harmony which really exists between Catholicity and science, both physical and historical." He could not yet abandon the position at which he had arrived by reason; and so he justified it once more. He could not yet deny that authority in whose interests he had labored for so long; and so he clung to it once more. But in his frenetic attempts to cling to positions already clearly opposed, his friends and enemies alike must have seen the inevitable end. That end was all too close. But the suddenness with which its warning bell was sounded could not have been anticipated.

Close upon the decree proscribing the articles on hell as in opposition to Catholic dogma, there came the papal encyclical about Scripture, *Providentissimus Deus,* which was designed to establish Scripture once more as the inspired source of all truth. Interpreted literally it could mean the end of Catholic science except in the narrowest sense of the word. For Mivart, that "terrible" encyclical came "all of a sudden, like a bolt from the blue." If he had been in doubt as to the direction in which Catholicism was moving, such doubts were now dissipated. For him the meaning of the papal message was all too clear and unequivocal. Against Mivart's hope that Scripture would eventually lose all of its authority in matters of science, Leo XIII spoke with the strongest of authority:

It is absolutely wrong and forbidden, either to narrow inspiration to certain parts only of Holy Scripture, or to admit that the sacred writer has erred. For the system of those who, in order to rid themselves of these difficulties, do not hesitate to concede that Divine inspiration regards the things of faith and morals, and nothing beyond, because (as they wrongly think) in a question of the truth or falsehood of a passage, we should consider not so much what God has said as the reason and purpose He had in mind in saying it— this system cannot be tolerated. . . . It follows that those who maintain that an error is possible in any genuine passage of the sacred writings, either pervert the Catholic notion of inspiration, or make God the author of such error.[36]

There was more; but the net effect of the encyclical was to so restrict the Catholic scientist as to make of him nothing more than a cataloguer of nature. Gone was the authority and power which Mivart would have vested in the scientist in his realm as in the theologian in his; gone was Scripture as a simple cultural document from a bygone age, useful in its time but subject to the limited intellectual horizons of a less enlightened social intellect; gone was the vista of a reign of reason within the Church and for all mankind. Instead there was an infallible Scripture held aloft by an infallible pope.

XI. EXCOMMUNICATION

Under the weight of the newly crystallized Catholic position so positively enunciated in the encyclical of 1893 the whole system of conciliation which Mivart had so patiently constructed crumbled into heresy. Even his most cherished contribution to the harmony between science and religion was to fall victim to the new orthodoxy. Within a few years the assertion of scriptural infallibility condemned as erroneous the Mivartian theory of man's bodily evolution. One by one its advocates, faced with the abrupt ideological about-face, recanted. Père M. D. Leroy, who in his *Evolution Restricted to Organic Species* in 1891 had adopted Mivart's point of view, was called to Rome early in 1895 where he learned that his "thesis, after examination . . . by competent authority, has been judged untenable, especially in what relates to the body of man—being incompatible with the text of Holy Scripture and with the principles of sound philosophy." Others, including Father Zahm, whose *Evolution and Dogma* was a virtual restatement of the *Genesis,* followed, until by 1899 Bishop Hedley, Mivart's first champion among the hierarchy, was able to write in announcing his own recantation that "the 'Mivartian' theory . . . can no longer be sustained." [1]

With the circulation of the encyclical, Mivart's position as a Catholic became exceedingly difficult. Although still maintaining the outward forms, he came to realize for the first time the real nature of the conflict between his status as scientist and as Catholic. "It then seemed plain to me," he later wrote Vaughan, "that my position was no longer tenable, but I had recourse to the most learned theologian I knew and my intimate friend. His representations, distinctions, and exhortations had great influence with me and more or less satisfied me for a time; but ultimately I came to the conclusion that Catholic doctrine and science were fatally at variance." [2] Until he arrived at that final and, for him, awful and irrevocable conclusion, he continued, impelled by a sort of intellectual inertia, on the path he had worn so deeply in the years since he first saw himself as the "peacemaker" between the forces of science and theology.

The years which followed his censure by Rome were years of relative inactivity insofar as matters of theology were concerned. Once censured, he appeared unwilling to incur again the wrath of Rome. His belief in his own rightness was, however, undiminished. These were years of reservation during which his resentments toward the new trend in Catholic conservatism, far from abating, waxed into the bitterness which so strikingly colored the last months of his life. These were the years during which, as he realized the loneliness of his own position, with friends and issues dead and dying, he sought the truth not for Catholics or non-Catholics, but for himself. "I feel I should not be honest if I did not try to make my meanings more clear as to our starting point, where we do seem to differ," he began a long and significant letter to Bishop at the beginning of 1898. While the letter was to Bishop, it might just as well have been addressed to all his friends who could follow him no longer. "Of course," he continued,

Catholics should not hold one of the objects of the Bible was to teach physical science. It is obvious that the description of Joshua's asserted action with respect to the relations between the earth and the sun, must have been expressed as it is expressed and that the language of modern science could not reasonably have been used thousands of years ago. Neither need one assert that God intended to write critical history for us and altogether with views such as those of Newman somewhat developed, one might be comfortable.

But if we have to say the Bible is verbally inspired and in all its parts is practically written by the finger of God (Vatican decree and Encyclical) then it is very difficult to be at all comfortable. As to the account of Creation, God need not have written such misleading words as "and the evening and the morning were the first (second, third, etc.) day." Neither need he have said that the grass and trees existed before the sun and moon! These statements are *absolutely* false. As to the tower of Babel and the categorical description given of Noah's ark in the deluge: They are mere fables and quite divergent from objective fact. The account of the formation of Eve and of Adam, naming the animals who came for the purpose, are utterly incredible. But if so, how about the account of the Fall and what certainty have we even as to the *existence* of Abraham?

I shall be told that it is the Church which has to decide what the Scriptures mean. But the *whole authority* of the Church rests on Scripture for if there is one thing certain it is that the earliest Christian teachers and propagandists appealed to the Scriptures as *the* proof of their religious truth, so many prophecies (to many of which no serious and at all learned person would attach the *slightest* importance) having been minutely and accurately fulfilled.

Now of course all I say will not weigh with you and I hesitate(?) *indeed* from writing that it should weigh with you. One is so much happier without all this scepticism. Still, friends as we are, I think I ought to let you know (for your *own* information) exactly where I stand. I have no controversial intention. I only want to be honest and true and *liberavi animam meam!* [3]

Only thus, within the privacy of the circle of his friends, those who not agreeing could yet understand, did Mivart feel able to express the deep anguish he felt, an anguish which was driving him toward inevitable schism.

Occasionally he reentered the lists in support of modernism against its more orthodox opponents—but only occasionally, and then in areas relatively unrelated to questions of theology.

Beneath the restraint in his public utterances there remained the growing bitterness of disillusionment which he was sometimes unable to conceal entirely in his private correspondence. The few letters to Meynell, his close friend and fellow liberal, indicate that his antipathy toward the new orthodoxy and its champions had lost none of its strength. Thus, referring to a recent meeting of Catholic scientists in 1897, he wrote

entre nous soit dit, there were no representatives of *Science* from England. Moreover I do not understand "Catholic Science" and on that account I refused to go to Brussels and my colleagues at Louvain, to whom I spoke about it, saw the force of my objections. . . . As nobody knows better than you, we must get a great deal further . . . and have a Catholic public to whom Brandi may be shown preserved in methylated spirit as a specimen of an ancient monster, now extinct—a cave monster who lived in an environment which made blindness an advantage in the struggle for life. [4]

The time was approaching when private criticisms were insufficient to ease the emotional pressures building up in the prophet scorned, to alleviate the gnawing conscience of the intellect pressed to serve the cause of error. The time was approaching when he, in opposition to his "liberal Catholic friends," was to argue that

we ought to know whether our position was, or was not, an honest and secure one; that it was useless to go on living in a "fool's paradise," and that for my part I was utterly sick of verbal jugglings which could only bring discredit on a faith for which they were offered as apologies. I was determined to rest satisfied with ambiguous teachings no longer, but to find out whether it was possible for me and my friends to remain in the Roman Communion, or whether we must leave, or be expelled from, the Catholic Church.[5]

2

The Church has often tolerated malcontents and critics within its body, but only so long as these expressed themselves within the body of the Church and within the sometimes broadly defined limits of accepted doctrine. When, however, authority speaks, the critic must submit, the malcontent must accept the answer of the infallible teacher. Had Mivart been content to acknowledge dutifully the authority of Rome, as was implied in his submission to the censure of 1893, his conflicts would have been resolved—and forgotten—in death. However, isolated events in the last years of his life, the years when his era was dying, seemingly conspired to make him break his silence and expose his wrath in a series of public denunciations.

It was in 1899 that the illness from which he knew he could not fully recover began. It was in 1899 that the forced recantations of the Catholic evolutionists became known. And it was in this year too that Mivart had his last personal exchange with the Congregations of Rome, an experience so unsatisfying that his fury came to be focused upon the authority of Rome itself. Upon this authority he placed the full blame for obstructing the necessary progress of the Catholic Church.

Mivart had hoped, with the optimism in which he so often indulged, that his condemnation in 1893 was but an act of expediency, a necessary brake on the too hasty liberalization of doctrine. But 1899 saw the reissue of the Index—and the articles on hell had not been removed. Faced with death and anxious to know the stand of the Church, Mivart wrote in August of that year "directly to . . . the actual Prefect of the Congregation of the Index. . . . I begged him, very respectfully, to have me informed who had denounced me and what propositions of mine were found fault with; adding that if His Eminence could not, or would not, furnish me with the information I desired, I must withdraw my submission." [6]

Thus did the end begin. Thus was the challenge cast, whose outcome could not have been in doubt.

"I received a reply saying that my writings on hell had been denounced to, and censured by, the Holy Office. . . . No further information was vouchsafed me, so my submission was withdrawn accordingly." [7] Thus the voice of the pope himself had finally been added to the surging chorus of opposition which, beginning with the Wards and the Murphys, had steadily risen—finally to stifle the anguished cry of Mivart's liberalism. He who had felt so confident that the highest, the infallible authority of the true Church must, by its very position of infallibility, be governed in the end by the authority of reason was convinced, at last, that it, too, was bound by the superstitions of tradition.

The future course of Mivart's opposition had been set; and in consequence he wrote the articles which were to result a few months later in his excommunication.

Added, however, to his personal grievances, there was one more drama whose final acts, then inflaming the emotions of the world, were to cap the personal defiance of Mivart with some semblance of universal justification. For 1899 was also the year of Dreyfus. And the intensity of feeling engendered by that recently reopened tragedy of France provided Mivart with an immediate opportunity for his strongest attack upon Catholic orthodoxy and, more significantly, his first attack upon the Holy Office itself. The persecution of Dreyfus, with its unmistakable overtones of anti-Semitism in the clerically colored political structure of France, had, in the months immediately preceding and following his second trial in August, 1899, placed Catholics on the defensive in an area in which no apologetics had been devised. Moreover, for English Catholics who still remembered vividly their own disabilities, the role of the French clergy was evil incarnate. The virulence of the Catholic press in France in its support of the anti-Dreyfusards and the peculiar role of the French clergy in the whole affair led many to infer, with no little justice, that the Church itself had contributed no small part to the persecution to which Dreyfus had been subjected and of which he was but a symbol. Although Catholic officials sought to absolve the Church of any responsibility, that inference was widespread among both Catholics and non-Catholics.[8]

The Catholic press of England was almost unanimous in condemning the role of its counterpart in France. Nowhere was the case more strongly stated than in Meynell's liberal *Weekly Register* which, in an emphatic editorial, remarked that "the crime of Rennes . . . reflects as well on the French Church as on the French Nation and . . . on Catholics throughout the world." The secular press was even more direct; and the London *Times* placed the responsibility for the Dreyfus affair squarely at the door of the Church. Following its denunciation, the *Times* received a steady stream of letters dealing with the relationship between the Church and Dreyfus. Most of the writers deprecated the position of the Church; and, of the Catholics, most, with the significant exceptions of Cardinal Vaughan, Wilfrid Ward, and the spokesmen for the Jesuits, hoped for some definitive action of authority or regretted that there had been none to curb the unjust excesses of French clericalism.

In view of his already developed hostility to authority, it is not surprising that Mivart is represented in this correspondence. His letter, published on October 17, was one of the last, one of the longest, and certainly the strongest condemnation of the Church to come from a Catholic. Commenting on the general features of the case, he wrote:

As to its iniquity (i.e. that of the second verdict by which, despite the obvious baselessness of the charge, Dreyfus was convicted again), the baseness which attended the first trial and the monstrous injustice of the second, the mendacity and cruelty of part of the secular, and of the entire religious, French press, we are all agreed. . . . That the great majority of French Catholics, with their priests and Bishops, are justly to be reprobated is, I believe, unquestionable. The Bishops, especially, have disgraced themselves in a deplorable manner by their toleration of the vilest newspapers and the bestowal of their *imprimatur* on publications the iniquity of which is only exceeded by their marvellous absurdity.

These are strong words even when restricted to bishops and priests; but Mivart was not content to so restrict them. Noting that the pope had done nothing, that he had, in fact, received in cordial audience the editor of one of the most violent of the anti-Semitic papers, Mivart continued with a scathing and disillusioned commentary on what he considered to be the sorry role played by the leader of Catholicism:

But what Catholics have for the most cause to lament is the Papal silence. On such a subject I only write with the greatest reluctance, but . . . it is "weakness" to "minimize" defects; whilst I am convinced that no cause can be served by hushing up the truth, and can only benefit by its being openly and honestly declared. But it is not only the absence of any condemnation of the extravagances in French and Italian religious publications, . . . it is the reception, not only without any public censure, but with positive commendation, of the Redemptionist miscreant, Bailly of *La Croix!* So scandalous a circumstance all Catholics must deeply deplore.

This was, however, not enough. Why did the pope not act as he should have acted? Why must Catholicism in this affair of such importance be shown in such hypocrisy? To Mivart the answer lay, not so much in the pope, as in the Congregations of which he had become only the spokesman. In a few paragraphs which have the faint ring of a Luther he noted regretfully that it is impossible for the pope to censure such acts as those of the French press and clergy for they are but the

modes of proceedings which are daily carried on under his own eyes, and are supposed to be due to his express initiative. How can he condemn flagrant injustice when his mouth is closed by the flagrant injustice of his own special agents, the "Roman Congregations"? . . . The Roman Congregations consist of men who have obtained more or less of what most men care for—influence, power, and some "ways and means." Doubtless many of them are excellent

and holy men . . . ; but it is only natural that, as a body, the Curialists should try to move heaven and earth to keep the advantages
they have obtained.[9]

As he noted the reception without censure given to the pur-
veyor of injustice and calumny, Mivart must have compared
that implicit support of intolerance with his own recent treatment at the hands of the Curia as he sought to intellectualize
his faith. He could feel that the man of truth had no place at
Rome, that the infallible voice was only the empty echo trapped
by the collective arch-enemy, the Curia. He could know now
in his disillusionment that "the lesson taught by Galileo [which
Mivart had spelled out so often since 1885] will never be
thoroughly learnt by the Roman Curia." But the case of
Galileo was a case in science and reflected only upon the authority of Rome in such matters, while that of Dreyfus was a
case in morality. And by its action in the latter, Rome had
forever proved its fallibility even in the area of morals, the
province which the Church had claimed as its legitimate right.
Thus, in his most significant paragraph, Mivart cast off the
yoke of papal infallibility in any and in every area: "Dreyfus is
the Galileo of the nineteenth century, and through him authority has now misled the world with respect to morals, with
the probable result that other millions of Catholics will, one
by one, abandon Catholicity." [10]

With this utterance Mivart, for all practical purposes, left the
Church. His later articles which led directly to his excommunication were, in a sense, anti-climactic.

The initial attack on Rome was more startling than even his
friends had expected. And Mivart soon found that, although
they sympathized with him in his outlook, they could not completely follow him in his methods. Three letters to Meynell
illustrate the position in which he found himself even with
respect to one who had been his closest friend. The first, dated
November 25, 1899, reads simply:

I confess I *have* wondered that I have not seen or even had a line
from you at a recent somewhat critical time. I saw you last on the
stairs of the Savile.

I send this line to say that I shall be here, at your service, from 11 a.m. to 12:30 p.m. on tomorrow the first day of the week wherein I saw (probably without any consciousness thereof) the light of day.[11]

Two days later he wrote, probably with reference to Bailly and *La Croix:*

I could not explain my views yesterday, the ladies being present. As to my term "miscreant" I might be supposed thereby to mean a man "unfortunately mistaken in his views." This I did not mean: I meant it in a *bad* sense and think the man *fully* deserved the epithet.

It seemed (and seems) to me that the fellow scattered broadcast over France his various damned . . . . [illegible] (of various geographical denominations) with their venomous lies, their atrocious calumnies, and their utter disregard of justice, careless of the mischief, pain and misery he might cause, carried away by his ignorant fanaticism, due to his pestilent superstition.

If he were to get fully what he deserves, I think he should be hanged.

You, my dear Wilfrid, who have always been so philanthropic, so considerate for the oppressed and so free yourself from the belated superstitions still common about us, should, it seems to me, feel *with me* in this matter and ought to execrate this "enemy of the human race."

Yours always as ever my dear Wilfrid (calling on your benevolence and humanity).[12]

A week later, in the last of his letters to Meynell, recognizing the extent of the opposition which he had aroused, aware of the widening gulf between him and the friends of a lifetime, he still clutched at the occasional straws of approval, still raised himself at the occasional nod of sympathy:

Is it because the English and Irish Catholics so much desire my death that I did not receive from *you* a "many happy returns" on the 30th [his 72nd birthday]?

Evil desires toward me were so far successful that on my birthday I became unwell and am now laid up with a bilious attack which I trust will very soon be a thing of the past. I should much like to chat with you alone.

By the way if E. and I. Cats do not like me and my ways that is by no means the case everywhere. Thus I am asked urgently by the Catholic Committee "in defense of right" at Paris to allow myself to be nominated an honorary member and correspondent and the Abbe Pichot is determined to publish my letter in French. He says "it would be immoral and tend to deprive the public conscience to allow 'notre presse Catholique' to go unrebuked for its intolerance, insolence, malignity and stupidity."

For myself I am getting rather sick of all this but a Roman priest who knows the Curia well writes to me saying "if anyone thinks that amongst these Curialists there is one spark of evangelical zeal—he must be a lunatic."

Surely we of the liberal party, who desire the advance of knowledge ought to hold together. You *know* that in thus speaking I speak unselfishly.[13]

3

Having already gone so far, Mivart did not await passively the official censure which his letter could well have elicited. His course of action had become clear. "After mature reflection and many mental struggles," he wrote as part of a symposium on "Reason and Religious Belief" in the *North American Review,*

I had come to the conclusion that the Roman Catholic Church must tolerate a transforming process of evolution, with respect to many of its dogmas, or sink, by degrees, into an effete and insignificant body, composed of ignorant persons, a mass of women and children and a number of mentally effeminate men. I was acquainted with a not inconsiderable number of cultured English Catholics—clergy as well as laity—who were severely tried by the reactionary policy which has shown itself of late years at Rome. To my mind it was clear that, unless the infallibility of the Church could be seriously disclaimed and the possibility of error in passed conciliar decrees allowed, the needful evolution of dogma was impossible.

It is imperative, he continued, that the dogma of infallibility be modified so that "by such a course, the way will be prepared for the play of evolution in Church dogma through the future centuries, and for the gradual construction of a Catholicity which shall embody all scientific truth and all the religious truths held by all forms of belief, including the beauties and noble precepts of the old Paganism, which were too quickly and carelessly thrown aside." [14]

Here was Mivart's theism. Here was his universalism born of his devout evolutionism. Here was the universalism toward which he had striven his life long; a universalism which he had equated with Catholicism in the fullness of his belief during the eighties; a universalism which resembled hardly at all the Catholicism of the nineties.

Like Luther centuries before, like Newman, the hero of his youth, and, more pertinently, like Döllinger and his disciples, Mivart saw, in his theism, Catholicism stripped of its superstitions and bedded again upon the rock of a faith only in God, the foundation of universal and absolute religious truth. For him, in his knowledge of and feeling for the philosophy of evolution and of change, of which the human mind was an ever progressing part, Catholicism could exist only as the never-ending, never-completed, never-fulfilled product of an evolutionary process initiated by an infinite God. And for him the authority of Rome, the Curia in all of its aspects, stultified that evolution, mocked that God, and mired the Church in the muck of a primitive level. To him Catholicism must be dynamic, its essence, change; and for its static distortions, its binding dogmas and the authority which maintained them, he coined the word "Curialism"—an expression of utter contempt.

To prove that true Catholicism, his brand of Catholicism whose flame burned through history, was constantly changing, he wrote "The Continuity of Catholicism" for the *Nineteenth Century* and "Some Recent Apologists" for the *Fortnightly Review*. These articles actually form a pair; but so great was the urgency with which their author regarded their appearance, so close did he feel death to be, that he published them simultaneously, the better to assure himself of the position of the Church.[15]

For anyone who had followed sympathetically the course of Mivart's previous writings, there was little new in these articles. One could note only that the writing was more positive, the denunciation of authority more sweeping, the attitude toward the faith less reverent, the whole mood and tone less temporizing. Their author, it was clear, was no longer a Catholic critic; he had become a critic of Catholicism.

The final assumption of his new position, following his own personal crisis during the early summer of 1899 when twice he was "expected to die and once was supposed to have gone," is clear in his long letters to Bishop, who had become his most intimate confidant in matters of theology. The substance of the position he had come to realize is feelingly contained in the three long letters of August 19 and 29 and November 30, 1899. With his world fallen away and his end figuratively and literally at hand, he seeks not so much for agreement as for understanding. "I thank you much for the information," he began the first of these letters,

But you must not imagine that I do not take the same views you do. Ever since 1844, I have never ceased to think the Anglican position entirely untenable and illogical and the notion of "continuity" in their case an absurdity. You have not seen, I dare say, my article in the 19 Century of this month.

Nevertheless as a curiosity and trying to put myself in an exaggerated Ritualist's absurd point of view (. . . one holding all to depend on convocation). . . . However all this is only a game. Given Christianity, a Roman Catholicism is the only tenable position; but the Curialists make that position a trying one, with their absurd nonsense about "Americanism" "Evolution" "man's bodily origin" etc etc. They have no comprehension of the spirit of the English speaking people and how we have utterly shaken off forever and will never endure despotism of any kind; but only rational, moderate, constitutional government. The Curia seems to think we are still in the 16th century.[16]

The letter continued the condemnation of the despotism implicit in current Catholic policy and concluded with a pessimistic rejoinder to Bishop's suggestion that the memories of the good things place in proper perspective the immediate impression of the seemingly bad: "No, you are right, *we* must not undervalue the pleasures of memory. They become more and more precious to us as the pleasures of hope shrink and dwindle. The next world is, to me, all too uncertain and utterly unimaginable for me to hope much about it."

To Bishop's probable criticism of this sort of scepticism, Mivart replied:

I will now endeavour to supplement the short and imperfect answer (to your kind long letter) I sent you the other day.

No! I have no very serious doubts about a future life but very serious ones as to the possible *nature* of it. You see, you and I, and our friends, all belong to a *very* small and exceptionally well-off minority of the whole human race now living. What reasonable

grounds have we for thinking that, in the next life, we shall be
nearly so fortunate? May it not, at the best, be parallel to temporal
existence of "William Sprogget" as depicted by Joseph Jacobs in his
article "The Mean (i.e. average) Englishman" in the July Fortnightly R.?

Of course, most of our friends, immersed in ecclesiasticism, probably think of the future life as a mainly religious one under the eye
of a Deity who has such a dominant attribute of "Holiness" that all
his other attributes are dwarfed and overshadowed thereby. That
is *not* the notion of the primary and universal cause which my life's
study of the world (man included) has impressed, as a result (ultimate or far), on *my* mind. With you I love nature and I have
always loved it, my instinctive tendencies have ever been towards
Biology and human history. But I have not, and never had, a temptation to Pantheism, although I regard God so immanent in every
existence and activity and am disposed to consider everything which
takes place as, in a sense, a miracle. As to God in Nature, though
as you know I enjoy ritual, the pomp of stately worship and, even
more, the sweet devotion of a low mass said where none are present
save the Priest and myself as server, yet I often feel we have such a
direct and immediate access to God and can always find him present
within our own living hearts, that all rites, ceremonies and everything external seem mere obstacles and hindrances. This I daresay
has also been the case with you. . . . [17]

And, finally, the confident despair of existing conditions:

I thank you for your long and interesting letters, no part of which
do I "Laugh at." . . . For my sake and for the sake of others as well
as for your own, I regret that you are not stronger so that we cannot
exchange *viva voce* ideas and possibly make plans together for the
future. I am, I think you will admit, pretty willing to accept advice
and direction from *you* and I am sure my "Times letter" would
have been better had I had you at my elbow. I am naturally a
rather pugnacious and provoking writer I know, but lying and humbug in matters of religion disgust and exasperate me. Greatly do I
wish that there were an organ such as you suggest, but that I am
sure is impossible. The Rambler, the Home and Foreign, and the
North British (in Lord Acton's hands) almost demonstrate the truth
of what you say that there is a "fixed and dogged intention" that no
such thing shall be. Otherwise I should gladly write for it *gratis*.
But I believe no avowedly Catholic journal, honest, truthful and
intelligent, is possible. Attempts in that direction are being made
by the *"Weekly Register"* and the "New Era." But Thurston, S. J.
has fixed himself, like the vampire "Desmodus" on the former;
while Dell, the editor of the latter, has to go very piano, piano feeling his way. The only thing to do would be to have a new journal

—not avowedly Catholic or even Christian, but devoted to religious matters, edited by a Catholic and with Catholic writers (who must also be intellectually up to the work, also in education, and of *scrupulous integrity*). It should deal with all forms of religion and their manifestations, with justice and intelligent appreciation, and I feel sure it would command a very large amount of support; for religious matters interest an enormous number of people at the present time.

What you say about the Curia and the Papacy tends to confirm my despair of any good from thence. This horribly worldly spirit and constant seeking after what is likely "to pay" is *most* revolting. In spite of human defects—of which I well know I have my share— I believe that the immense majority of mankind will respond to frank appeals, boldly made to to their ethical judgment and their ethical sentiments; but there must be no insincerity, no shuffling, no assertions that the Bible does not contain errors, and *heaps* of them. No edifice can be securely reared (of the kind I refer to) save on a foundation of absolute truth so far as it is known when the building process begins. I do believe that a noble and true Catho-licity is possibly developed in continuity with the Catholicity of the past but it must be a continuous development like that of the but-terfly from the grub. . . . [18]

While his friends were aware of the position to which his own evolution had taken him, his public testament of the hope-lessness in the contemporary Roman Catholic Church was con-tained in the two articles mentioned above.

These two articles constitute his public farewell to the Church in whose cause he had so long and so valiantly labored. They are a recapitulation of disillusionment as they are, too, a testimony of hope. They are the explosive expression of the restrained grievances of a decade; and they are the rallying cry of a new faith. They are a condemnation of the institutional-ized structure that had come to be Catholicism; and they are the vindication of the theism of a rationalist. With these articles Mivart hoped to leave the world with a mind and a faith unsullied by the ambiguities, the hypocrisies, the incon-sistencies which he saw flow from the impact of a rapidly changing science upon a static theology. In this farewell he summed up what had been the goal of his life:

It was evident to me, when I began to write, that a serious conflict existed in the minds of many persons, between their religious beliefs and certain convictions and sentiments with which my innermost nature compelled me to sympathize. For as in youth I loved both natural science and history, and also early attained the convictions that there exists, pervading the universe, an intelligence utterly unfathomable by man, and that the world could not be explained or understood by mechanical conceptions only, I also became assured that Catholicity, well understood, is the most developed form of Theism, and that, in addition to its other claims on acceptance, it acts as a very potent social bond, and supports and promotes (with whatever local or temporary drawbacks) the most benevolent and noblest aspirations. . . . I therefore felt bound to do my best to remove misunderstanding and promote concord as far as I could honestly promote it.[19]

What follows is not only the story of his own limited attempts to interpret the Church as a changing body of doctrine; but, more significantly, it is an attack upon the whole structure of dogma with which he considered the leaders of the Church to have bound, unnecessarily and irrationally, the truth which is implicit in Catholicism. Not only, according to Mivart, must dogma change, but it has changed and is changing whether the hierarchy recognizes those changes or not. Just as dogmas once held have ceased to exist, so must dogma now held change in conformity to advancing knowledge and reason. Unchanging dogma is stultification; change is life itself. Dogma is authority wrongfully and arbitrarily imposed; as such, it is unjust, violating the most fundamental right of individual conscience. With this indictment of dogma, he concluded with a sweeping annihilation of the authority recently vested in Rome. With past errors of authoritative pronouncements in mind, "Catholics, to be logical, must say to any Roman congregation which should attempt to lay down the law about any branch of science: 'You have blundered once, and we can never trust you again in any scientific matter; whether it be astronomy, biology, political economy, history, biblical criticism, or ecclesiology. You may be right in your dicta, but also you may be wrong. The only authority in science is the authority of those who have studied the matter and are "men in the know." As to all that comes within the reach of inductive research, you must humbly accept the teaching of science, and nothing but science. And for this you should be grateful.' " [20]

Condemnation of this sort, following so rapidly upon his indictment of the Catholic hierarchy from top to bottom in his Dreyfus letter to the *Times* roused to action the religious authority to which he was immediately subject. Cardinal Vaughan himself called upon Edmund Bishop "to help Mr. Mivart," although he already had reason to believe that events had moved too far and too fast for the appeals of friendship and loyalty to have any effect. "A Priest who has known him [Mivart] most intimately," wrote Vaughan, "writes: 'I can prove by his own letters to me that for over two years he has ceased to believe in Christianity.' It is better for the body that poisonous and deadly humours should be got out of it— lest the whole become infected." Bishop's intercession failed. "A short conversation sufficed to shew that it was too late; that things just now must take their course, whatever that may be." [21] That course had already been dictated; authority now acted.

While nowhere did the Catholic press look with favor upon Mivart's arguments or the manner in which they were presented, it was the *Tablet,* now completely under the control of Cardinal Vaughan, which passed the severest judgment. In an unsigned leader, Mivart was ridiculed as a Catholic, as a writer, and as a gentleman. "There is," the editor noted, "a form of inordinate intellectual vanity which takes the shape of reading acquiescence to its own views into the minds and speech of all around it, and a jaundiced state of mind which colours with its own scepticism and pitiable disease of the faith all whom it looks upon." [22] In the "ludicrous effusions" and the "diatribes" which have come from Mivart's pen, the Church has been maligned as have been its communicants to whom have been credited, with an unjust anonymity, heretical notions. Stronger language, language whose only interpretation could be a personal charge, was reserved for Mivart's characteristic use of the anonymous informant:

The anonymity of the persons spoken of, acts like a charm for protection of the lie. When the outraged denomination demands that the accuser, in the name of justice and truth, shall substantiate or withdraw his charges, then comes the second part of the trick, and he has only to whine forth his plea that he cannot betray private confidences, or, forsooth, he cannot expose the persons referred to to the risk of ecclesiastical persecution, etc. Thus protected, he can slander at will on the strength of his own *ipse dixit,* or his own vicious interpretation of words and acts which are utterly innocent of the meaning attached to them. This method is simply the "Art of Bearing False Witness against your Neighbour, without risk of being brought to book." We submit that as often as we have to deal with this infamous method, and this cowardly making charges whilst skulking under the cover of anonymous witnesses, there is but one course open to us or to any other body similarly assailed. Until such charges are substantiated by names and proofs and verifiable evidence, they must be treated as slanderous falsehoods, and their authors as contemptible calumniators of their brethren.[23]

Whatever the relative merits of the method Mivart had used to expose and argue the positions he wished to defend, the violence and personal abuse which characterized the *Tablet's* charge had its effect. As in his debates with the Darwinians a quarter of a century earlier, Mivart found—and for similar reasons—the debate translated to a personal level. And, as in the earlier controversy which marked his estrangement from the community of science, so bitter was the tone of conflict that reconciliation was impossible—as both parties knew. The virulence of the attack, however, even in so authoritative an organ and even though it was "inspired, as is only too obvious, in high quarters," did not so much reflect the feeling of the Catholic community as it set for its members the tone for future action. It was preparatory rather than final, for Mivart was no ordinary member of the Church in England. Either by coincidence or by design the *New Era,* a liberal Catholic periodical, featured a highly laudatory biographical review of Mivart's long life and accomplishments while he was being vilified by the *Tablet.* And its editor, while showing little sympathy for the opinions which Mivart espoused, still reserved his bitterest condemnation for the manner in which English Catholicism's most distinguished man of science had been handled, a manner which "has excited widespread disgust among Catholics of every shade of opinion."

Mivart himself felt more than disgust. He was outraged at the personal abuse, at the accusations of cowardice and false-

hood to which he had been subjected in what he had considered a serious area of significant issues. So noble had been
his intent; so base had the dispute become.

Placing the formal responsibility for the slander upon
Vaughan, he demanded an apology. On January 6, immediately after reading the *Tablet's* editorial, he wrote to the Archbishop of Westminster who, in better days, had been his friend:

Although I believe the *Tablet* belongs to your Eminence, I am
fully persuaded that you could not have known and approved of
the monstrous article on me which appears therein.

I should not think of complaining of any criticism of opinions
referred to by me, however hostile; but when I am personally abused
as a liar, a calumniator, and a coward, I feel I have cause to complain. I have never before been accused of cowardice in making
my views known, but rather of too much boldness and presumption.

The article will surely shock all earnest Christians, for it sins
deeply against that greatest of Christian virtues—charity. Its author
represents me as falsely citing anonymous witnesses. I give you my
honour I do not refer to one save with complete truthfulness.

As to the points he especially refers to, the persons I cite are well
known to your Eminence. As to the birth of the Lord, I did not
merely hear, but had written evidence, a verbatim copy of which is
now in my library. As to the resurrection, my informant was almost
as much known to your Eminence as Bishop Brindle. He did not
bind me to secrecy, and If your Eminence cares to know who he
was and will keep his name a secret, I will mention it.

The articles were written by me under a sense of duty, thinking
death not far off, and (like my antecedent ones) with a view of opening as widely as possible, the gates of Catholicity; the *Fortnightly*
one to make conformity as easy as might be, the *Nineteenth Century* one to point out the changes tending to facilitate that conformity—changes the existence and importance of many of which it
is absolutely impossible to deny. My aim may have been Quixotic,
my measures unwisely selected; but whatever criticism I may merit,
I am sure that scurrilous personalities can never be approved by
your Eminence.[24]

How could the cardinal answer? Leaving it to his editor to
assume full and sole responsibility for the personal attack,
Vaughan immediately, in his reply, placed the issue upon the
much more significant level of orthodoxy as opposed to heter-
odoxy, private judgment as opposed to authority. With only a
hasty reference to Mivart's complaint, he answered:

Before touching on these points, it is necessary to be clear as to the substance of your position.

You have publicly impugned the most sacred and fundamental doctrines of the faith, while still professing yourself to be a Catholic. It becomes, therefore, my primary duty, as Guardian of the Faith, to ascertain whether I am still to treat you as a member of the Church and subject to my jurisdiction or to consider you outside the unity of the faith.

As a test of orthodoxy regarding certain doctrines dealt with by you in your articles in the *Nineteenth Century,* I herewith send you a Profession of Catholic Faith. I invite you to read and return it to me subscribed by your signature. Nothing less than this will be satisfactory. I need not say how deeply I regret the necessity which compels me to take official action of this kind, and how earnestly I hope and pray that you may have light and grace to withdraw from the position in which you stand, and to submit yourself unreservedly to the authority of the Catholic Church.

The point of final decision had come.

Once before Mivart had professed a faith. But then, a lifetime away, it had been a creed of hope, a profession of life, a free and joyous submission to the spirit of the future. Now, the life was over. Here was a profession of capitulation and defeat.

The profession of faith tendered Mivart by Vaughan in his capacity as the highest Catholic authority in England was couched in such terms that its acceptance in totality would have meant complete abdication from the position which Mivart had sacrificed so much to occupy and defend for the better part of his adult life. It was so written that it would have been impossible for him to have signed it without signing away his dignity. It read:

I hereby declare that, recognizing the Catholic Church to be the supreme and infallible guardian of the Christian faith, I submit therein my judgment to hers, believing all that she teaches, and condemning all that she condemns. And in particular I firmly believe and profess that Our Lord Jesus Christ, the only begotten Son of God, born of the Father before all ages, in the fulness of time, for us men and for our salvation, came down from heaven and was conceived by the Holy Ghost, and born of the Virgin Mary—that is to say, that the same Jesus Christ had no man for His father, and that St. Joseph was not His real or natural father, but only His reputed, or foster, father.

I therefore firmly believe and profess that the Blessed Virgin Mary conceived and brought forth the Son of God in an ineffable manner by the operation of the Holy Ghost, and absolutely without loss or detriment to her virginity, and that she is really and in truth, as the Catholic Church most rightly calls her, the "ever Virgin"; that is to say, virgin before the birth of Christ, virgin in that birth, and virgin after it, her sacred and spotless virginity being perpetually preserved from the beginning, then, and forever afterwards.

I therefore condemn and reject as false and heretical the assertion that doubt or denial of the virgin birth of Christ or the perpetual virginity of the Blessed Mary, mother of God, is—or at any time ever can be in any sense whatever—consistent with the Holy Catholic faith.

I believe and profess that Our Lord Jesus Christ, after his death and burial, rose again from the dead, and that His body glorified in His resurrection is the same as that in which He suffered and died for us upon the cross. I reject and condemn the statement that the body of Christ rotted in the grave or suffered corruption as false and heretical, and contrary to the Holy Catholic faith now and in all future time.

I firmly believe and profess, in accordance with the Holy Council of Trent, that the first man, Adam, when he transgressed the command of God in Paradise, immediately lost the holiness and justice in which he had been constituted, and that he incurred through that prevarication the wrath and indignation of God, and that this prevarication of Adam injured, not himself alone, but his posterity, and that by it the holiness and justice from God were lost by him, not for himself alone, but for us all.

I firmly believe and profess that our Lord died upon the cross, not merely (as Socinus held) to set us an example or an "object lesson" of fidelity unto death, but that He might give Himself "a redemption for all" by "bearing our sins in His body upon the tree"— that is, by making a true and full satisfaction to the offended justice of God for the sins original and actual of all men, and that these sins are taken away by no other remedy than the merit of the "one mediator, our Lord Jesus Christ," who has reconciled us to God in His own blood; "made unto us justice, sanctification, and redemption."

I reject and condemn all doctrines which deny the reality and transmission of original sin, and the perfect sufficiency of the atonement by which man is reconciled to God in the blood of Jesus Christ, as false and heretical, and contrary to the Holy Catholic faith now and at all future time.

I firmly believe and profess that the souls of men after death will be judged by God and that those who are saved will "go into everlasting life," and those who are condemned "unto everlasting punishment.' I reject as false and heretical all doctrines which teach that the souls in hell may eventually be saved or that their state in hell may be one which is not of punishment.

In accordance with the Holy Councils of Trent and of the Vatican, I receive all the books of the Old and New Testament with all their parts as set forth in the fourth session of the Council of Trent, and contained in the ancient Latin edition of the Vulgate, as sacred and canonical, and I firmly believe and profess, that the said Scriptures are sacred and canonical—not because having been carefully composed by mere human industry, they were afterwards approved by the Church's authority, nor merely because they contain revelation with no admixture of error; but because, having been written by the inspiration of the Holy Ghost, they have God for their author and have been delivered as such to the Church herself. Wherefore in all matters of faith and morals appertaining to the building up of Christian doctrine, I believe that to be the true sense of Holy Scripture which our Holy Mother the Church has held and now holds, to whom the judgment of the true sense and interpretation of Holy Scripture belongs.

I firmly believe and profess that the doctrine of faith which God has revealed has not been proposed like a philosophical invention to be perfected by human ingenuity, but has been delivered as a divine deposit to the spouse of Christ, to be faithfully kept and infallibly declared, and that therefore that meaning of the sacred dogmas is to be perpetually retained which our Holy Mother the church has once declared, and that the meaning can never be departed from, under the pretense or pretext of a deeper comprehension of them. I reject as false and heretical the assertion that it is possible at some time, according to the progress of science, to give to doctrines propounded by the church a sense different from that which the church has understood and understands, and consequently that the sense and meaning of her doctrines can ever be in the course of time practically explained or reversed.

Moreover, I condemn and revoke all the other words and statements which in articles contributed by me to the "Fortnightly Review" and the "Nineteenth Century", or in any other of my writings, are found to be, in matter of faith and morals, contrary to the teaching of the Holy Catholic Faith according to the determination of the apostolic see; and in all such matters I submit myself to the judgment of the said see, receiving all that it receives and condemning all that it condemns.

Vaughan, symbolic of the authority of the Church, was to be satisfied with nothing less than complete submission, the unconditional surrender of the enemy.

Mivart, however, could have expected—and perhaps he sought—nothing except such a forthright statement of the official stand of the Church. In reviewing these events a few months later, he wrote, in fact, "On purpose I made them [the articles which led to Vaughan's action] of startling character, so that I might be able to ascertain whether the position I, and not a few other Catholics, occupied in the Roman Church was, or was not, a tenable one—whether it was in any way possible to continue in that communion." The action he elicited was, perhaps, more drastic than he had anticipated; but it left no doubt in his mind as to his future in the Church. And for that he was grateful. "Though I deeply regretted, and regret," he wrote, "this clear demonstration through the action of Archbishop Vaughan and his advisers, that the Roman Catholic Church has thus shown itself to be essentially a *petrified* and not a *progressive* Church, I feel none the less convinced that it is better that such a fact should become distinctly known than that it should remain concealed by subterfuges and evasions of ecclesiastics who seek to retain, and gain, adherents through a pretence of logically impossible liberalism." [25]

To Vaughan's dogged demands that he sign the profession of faith, Mivart answered first with questions, then with explanations, and finally with an unequivocal rejection: "I categorically refuse to sign the profession of faith. . . . Happily I can now speak with entire frankness as to all my convictions. *Liberavi meam animam.* I can sing my *Nunc dimittis* and calmly await the future." [26]

Having initiated a situation, with whatever wisdom, from which there could be no retreat, Cardinal Vaughan had no alternative but to regard as a heretic him who had been one of the Church's staunchest supporters. On the Feast of St. Peter's Chair, Vaughan, as Archbishop of Westminster, addressed the following circular letter to all the clergy of his diocese:

Dr. St. George Mivart, in his articles entitled "The Continuity of Catholicism" and "Some Recent Apologists" in the "Nineteenth Century" and the "Fortnightly Review" for January, 1900, has declared, or at least seemed to declare, that it is permissible for Catholics to hold certain heresies—regarding the virginal birth of Our

Lord and the perpetual virginity of the Blessed Virgin; the gospel account of the resurrection and the immunity of the sacred body from corruption; the reality and transmission of original sin; the redemption of a real satisfaction for the sins of men; the everlasting punishment of the wicked; the inspiration and integrity of Holy Scripture; the right of the Catholic church to interpret the sense of Scripture with authority; her perpetual retention of her doctrines in the same sense; not to speak of other false propositions. As he has thereby rendered his orthodoxy suspect, and has, moreover, confirmed the suspicion by failing after three notifications, to sign the annexed profession of faith when tendered to him by me, it now becomes my duty to take further action, and I hereby inhibit him from approaching the sacraments, and forbid my priests to administer them to him, until he shall have proved his orthodoxy to the satisfaction of his ordinary.[27]

His denial to Mivart of the sacraments was tantamount to excommunication, prohibiting, as it did, burial in hallowed ground.

Although submission and repentance were always possible, it would have been extremely inconsistent with the whole of Mivart's character for him to alter the step he had taken. He was, moreover, fully aware of what he had done. Still full of fury at his treatment by the *Tablet*'s editor and its proprietor, he wrote on February 10 to the former: "I was not fully aware, till the reception my recent articles met with made it evident, how great was the inevitable divergence between the Catholicity to which I was, and am, attached and the Catholicity which alone can find toleration from ecclesiastical authority. It was the former Catholicity I wished, and wish, to strengthen; certainly not that of Cardinal Vaughan—my possible and unintentional part promotion of which I have desired to atone for and undo." [28]

Liberavi animam meam. "I have freed my mind and my spirit," Mivart chanted as he cast off the chains of the ultimate authority external to himself. But what this final effort, this final victory of his intellect, meant to him was known only to those few close friends whose sympathy he sought in the vacuum of the new freedom. How ardently, in his new loneliness, he must have tried to convince them of the rightness of his actions! How painful must have been the readjustments in the patterns of his life! How he must have sought to hide his final disillusionment! In all of this he may have been successful. But that apparent success must have been only superficial. Those able to penetrate the mask of satisfaction saw the heart broken by a lost faith. Late in March of 1900 Alice Meynell, poet, critic, and Catholic, the friend of many years for whose child Mivart had been godfather, wrote him in answer to his search for sympathy, for understanding, for the earlier, the better days to be again:

I should not have offered you my criticisms, but in reply to your question, I have to say that I do think what you are doing to be wrong.

It seems to me wrong to influence others to give up a faith that is a restraint upon human passions. Your own abandonment of Christianity, however rational you may consider it, is no more than the result of an opinion. And there can be no sufficient reason for urging an opinion upon others; whereas the reason for not urging *this* opinion upon others is most momentous. Mankind is absolutely in need of fundamental morality in the first place, and of a code of morals in the second place. I do not know how much fundamental morality you now acknowledge; probably you think mere cruelty to be wrong. But the pursuit of pleasure for its own sake leads to cruelty—not merely accidentally, by way of egoism, but directly, as to an end. This is one of the mysteries of human nature, and against this descent into infernal evil mankind needs a safeguard which must be dogmatic from the beginning. I am quite sure it is wrong to take away such a safeguard because *on the whole* you think it an imaginary one.

Moreover it seems to me wrong and lamentable that a man should be eager to write and talk about his loss, when he has lost Jesus Christ. To have to relinquish that figure and that person ought to be a great grief—certainly a grief imposing silence for a time. Only a cold and corrupt heart would fail to suffer. Therefore I think you must suffer more than you know, and I wish I had words to persuade you to respect your own distress.[29]

Contradicting all subsequent charges of mental breakdown, Mivart's answer to his old friend summed up the world of compassionate reason into which he had entered after so long a journey. "I must send a few words in rejoinder," he wrote immediately upon receiving Mrs. Meynell's uncomprehending criticism, but I know how precious your time is so I will be as brief as I can.

My experience of life makes me *deny* that Catholicity is as moral as cultivated natural ethics and common sense. I have known admirable Catholic men and women but they are not the best I have known; while the absolutely worst, *by far*, of both sexes have been Catholics, greatly attached to their faith, devout, practical, and some, though English, attached to the Papal court. I refer to sexual morality, but if I extend it to truthfulness and honesty in money matters it is much the same.

Of course men need fundamental morality and if they will use their reason it stares them in the face. And a code founded on reason and independent morality is surely being evolved. But it will not coincide in all things with the Christian code, which is partly based on an exaggerated asceticism, and an absurd estimate of virginity as a state to be admired in and for itself.

Unbridled passion and the pursuit of pleasure as an exclusive end, sacrificing other considerations, are, of course, hateful, base and tend to cruelty—as I have often urged and, as long as I live, shall continue to urge. Worldliness and an exclusive pursuit of wealth and power are detestable also. There is no need to be a Christian to have moral convictions and ideals. You speak of the rejection of Christianity being "the result of an *opinion*,"—it should be the result of a careful intellectual judgment, and the *acceptance* of Christianity can claim no higher sanction. If you think we have some faculty higher than the intellect, all I can say is it is utterly unknown to me. As to the character of Jesus Christ, I have during my long illness made as careful a study of it as I could, and I think the sentiment so many feel about it is due to traditional reverence and what they have been taught from infancy. What *God incarnate* did and said I used to reverence as divine and never criticized. But calm judgment of Jesus Christ as a mere man is a different matter. St. John's account I put aside as ideal and fictious. Of what we read in the Synoptics how much is *true* history? But if we accept most of it, it seems to me that certain parts are admirable, some teaching distinctly immoral, and other parts ignorant and foolish. Altogether had I lived then, I do not think he would have attracted me. With many thanks for your letter. . . . The confessional I regard as rather an encouragement to sexual immorality as regards men, than as a restraint. Absolution is given so very easily and freely as often as wanted. It is recorded of Henry VIII that he would sometimes go several times a day.[30]

So far had his probing taken him.

But suffer he did, as Alice Meynell's poet-heart knew he must. A week later, Mivart was dead, suddenly; though the mind had conquered, the heart had failed.

4

On Saturday evening, April 1, Mivart was to speak as guest at the dinner of the Authors' Club. Perhaps the reappearance of his novel of ideas (published under a pseudonym a decade earlier) had established him as an author to be so honored; or perhaps it was the style and feeling exhibited in his now-public exchange with Cardinal Vaughan; or perhaps it was his last— almost frantic—attempts through the popular journals to alter the course of the Catholicism of which he was no longer a part; or perhaps it was just that events had made him a figure of public note. Whatever the reason for the invitation, whatever blast he had reserved for the occasion, this last platform for his exaltation of reason in all of life was denied him. On the afternoon of his scheduled appearance he suffered the last of a series of heart attacks and died.

His friends sought, during the following week, to lift the ban which prohibited Catholic burial. They used as their justification the illness from which he suffered, suggested that his mind was diseased, argued that he was not responsible for the positions he had taken. But Vaughan, himself on his deathbed, was unable to relent. And thus, still in the midst of controversy, Mivart was buried in unhallowed ground.

It was for his friends and his family, those who had learned from him and those who had counseled him, to search for the ways of reunion once death and time had softened the bitterness of rebellion. In so doing, however lofty their motives, they were reducing to pygmy proportions the intellectual stature which Mivart had finally achieved. By attributing his revolt to a disease of the mind, they demonstrated that, in the final analysis, Mivart was alone, that his life, whose pattern had been so clear, was in vain.

As he was reburied, a Catholic once more, in sacred ground four years after his death, the Church sealed the schism; but the intellect that was Mivart had gone down in defeat.

EPILOGUE

Only when a life is over, in an epilogue such as this, may the biographer attempt—in hindsight and with the bias of the present—to evaluate the impact, the failures and successes, the twisted turnings and the goalward sprints of the human life, and the activities to which it gave birth.

Evaluations of whatever kind are difficult because they imply the existence of some standard, usually arbitrary and culturally subjective, by which the evaluative judgments can be made. The evaluation of an historical figure or event is doubly difficult because it is hardly possible to disregard the reorientation in values which follows from the inevitable temporal change in the culture in which and through which the evaluator makes his judgments. This is particularly true in the recent history of science, where the data and the problems to which they have given rise have increased so rapidly and where the currents of thought have shifted so drastically.

In his own evaluation of the scientific greats of the nineteenth century, Osborn cautioned: "It is well to remember that we may not estimate either a man of science or his conclusions as of our own period, but must project ourselves in imagination into the beginnings of his thought and into the travails of his mind, considering how much larger he was than the men about him, how far he was an innovator, breaking away from the traditions of his times, how far his direct observations apart from his theories are true and permanent, and how far his theories have contributed to the great stream of biological thought." [1] It is only in these terms, I think, that we can evaluate the work—and the life—of St. George Mivart.

His life was one of almost continuous controversy. The seeds of his criticisms, ranging over many fields, lay not so much in the material as in the man. As every man is ruled in his estimation of others by his estimation of himself, so was Mivart. His estimate of himself made it imperative that he assert his own personality and not become a subordinate cog in the system of any other.

Except for the usual banalities of the obituaries, there is hardly any direct, candid testimony bearing upon Mivart's character. And yet, on the basis of his writings and the manner of his expression, particularly in controversy, there can be little doubt that he felt that to him were given the keys of wisdom. There is little real humility in any of his writings; on the contrary, they display an author pompous and positive. Even the apparent humility with which he cloaked his letters to Cardinal Newman—whom he respected beyond any other— cannot conceal the stubborn and willful writer whose every action and every thought could be justified in terms of absolute truth. He was positive—and it was this very positiveness which led him time and time again into controversy with those who for good reason or bad refused to accept the authority which marked his utterances. Though the last to admit that he knew truth—only to God was that ability given—he was certain that his was the path to its most complete elucidation.

He could admit his fallibility as he did, for example, in a letter to Poulton, in which he generously remarked: "I have but one wish which is that by our combined but diverse and diverging efforts we may help on truth. I should [think] not many people have a more lively sense of their fallibility than I have of mine." [2] But such confessions were rare and restricted to matters of detail. In his philosophical outlook, in his whole approach to the universe, natural or supernatural, he was convinced that he was basically correct—because his reason told him so. Thus, even when forced to apologize publicly to George Darwin in a matter of misquotation, he could do so in a manner which simply reiterated the charge for which the apology had been demanded; or, after his articles on hell had been placed on the Index, he could publicly accede to the decree of

Rome in such a manner as not to prejudice the position for which he had been censured. It was this faith in the soundness of his own reason which could justify, in anonymous reviews, his use of himself as an authority for the point he wished to make.

Only a man convinced of his own rightness could rail against his adversaries with the righteous indignation and benign condescension which were so characteristic of his controversial writings. Only a man convinced of his own rightness could proclaim it so long and with such force.

It is this same attitude which, generalized, marks his tolerance as a Catholic of adherents of other creeds. Positive in his own Catholicism, he recognized—as he had to recognize—the right of others to other beliefs; but they were in error. And it was his aim to demonstrate their error to them. A great part of his writing, particularly as it attempted a reconciliation between science and religion on intellectual grounds and through an amelioration of antiquated theological beliefs, was designed to convert those outside the pale of the Catholic communion to the only true faith. As an intellectual, he appealed to their intellects. "I know you think with me," he wrote Meynell in 1885, "that it is a great pity so many men (especially the younger) should leave the Church openly or practically because they are convinced that they cannot honestly and without violence to their *intellect* be in thorough harmony with it. My *whole object* is to keep liberal and intellectual men inside and if this is to be done the *strain* must be relaxed." [3] The rejection of Catholicism, with its complex of truths, could lead only to final error. Typical of this attitude regarding the correctness of the Catholic view was his reaction to the repeated charges that the Church hindered the advance of science and knowledge. "So far from the Christian [i.e., Catholic] religion tending to cramp or fetter intellectual development," he wrote in answer to the strictures of Huxley, "it is notorious that some of the profoundest thinkers of recent as of more ancient times have been believers in Christianity, and I am convinced that every man who rejects that belief is *ipso facto* necessarily condemned not only to a moral but also, and as inevitably, to an intellectual inferiority as compared with what he might attain did he accept that system in its fulness." [4]   Only one convinced of the absolute correctness of his own system of belief could make such a wholesale condemnation of those whose right to believe he affirmed.

Nor was Mivart unaware of his own egoism.   In fact, he seems at times to have reveled in it, using it to answer his critics and choke off controversy.   The imperious statement with which he declined controversy with a theologically inspired critic of the *Genesis* is not atypical.   To this anonymous correspondent in the columns of the *Tablet,* Mivart replied:

> I beg to say that I fully hold that the doctrine of human liberty and the spirituality of the soul can be proved by reason alone, and that I am sure that nothing in my book even *tends* to support a contrary belief.   I cannot, however, undertake to make this clear to the mind of A. B. whose opinion that "the difference between the intelligence of an ape and a savage is by no means so clear, or even . . . so essential" as that between crystalline and colloidal matter, I believe to be as scientifically false as it is dangerous to religion.
>
> For my part, my reason *alone* convinces me that there is far more difference between the lowest savage and the highest ape than there is between the highest ape and a lump of granite.
>
> With this comment I must decline further controversy.[5]

It is to this sureness, which he recognized in himself, that he alluded in a conciliatory letter to Huxley in 1886.   Complimenting his friend of former days on the excellence of a recent article, Mivart went on to say, however, that he could not "pretend to altogether agree with you.   I still hold and think I always shall hold the supreme certainty, to me, of my own existence—the certainty about that is what 'in the *schools*' is called 'cock.'   That's his d———d egotism you will say."   And remembering the pain of former conflicts, he concluded with a rare, though in its generality meaningless, admission of error: "Well! so be it, for I have not the slightest inclination for controversy.   I know only too well *I* have made mistakes and life is short—alas!" [6]

To such a man, supreme in his own ego, no one could be entirely right; nor could anyone, in the final analysis, be regarded as authority unless it be he himself.   In that "synthesis of truths" which he sought to propound in the world of the intellect, it was *he* who was to be the arbiter between truth and error. The truths were *his* truths derived from the application of *his* judgment and reason. For Mivart it was Mivart who was the court of last appeal in matters of controversy.

His whole approach, impelled by the fervency of his belief, was one calculated not so much to persuade as to bludgeon. Convinced of his own truths, he, like most crusaders, was intolerant of "indecision and equivocation." To him there could be no "may be's" but only "can only be's" with respect to important propositions. Regarding his own, he suffered from the very dogmatism which he so condemned in others. He was unwilling to allow the relativity of truth, but insisted upon its absoluteness. For him the contrasts were the blacks and the whites; and he ignored the weakness of the grays. There is, in short, a lack of humility in Mivart's writings, whatever share of that trait he may have exhibited in ordinary social intercourse. He was the prophet of truth—and he knew it.

Beyond all, however, he possessed a deep and devoted love of truth—not the relative truth of the later nineteenth century, but truth absolute, laid down at the beginning of time, resting in the inscrutable intelligence of the Divine Creator. For the enunciation of that truth, he was willing to sacrifice all, because the meaning of life lay in its discovery. "It was with no little pain," he wrote concerning his difficulties with Darwin, "that earnest conviction impelled me to criticize two of his subsequent works, but no scientific man can reasonably blame me for not refusing to sacrifice what I believed to be truth at the shrine of private friendship." [7] It was this same refusal "to sacrifice what I believe to be truth" which, having driven him from the Darwinian circle, finally forced him from the church of his faith.

2

As a scientist, Mivart can be ranked only as one in a large body of individuals who, in the latter half of the nineteenth century, laid much of the factual foundation of modern biology. By no means a Darwin nor even a Huxley, he followed in most of his work the paths laid out for him by his predecessors with respect both to the collection of his data and its philosophical interpretation. In no area was he strictly speaking an innovator; he seems to have been content to exploit the methodological and philosophical innovations of others, as his frequent reference to and reliance upon the theoretical work of others indicate. Nor do I believe that he considered himself an original thinker or pioneer in any of his fields of interest and activity. He was and, I think, he felt himself to be essentially eclectic in his approach to the solution of those problems which pricked the intellectual curiosity of the nineteenth century. His approach was a synthetic one; and his role that of a selector and coordinator, producing a synthesis of truth from the mass of data emerging from the new science. He was an omnivorous reader and an avid conversationalist and writer, but in what he wrote he proved himself an organizer of material rather than an original thinker; and it was from his broad and catholic intellectual associations that he selected those conclusions which best harmonized with his rational a priori judgments.

Nevertheless, despite the crystallized point of view which gave direction to his synthesis, he was by no means incompetent or valueless as an empirical investigator. No mere arm-chair speculator, he was equally at home in the laboratory and in his study; his scalpel was as familiar to him as his pen. It is, in fact, upon his "direct observations apart from his theories" that, in the main, his claim to scientific fame must rest.

Although almost forgotten by modern workers—or, at best, quoted only in the most comprehensive of bibliographies— many of his technical papers are fundamental contributions to the specific fields with which they deal. His skeletal studies of the Primates, particularly those of the Lemuroids, were the best and most complete studies of the kind for almost half a century and suffer today only through the later refinement and systematization of metric techniques. His subordinal distinction between the Lemuroids and the Anthropoids has never lost its utility despite the recent expansion of the former and the terminological revision instituted by Simpson.[8] His papers on the

Lemuroids, in fact, are unique for the period in which they were written. Mivart was, furthermore, one of the pioneers in the osteological investigation and classification of those Primate-like Insectivores (or Insectivore-like Primates), the *Tupaiidae*. In his then definitive work on that group,[9] Lyon paid tribute to Mivart, not only as the first to define and name the family but also as the earliest of the few anatomists whose "rather careful" skeletal studies formed the basis of his own work.

The lasting value of Mivart's technical work, with whatever group it dealt, lies in his zealous attention to detail and the consequent construction of a body of data in relatively unexploited areas upon which theoretical structures could be based. It is this value which his contemporaries recognized. The result of his anatomical work, wrote one of his colleagues at Mivart's death, "was largely to increase our knowledge of the anatomy of these groups; the most remarkable feature connected with these investigations being the care bestowed on the arrangement and tabulation of the data acquired. In this respect Dr. Mivart's work is a model for future investigators."[10] And Howes remarked that through his work Mivart had "placed the world of working zoologists under a deep obligation for his numerous memoirs and papers, which are for the greater part painstaking records of structural detail, of immense service for reference."[11]

His more general, and often theoretical, works, when divorced from the philosophical biases which often inspired them, are, I think, of even greater interest when viewed from the vantage point of today. Judged by Osborn's criterion, however, they must be considered almost valueless, for they contributed hardly anything to "the great stream of biological thought." Despite Morgan's allusion to Mivart's valuable conceptual contributions to his own empirical psychology and despite the turmoil which surrounded much of what he wrote, Mivart's influence upon the thought of his own or immediately succeeding scientific generations was insignificant. Unlike Huxley, with whom he must inevitably be compared because of the parallel nature of their interests, Mivart left only the faintly discernible mark of the critic on nineteenth century science. Unlike Huxley, who must stand as the peerless teacher of post-Darwinian biology, whose students, even those several generations removed from his direct influence, carried on and developed his approach to scientific investigations, Mivart left no one to propagate the scientific faith that was in him. His science died with him; and like his body it was buried a virtual outcast from the community which had given it life.

The interest of Mivart's ideas, apart from his observations, lies rather in their anticipation of things to come than in any specific contribution to the coming.

Of these ideas, the most significant is his emphasis upon the independent development of similar structures in the evolutionary process and its specific application to the problem of the origins of man. If not the first to note, Mivart was certainly the first to call attention to the facts of convergence and parallelism not only as significant factors in evolution generally but also as complicating ones in the definition of particular evolutionary lines. And it was on the basis of this probable parallelism in the evolution of the Primates that he argued against the deceptively simple anthropoid theory of human origins which came to be regarded more as fact than as hypothesis by the Darwinian enthusiasts of the latter part of the nineteenth century and the earlier decades of the twentieth. Mivart's adroit separation of the human line of descent from that of anthropoid apes, which he first set forth so convincingly in his soon-forgotten *Man and Apes*, was a precursor of the similar views of such contemporary Primate anatomists as Frederic Wood Jones and William L. Straus, Jr.[12] Neither of these "neo-Mivartians", though each has expressed admiration for Mivart's work, can be said to have been influenced by him. They have reached their similar views by approaching the problem from Mivart's vantage point—the detailed anatomical investigation of the Primate order as an order. And, like Mivart, they have been forced to the same conclusions.

Recent emphases, Mivartian in tone rather than in origin, in philosophy rather than in psychology, provide a key to an un-

derstanding of the mystery of human mentality without, however, solving it.   And that key is essentially the same as the
one with which Mivart tried to unlock the door of the human
mind.   The philosophical interest in man's symbolic activities
gives promise of clarifying the foundations of human behavior
as distinguished from that which man shares with his biological
kin.   In the recognition of symbolic behavior as the uniquely
human component in the total entity that is the human mind,
there is a return to the Mivartian definition of man.   For to
Mivart, too, it was man's "representative" abilities, evidenced
in his powers of abstraction and in his construction of language,
which set him apart from the "merely sentient" brutes to whom
he was but morphologically linked.

One need not make the distinctions in origins which Mivart
made, in order to agree with the logic of his analytic distinctions.   Whatever the biological relations involved are eventually proved to be, the recognition of the difference between
"sign" behavior and "symbolic" behavior—whether it is or is
not a qualitative distinction in Mivart's particular sense is unimportant—is a fruitful one for an understanding of man.

I have said that these ideas, among others,[13] are of interest
when divorced from their theological and philosophical biases.
The tragedy of Mivart, as a contributor to the intellectual
growth of his time, was that he could not accomplish such a
divorce.   The idea was both an outgrowth and a support for
his point of view; the two were inextricably linked in a single
conception.   In his failure to make the separation, Mivart was
frustrated in any attempt to probe more deeply into the nature
and implications of the data, phenomenal as well as ideational,
whose meaning he was able to recognize.   Thus, whenever he
was faced with a problem, either on an empirical or rational
level, which more intensive investigation might have clarified
in causal terms, he was content to provide the easy answer of
his Divine Intelligence.   The First Cause, as an answer, was too
readily available for him; and too often he was unable to resist the temptation of using that answer to cut knots, instead
of untying them.   For any positive contribution to the world
of ideas, his preconceptions too often distorted and inhibited

his conceptions; and the consequent intrusion of nonscientific factors in scientific matters, an appeal to faith under the guise of reason, led to his virtual exclusion from the close circle of those who were enamored by the vision of a pure science grounded upon the ideal of induction.

One reads Mivart at times with wonder as he moves from the natural to the supernatural and back again with the ease of an acrobat. The distinction between natural and supernatural, which was so real to his critics, was for him, however, illusory. God was real and nature gave witness to his reality; and with the reality of God established as a basic premise, that premise had its rightful place in scientific reasoning. In answer to protests against such a method, he would calmly and condescendingly accuse the protestant of a misunderstanding of the nature of science, or, at best, a too-limiting overspecialization. It was this intrusion of God, and the conclusions derived therefrom, into the domains of science which irritated his opponents; and yet it was this very intrusion which Mivart constantly sought to justify. The search was compulsive, since in its success lay Mivart's own adjustment to the religio-philosophical system which he had assumed as his own.

3

Mivart was, however, not only a biologist; and thus he cannot be seen only in terms of the position he occupied in the somewhat restricted area of science. He considered his role in the Roman Catholic Church to be of equal value. It was his Catholicism which provided him with the outlines of his philosophy with its consequences for his science. But as his science was tempered by his Catholicism, so was his Catholicism tempered by his science.

To the Church which was for him the source of truth he brought the fruits of science. It was not so much the scientific method itself which he offered as it was the essence of nineteenth-century science—the concept of an eternal and inevitable change throughout the whole of the universe. With this concept he sought to perfect the divinely inspired instrument of truth through a process of growth which was as natural as it was inevitable. To an institution which seemed to him to be withering in the staticity of its traditional dogmatism, he offered the hope of eternal life through the natural—and, because it was natural, divine—principle of change.

Mivart was not alone in his attempts to revivify the Catholic Church. But he was, in England, the most ardent, the most articulate of its lay reformers. And of these liberals he was, perhaps, the most impatient as well.

Had his attempts at the liberalization of Catholic dogma and doctrine been successful, had he succeeded in welding together the twin truths of science and theology into a harmonious intellectual unity through which both would have benefited—had he accomplished the impossible—he might have stood, as he sometimes saw himself, as a nineteenth-century Galileo. But his was a vain and lonely voice of protest lost in the tempest of tradition.

Viewing Mivart's liberal theological ideas out of the context of history, it is tempting to see him as a paramount figure in the modernist movement which swept over the Catholic world at the turn of the century. But as he was rejected by the traditionalists, so was he rejected by the modernists. For those to whom he should have been a champion, he was but "a useful object lesson . . . on the necessity of keeping one's temper"; [14] those whose burden he had assumed "blamed him for having lost his temper in the quarrel." [15] Alone he fought the initial battles of the modernists; alone he reaped the galling punishment. Always he was alone. Although he was supremely confident that his was the way to truth, he wandered, ever a lonely figure, through the world of ideas.

4

Throughout his writings there is a recurring emphasis, an underlying theme, which unites all that he did and all that he attempted, in science and theology, in history and philosophy, into a consistent and meaningful whole. In the lyrical passage with which he opened his philosophical attack on Hume and his "materialistic" adherents Mivart sang of the nature he loved:

In a small ravine on the verge of Sheffield Forest, in Sussex, there is a shady nook, where on hot summer days the author has loved to sit and where much of this work was done. There, between banks so steep and woody that the sky is almost hidden by the meeting boughs of birch and oak, alder and chestnut, a tiny streamlet winds its way, and falls with ceaseless, copious drip from moss-grown rocks into a small pool. All around, tall bracken ferns stretch up towards the light, while masses of blechnum, with their twofold, graceful fronds, clothe the banks lower down. Where moss is wanting, on jutting pieces of sandstone, there liverworts have their hold, and campanulas, potentillas, scabious, and agrimony, with corydalis, foxgloves, and asphodels have each their station, which they struggle to extend. Besides the drip and ripple of the streamlet, is heard the constant hum of active insect life, and occasionally the drowsy note of over-sailing rooks. Busy ants pass perseveringly to and fro along their well-trod paths, and every now and then a butterfly or moth quivers in the chequered light, and the beautiful dragon-fly hovers over, or darts down upon, the pool in which another tiny world may be watched in rapid motion. What is the special charm of a bit of nature of this kind? It is not in a mere soothing of the senses or a vague revival in the imagination of pleasures formerly experienced. A mere rustic may indeed have pleasure in such a spot, and every lover of the picturesque may feel its charm, and indistinctly perceive at least some part of its meaning. Only the skilled lover of nature, however, who knows much of her laws and of different classes of living creatures, can thoroughly appreciate all its interest and charm.

What the man of science therein appreciates is, the display of natural harmony, the unity of multifold variety, and the delicate balance of physical and vital activities which it manifests. Evidently the greater his knowledge, the more fully his mind will be able to embrace the complex inter-relations of its animal and vegetal inhabitants, and the more intense will be the intellectual pleasure he may derive from its contemplation.[16]

Harmony—this was the keynote in all of Mivart's attempted solutions to the problems of science, of philosophy, of life itself. For him all phenomena, of whatever level of abstraction, were united in a harmonious expression of that universe-pervading Divine Intelligence whose existence was as real to him as his very own. It was this deep and abiding sense of the basic oneness of the universe, the universe of thought and sense, of science and religion, which spawned his cravings for synthesis. In the atmosphere of the prevailing science of his day he breathed the air of phenomenal separateness; and he found it noxious. The thread of harmony founded upon the absolute world of his theism ran through his life, providing that intellectual sustenance upon which his mind thrived.

It was this belief in the relatedness and harmony of nature that lay at the root of Mivart's evolutionism, and led him early to expand biology to include the science of *Hexicology* as that "special science . . . devoted to a study of the relations which exist between organisms and their environment as regards the nature of the localities which they frequent, the temperatures and amounts of light which suit them, and their relations to other organisms as enemies, rivals, or accidental and involuntary benefactors." [17] It motivated his lifelong attempt to reconcile science and religion and to unite science and philosophy into a science of sciences. Finally, in his later years, it led him into the byways of epistemology in the hope that here he might discover the unifying forces of knowledge from which both science and philosophy stemmed. It was a noble attempt; but it could not succeed.

5

However much Mivart searched for the harmony in the macrocosm, he rarely achieved it in the microcosm of his own social relationships. Although "his friendly geniality, his refined manners, his interesting conversation and fund of anecdote of the most varied kind, rendered him a charming companion," [18] he seems almost always to have been at odds with even the best of his friends. His controversies generated personal animosities. While he was always quick to disclaim the personal character of his criticism, "criticism which I can conscientiously aver has been free from personal animosity," he was often unable to separate, in his forceful attacks, the individual from the ideas he expressed. His was a vitriolic pen; and he flourished it broadly and on the least provocation.

His son explained his controversies by saying that his father "was a voluminous and many-sided, though often too rapid if not at times also a careless writer, too easily induced to extract burning chestnuts for persons unwilling to do the job for themselves." [19]   Certainly this was true.   Too often he entered the lists at the behest of others who thought it more prudent to remain silent.

His more spectacular controversies follow a pattern which transcends both service to others and the expression of his own ego.   Mivart was the eternal protestant, the ever-ready battler against the imposition of authority.   Theology was not the only realm in which authority existed; Mivart saw its expression in matters of science as well.   As early as 1869, he commented scathingly upon the position which he considered the apostles of materialism held in the eyes of the lay public:

A lamentable sign of our present intellectual decrepitude is the way in which even the so-called educated public is ready to fall down at the feet of any teacher of physical science who has attained a certain degree of fame or notoriety.   Two or three such, with as many soi-disant philosophers, reign at the present moment, in English public opinion in a way which would be ridiculous were not the consequences so serious.   Inverting the true order, we have unbounded submission, as to mere matters of opinion, where reason and not authority should be the sole arbiter.   In the name of truth, then, we cry out for more "free thought" and a greater exercise of "private judgment" in this, its legitimate field.[20]

Like his fellow Catholic and contemporary, the historian Lord Acton, he fervently believed in and fought for the freedom of the individual, the freedom of conscience, the freedom of belief, and "the assertion of private judgment."

By the end of his life, he had thrown off the last and strongest external authority to which he had been subject.   In the midst of his last great controversy, he announced to his archbishop and through him to his Church: "All of use, however submissive to authority, must in the last resort, rest upon the judgment of our individual reason.   How otherwise could we know that authority had spoken at all or what it had said?   It is impossible to accept anything as true which is a contradiction in terms.   Upon that truth all theological reasoning is based and all other reasoning also." [21]

Reason, reason, reason—like Descartes three centuries before, he worshiped reason.   Reason was the justification for his acts; and all of his acts were justified, for he was the rational man par excellence.

Here was a man sublimely confident in his own rational ability; and yet he constantly found himself placed in a position subservient to authority.   Not one authority, but two—his science and his religion.   It is little wonder that his life was a constant struggle against both.

NOTES

NOTES TO I: CONVERSION

1. For an excellent treatment of the labor pains of contemporary geology and the impact of its emergence upon the intellectual order of this period, see Charles C. Gillispie's *Genesis and Geology* (Princeton, Princeton University Press, 1951); in the more general field of the natural sciences as a whole, Loren C. Eiseley's *Darwin's Century* (New York, Doubleday, 1958) provides a readable and authoritative account of the events leading to the intellectual revolution of the mid-nineteenth century.

2. Leonard Huxley, *The Life and Letters of Thomas Henry Huxley* (2 vols., New York, D. Appleton and Co., 1901), I, 159.

3. Frederic Boase, *Modern English Biography* (6 vols., Truro, Netherton & Worth, 1897).

4. F. St. G. Mivart, "Early Memories of St. George Mivart," *Dublin Review*, CLXXIV (1924): 3–4. It is this source, reproducing autobiographical material recorded between 1881 and 1885, that provides the only information regarding Mivart's early years.

5. St. George Mivart, *An Introduction to the Elements of Science* (London, Osgood, McIlvaine and Co., 1894).

6. F. St. G. Mivart, "Early Memories of St. George Mivart," *Dublin Review*, CLXXIV (1924), 7–8.

7. John H. Newman, "Catholics in England from the Sixteenth to the Nineteenth Century," in W. S. Lilley, *A Newman Anthology* (London, Dennis Dobson Ltd., 1949; originally published in 1875), pp. 179–80.

8. F. St. G. Mivart, "Memories of St. George Mivart," *Dublin Review*, CLXXIV (1924), 16.

9. Augustus Welby Pugin, himself a convert to Catholicism, is regarded by many as the initiator of the Gothic revival in English architecture. Recreating, particularly in the Catholic parish church and cathedral, the grandeur of medieval religious architecture, he signaled the awakening of the Catholic community in England by drawing attention to its former glories. There were many who, like Mivart, were drawn to the Church which inspired so majestic a visible expression. See D. Gwynn, *Lord Shrewsbury, Pugin and the Catholic Revival* (London, Hollis and Carter, 1946).

10. F. St. G. Mivart, "Early Memories of St. George Mivart," *Dublin Review*, CLXXIV (1924), 17.

11. *Ibid.*, p. 19.   12. *Ibid.*, p. 20.

13. Philip Schaff, *The Creeds of Christendom* (3 vols., New York, Harper and Bros., 1877), I, 99.

14. Wilfrid Ward, *The Life of John Henry Cardinal Newman*, (2 vols., in one, London, Longmans, Green and Co., 1927; originally published in 1912), I, 119.

15. Quoted in Bertram C. A. Windle, *Who's Who of the Oxford Movement* (New York, Century, 1926), p. 53.

16. The regulations for admission to the Inns of Court, for example, stress as a condition for entrance that the candidate be a "gentleman of character and responsibility"; and they expressly state that "no person can be admitted a member who shall be engaged in trade." A further expression of the linkage of law, medicine, and divinity as the occupational trinity for the gentleman is reflected in what is perhaps one of the earliest scholarship bequests, that of Tancred in 1754, by which funds were provided to cover the educational costs of twelve students—four in each of the three fields—leading to the degrees of Bachelor of Arts, Bachelor of Physic, and Barrister-at-law. See Robert R. Pearce, *A History of the Inns of Court and Chancery* (London, Richard Bentley, 1848).

17. From the application form for admission, reproduced in *ibid.*, p. 386.

18. *Ibid.*, pp. vi–vii, footnote.   19. *Ibid.*, p. 395.

20. December 11, 1883; this letter is in the collection of correspondence and papers of Wilfrid and Alice Meynell (hereafter referred to as Meynell papers), pertinent items of which were provided me by Mrs. Olivia Sowerby of London. Buckfast Abbey is one of the oldest in England, having been founded, probably, in the middle of the tenth century. At first occupied by a Benedictine Order and a Cistercian, it was finally sold and left to ruin during the reign of Henry VIII. In 1882 it was reoccupied by the Benedictines, the first Church property to be so reoccupied since the Reformation. Immediate plans were made to reconstruct a new Abbey upon the ruined foundations of the old. In 1883, reflecting his interest in architecture as well as in the monastery traditions, Mivart became, as honorary secretary of the reconstruction committee, a prime mover in the subscription campaign to raise funds for the rebuilding.

21. This article, if actually written and published, was probably the first of Mivart's publications, and must have been written between 1852 and 1856, thus preceding by a decade his first acknowledged publication. It is not unlikely that it was an anonymous review, similar to many articles which Mivart must have written, but which, because of the fashion of anonymity, are impossible, except in isolated instances, to trace.

22. Alfred Russel Wallace, *My Life* (2 vols., New York, Dodd, Mead and Co., 1905), II, 44–45.

23. July 23, 1880; in the correspondence of Richard Owen (hereafter referred to as the Owen papers) in the library of the Natural History Museum (British Museum), South Kensington.

24. St. George Mivart, "Sir Richard Owen's Hypothesis," *Natural Science*, II (1893), 21.

25. St. George Mivart, *On the Genesis of Species* (London, Macmillan and Co., 1871), p. 186.

26. April 13, 1872; Owen papers.

NOTES TO II: SCIENCE

1. St. George Mivart, "Some Reminiscences of Thomas Henry Huxley," *Nineteenth Century* XLII (1897), 988–89.

2. *Ibid.,* p. 985.   3. *Ibid.,* p. 990.

4. December 31, 1886; The Correspondence, Manuscripts and Miscellaneous Papers of Thomas Henry Huxley (hereafter referred to as the Huxley papers) preserved in the Muniments Library of the Imperial College of Science and Technology, London.

5. Mivart had been, for four years past, professor of comparative anatomy at St. Mary's and it is not improbable that the lecture referred to was given at his instigation.

6. St. George Mivart, "Some Reminiscences of Thomas Henry Huxley," *Nineteenth Century,* XLII (1897), 993–94.

7. *Ibid.,* p. 993.

8. Thomas H. Huxley, *On Our Knowledge of the Causes of the Phenomena of Organic Nature, Being Six Lectures to Working Men, Delivered at the Museum of Practical Geology* (London, Harwicke, 1863), p. 134.

9. [Samuel Wilberforce], "Review of Darwin's *Origin of Species,*" *Quarterly Review,* CVIII (1860), 256.

10. Oddly enough, the names of neither Huxley nor Owen appear on Mivart's certificate of recommendation for election into the Fellowship of the Royal Society. Although only six references were necessary, Mivart's application received the support of twenty members of the society—some of the outstanding members of the nineteenth-century scientific community. He was, according to information kindly provided by the librarian of the Royal Society, supported by W. H. Fowler, James Salter, George Busk, P. L. Sclater, W. K. Parker, Francis Sibson, G. M. Humphrey, Henry Holland, George Rolleston, John Gould, William Fergusson, A. Mathiessen, J. Prestwich, Charles Darwin, Albert Gunther, T. Spencer Cobbald, J. W. Hulke, C. Pritchard, H. Charlton Bastian, and L. Smith Beale.

11. Thomas H. Huxley, "On the Natural History of the Man-Like Apes," first of three essays comprising *On Man's Place in Nature,* originally published in 1863; in Huxley, T. H., *Collected Essays* (New York, D. Appleton and Co., 1902), VII, 33.

12. St. George Mivart, "On the Appendicular Skeleton of the Primates," *Philosophical Transactions of the Royal Society of London,* CLVII (1867), 299.

13. See William L. Straus, Jr., "The Riddle of Man's Ancestry," *Quarterly Review of Biology,* XXIV (1949), 200–23; note also Hill's quotation of Mivart's definition with the notation that "the contemporary definition of Primates need depart little, if at all, from the classic statement made by Mivart in 1873," in W. C. Osman Hill, *Primates: Comparative Anatomy and Taxonomy,* (3 vols., New York and Edinburgh, Interscience Publishers Inc. and Edinburgh University Press, 1953–57), I, 5.

14. St. George Mivart, "On *Lepilemur* and *Cheirogaleus* and on the Zoological Rank of the Lemuroidea," *Proceedings of the Zoological Society of London,* 1873, p. 507.

15. St. George Mivart, "Specific Genesis," *North American Review,* CXIV (1872), 451–68; reprinted in his *Essays and Criticisms* (2 vols., London, Osgood, 1892), II, 104–5.

16. St. George Mivart, "On *Lepilemur* and *Cheirogaleus* and on the Zoological Rank of the Lemuroidea," *Proceedings of the Zoological Society of London,* 1873, p. 507.

17. *Ibid.,* p. 506; this position, once achieved, was never left. Compare the following paragraph written twenty years later: "In the early days of the promulgation of the theory of evolution nothing seemed easier than to answer such questions as to genealogical relations and ancestral origins of particular faunal forms. Genealogical trees of animal life were set up by very many naturalists—most conspicuously of all by Prof. Haeckel of Jena—with eagerness. Soon, however, they were found to need pruning, then 'lopping and topping,' and finally not a few have we seen cut down and torn up by the roots. Some of our own modest shrubs we have come to believe merit the same fate, though we have not to answer for much such arboriculture, on account of our having from the first believed in and called attention to the 'independent origin of different [*sic*] structures'." St. George Mivart, *Types of Animal Life* (London, Osgood, McIlvaine and Co., 1893), pp. 119–20.

18. St. George Mivart, "On *Lepilemur* and *Cheirogaleus* and on the Zoological Rank of the Lemuroidea," *Proceedings of the Zoological Society of London,* 1873, p. 510.

19. *Ibid.,* p. 508.   20. *Ibid.,* p. 509.   21. *Ibid.,* p. 510.   22. *Ibid.*

NOTES TO III: COMPROMISE

1. St. George Mivart, "Some Reminiscences of Thomas Henry Huxley," *Nineteenth Century,* XLII (1897), 994–95.

2. *Ibid.,* p. 992.

3. Charles Darwin, *On the Origin of Species by Means of Natural Selection or the Preservation of Favoured Races in the Struggle for Life* ([a reprint of the first edition, 1859], New York, Philosophical Library, 1951), pp. 413–14; Mivart was later (in "Primitive Man: Tylor and Lubbock," *Quarterly Review,* CXLVII [1874], 40–77) to imply that Darwin's omission of man from his work was purposeful and designed to limit opposition. This accusation that "Mr. Darwin disguised at first his views as to the bestiality of man" was essentially, in its context, an accusation of intellectual dishonesty; and, as such, it was bitterly resented by Darwin's friends. It was this resentment which led, in part, to Huxley's biting attack (see note 4 below) in which he defended Darwin against the unwarranted charge of duplicity.

4. Thomas H. Huxley, "Review article of *Anthropogenie, Entwicklungsgeschichte des Menschens* von Ernst Haeckel," *Academy,* V (1875), 16.

5. Thomas H. Huxley, "On the Relations of Man to the Lower Animals," third of three essays comprising *On Man's Place in Nature,* originally published in 1863; in his *Collected Essays* (9 vols., New York, D. Appleton and Co., 1902), VII, 152.

6. St. George Mivart, "Darwin's *Descent of Man*," *Quarterly Review*, CXXXI (1871), 47–48.

7. This charge is not technically correct. Only a single oblique reference is made to such an application in the *Origin*, although Darwin's attitude in this connection, published twelve years later, was no real secret.

8. Samuel Wilberforce, "Review of Darwin's *Origin of Species*," *Quarterly Review*, CVIII (1860), 257–58. Although reviews in the *Quarterly* were, at this time, customarily unsigned—thus permitting, under the guise of critical freedom, a great deal of license with respect to personal abuse and distortion—the authorship of certain articles became an open secret, not only through the pride taken in them by their authors and those "in the know," but also through the internal evidence of the articles themselves. On both counts, this review was reliably ascribed to Samuel Wilberforce, Bishop of Oxford, a man of some mathematical ability but one who possessed a total misunderstanding of the nature of science and, in particular, of the meaning of Darwin's theory. Though scientifically "crammed" by Richard Owen, Wilberforce's style was so characteristic that Darwin recognized the authorship immediately.

9. The signal for the coming of age of the post-Reformation Catholic Church in England was the reestablishment of the hierarchy in 1850 with Wiseman, perhaps the most significant figure of the Revival, as the first Archbishop of Westminster. The reestablishment of the hierarchy, however, ushered in a generation of bickering out of which was to rise the platform of Catholicism in England.

10. Edmund S. Purcell, *Life of Cardinal Manning* (2 vols., New York, Macmillan & Co., 1896), II, 76.

11. John Henry Blunt, ed., *Dictionary of Sects, Heresies, Ecclesiastical Parties and Schools of Religious Thought*, (London, Rivingtons, 1874), p. 603.

12. Wilfrid Ward, *The Life of John Henry Cardinal Newman*, (2 vols. in one, London, Longmans, Green and Co., 1927), I, 463.

13. *Ibid.*, pp. 459–60.

14. St. George Mivart, "Another Catholic's View of 'Helbeck of Bannisdale,'" *Ninteenth Century*, XLIV (1898), 649–50.

15. W. Ward, *Newman*, I, 565.   16. *Ibid.*, p. 567.

17. For a full treatment of the whole controversy relating to the attendance of Catholics at the Universities, see Ward, *Newman*, particularly Chapter 21. The only reference to Mivart's participation occurs in a letter from him to Newman (in the Papers and Correspondence of Cardinal Newman, hereafter referred to as the Newman papers, in the possession of the Oratory, Birmingham, England). In this letter Mivart mentions, in passing, that he did join in this petition. It is probable too that Mivart also lent his support to the movement, chiefly among the English bishops, to prevent the promulgation of the Dogma of Papal Infallibility. There was a great deal of political jockeying during the meeting of the Vatican Council; and it is perhaps not without significance that it was during the winter of the Council (1869–70) that Mivart was in Italy.

18. W. Ward, *Newman*, II, 69.

19. Monica Taylor, *Sir Bertram Windle: A Memoir* (London, Longmans, Green and Co., 1932), p. 53.

20. St. George Mivart, "Modern Catholics and Scientific Freedom," *Nineteenth Century*, XVIII (1885), 32.

21. St. George Mivart *On the Genesis of Species* (London, Macmillan and Co., 1871), pp. 2–3.

NOTES TO IV: ON THE GENESIS OF SPECIES

1. St. George Mivart, "Evolution and Its Consequences: A Reply to Professor Huxley," *Contemporary Review* XIX (1872), 168–97; reprinted in Mivart, *Essays and Criticisms*, II, 60–61.

2. St. George Mivart, *On the Genesis of Species* (London, Macmillan and Co., 1871), p. 38.

3. *Ibid.*, p. 61.   4. *Ibid.*, p. 23.   5. *Ibid.*, p. 67.
6. *Ibid.*, p. 128.   7. *Ibid.*, pp. 101–2.

8. St. George Mivart and James Murie, "Anatomy of the Lemuroidea," *Transactions of the Zoological Society of London*, VII (1872), 91; communicated March 27, 1866.

9. St. George Mivart, *Genesis*, p. 118.

10. *Ibid.*

11. *Ibid.*, p. 156.   12. *Ibid.*, p. 225.

13. Charles Darwin, *On the Origin of Species by Means of Natural Selection or the Preservation of Favoured Races in the Struggle for Life* (New York, Philosophical Library, 1951), p. 69.

14. *Ibid.*, p. 144.

15. St. George Mivart, *Genesis*, p. 17.

16. *Ibid.*, p. 20.

17. E. B. Poulton, *Essays on Evolution 1889–1908* (Oxford, Oxford University Press, 1908), pp. 96–97.

18. Francis Darwin, *The Life and Letters of Charles Darwin* (2 vols., New York, D. Appleton and Co., 1897; originally published in 1887), II, 122.

19. St. George Mivart, *Genesis*, pp. 239–40.

20. St. George Mivart, *The Cat, an Introduction to the Study of Backboned Animals, Especially Mammals* (New York, Scribners, 1892; originally published by John Murray, London, 1882), p. 528.

21. *The Athenaeum*, London, April 7, 1900, p. 438.

22. St. George Mivart, *Genesis*, p. 260.

23. St. George Mivart, *Man and Apes, An Exposition of Structural Resemblances and Differences Bearing upon Questions of Affinity and Origin* (London, Hardwicke, 1873), pp. 189–92.

24. St. George Mivart, "Primitive Man: Tylor and Lubbock," *Quarterly Review*, CXLVII (1874), 75–77.

25. St. George Mivart, *Man and Apes*, p. 7.
26. *Ibid.*, p. 133.   27. *Ibid.*, pp. 172–75.

NOTES TO V: BREAKING POINT

1. The *Tablet*, February 25, 1871, p. 232.

2. "Mivart's *Genesis of Species*," *The Month*, XIV (1871), 528.

3. "Review of Mivart's *Genesis of Species*," *Dublin Review*, LXVIII (1871), 482.

4. *Ibid.*, p. 486.   5. *The Tablet*, March 4, 1871.

6. The *Tablet*, March 11, 1871.

7. January 15, 1871, Newman papers.

8. *Ibid.*, December 9, 1871.

9. Alfred W. Bennett, "Review of *The Genesis of Species*," *Nature*, III (1871), 270–73.

10. As the marginal notes in his copy indicate, Darwin read the *Genesis* closely, noting emphatically and often illegibly his objections as he read on.

11. Charles Darwin, *On the Origin of Species* (6th edition, 1872; New York, Modern Library, n.d.), p. 183. (Page reference to Modern Library edition.)

12. Chauncey Wright, "The Genesis of Species," *North American Review*, CXIII (1871), 63–103; "Evolution by Natural Selection," *North American Review*, CXV 1872), 1–30.

13. Darwin to Wallace, July 9, 1871, in James Marchant, *Alfred Russel Wallace: Letters and Reminiscences* (New York, Harper and Bros., 1916), p. 217.

14. Chauncey Wright, "The Genesis of Species," *North American Review*, CXIII (1871), 66.

15. *Ibid.*, p. 66.

16. Wright to Mrs. Lesley, May 7, 1871, in *Letters of Chauncey Wright* (Cambridge, Mass., J. Wilson & Son, 1878), p. 219.

17. Wright to Miss Grace Norton, June 6, 1871, in *ibid.*, p. 226.

18. Darwin to Wallace, January 30, 1871, in Marchant, *Wallace*, p. 211.

19. Wallace to Miss A. Buckley, February 2, 1871, in *ibid.*, p. 288. Lyell did read the *Genesis* and thought some of its arguments impressive. Still not convinced of the validity of Darwinism as a complete explanatory system, he wrote to Hooker on February 14, 1871: "I am reading Mivart's 'Genesis of Species', and am only half through; it improves greatly as I proceed. I thought his first objection, that so many other Ungulata ought to have long necks as well as the giraffe, a very poor one against natural selection. But the difficulty about the eyes of cuttle-fish, dragon-flies, and man, is very well put." *Life, Letters, and Journals of Sir Charles Lyell, Bart.*, edited by his sister-in-law Mrs. Lyell (2 vols., London, John Murray, 1881), II, 448.

20. "Evolution and Faith," *Dublin Review*, LXIX (1871), 7.

21. St. George Mivart, "Evolution and Its Consequences: A Reply to Professor Huxley," reprinted in his *Essays and Criticisms*, II, 101.

22. St. George Mivart, "Darwin's *Descent of Man*," *Quarterly Review*, CXXXI (1871), 52.

NOTES TO VI: FIRST CONFLICT

1. John Fiske, "Mr. Mivart on Darwinism" (1876), in his *Darwinism and Other Essays* (Boston, Houghton, Mifflin and Co., 1896), pp. 38–39.

2. James Marchant, *Alfred Russel Wallace: Letters and Reminiscences* (New York, Harper and Bros., 1916), p. 217. It should be noted that such

a charge, if true, would be a grave indictment since, in effect, it is an accusation of distortion with the implication in this case that the act was willful. But as Francis Darwin, the editor of his father's letters, points out in a footnote: "The passage from which words are omitted is not, technically, at least, a case of misquotation." In fact, the words omitted in Mivart's paraphrase are not, despite the concern of Wright, essential to the argument of either Mivart or Darwin.

3. Marchant, *Wallace*, pp. 218–19.   4. *Ibid.*, p. 219.

5. *Ibid.*, p. 220. It is interesting to note that this second postscript, as well as the first sentence of the second paragraph of the first ("I quite agree . . . especially against me."), is omitted in the published version of this letter in F. Darwin's *Life and Letters of Charles Darwin*, a circumstance which, while perhaps simply fortuitous, is noteworthy since the general impression created by the published treatment of the controversy is one of personal malevolence and willful misrepresentation on the part of Mivart.

6. Marchant, *Wallace*, p. 221.

7. Thomas H. Huxley, "Mr. Darwin's Critics" (1871), reprinted in T. H. Huxley, *Darwiniana*, (New York, D. Appleton and Co., 1896), p. 122.

8. Francis Darwin and A. C. Seward, *More Letters of Charles Darwin* (2 vols., London, John Murray, 1903), I, 332–33.

9. September 11, 1871, Huxley papers.

10. September 16, 1871, Darwin and Seward, *More Letters*, I, 332–33.

11. September 21, 1871, Huxley papers. This letter (dated September 21) and the following (dated September 30) are quoted in their entirety as they appear in the unpublished Huxley papers. Edited versions of both also appear in Darwin's collected correspondence. As published, however, they do not contain the most bitter comments with reference to Mivart, either because Mivart was still alive at the time of publication or because it was thought that such comments might reflect upon Darwin's personal character. Because of the significance of the omissions for an understanding of the passion of the controversy, I have felt it to be of some value in the context of the whole affair to include the unedited versions.

12. April 2, 1873, Huxley papers. This letter was written with reference to Huxley's Preface to his *Darwiniana* in which "Mr. Darwin's Critics" was included.

13. September 17, 1871, Huxley papers.

14. September 30, 1871, *ibid.*

15. No date, in Leonard Huxley, *Life and Letters of Sir Joseph Dalton Hooker* (2 vols., London, John Murray, 1918), II, 129–30.

16. October 4, 1871, in Darwin and Seward, *More Letters*, I, 333.

17. Thomas H. Huxley, "Mr. Darwin's Critics" (1872), in his *Darwiniana*, pp. 147–48.

18. *Ibid.*, p. 147.   19. *Ibid.*   20. *Ibid.*, pp. 125–26.   21. *Ibid.*, p. 146.

22. St. George Mivart, "Evolution and Its Consequences: A Reply to Professor Huxley" (1872), in *Essays and Criticisms*, II, 90.

23. *Essays and Criticisms*, II, 76.   24. *Ibid.*, II, 90.

25. Mivart's defense of his old friend Wallace was unnecessary; for in one of the most gracious acts in the history of science, Wallace had himself written to Darwin with respect to claims of priority: "As to the

theory of Natural Selection itself, I shall always maintain it to be actually yours only. You had worked it out in details I had never thought of, years before I had a ray of light on the subject, and my paper would never have convinced anybody or been noticed as more than an ingenious speculation, whereas your book has revolutionized the study of natural history, and carried away captive the best men of the present age. All the merit I claim is the having been the means of inducing *you* to write and publish at once." James Marchant, *Wallace*, p. 131. See also Wallace's eloquent statement upon receiving the Darwin-Wallace Medal of the Linnean Society at its Darwin-Wallace Celebration on July 1, 1908, in *The Darwin-Wallace Celebration Held on Thursday, 1st July, 1908, by the Linnean Society* (London, Linn. Soc., 1908), pp. 5–11.

26. St. George Mivart, "Evolution and Its Consequences: A Reply to Professor Huxley" (1872), in his *Essays and Criticisms*, II, 60–61.

27. *Ibid.*, II, 66.   28. *Ibid.*, II, 67.

29. *Ibid.*, II, 60. It is interesting to note that two phrases which appeared in the original published version of this article are omitted in the reprint a quarter-century later. These are "as a subaltern in science" (first paragraph) and "is *indeed* my superior officer" (second paragraph).

30. St. George Mivart, "The Rights of Reason," *Fortnightly Review*, XLV (1886), 68.

31. St. George Mivart, "Some Reminiscences of Thomas Henry Huxley," *Nineteenth Century*, XLII (1897), 996.

32. Something of the poignancy of this controversy can be seen in the fact that Mivart's son was, at this time, a student in one of Huxley's classes. And it is a measure of Huxley's personal character that the younger Mivart could write (F. St. G. Mivart to Sir Shane Leslie, August 30, 1923): "As regarded my humble personality, Huxley never allowed the quarrel to make the smallest difference. I have two or three quaint anecdotes bearing upon this side of the incident which would have placed me in an impossible position but for Huxley's personal kindness and the graceful way he had of turning things aside."

33. St. George Mivart, "Primitive Man: Tylor and Lubbock," *Quarterly Review*, CXLVII (1874), 40–77.

34. George Darwin, "On Beneficial Restrictions to Liberty of Marriage," *Contemporary Review*, XXII (1873), 412–26.

35. St. George Mivart, "Primitive Man: Tylor and Lubbock," *Quarterly Review*, CXLVII (1874), 70.

36. George Darwin, "Note on the Article 'Primitive Man—Tylor and Lubbock,'" *Quarterly Review*, CXLVII (1874), 587–88.

37. St. George Mivart, "Reply to George Darwin," *Quarterly Review*, CXLVII (1874), 588.

38. *Ibid.*, p. 589.

39. June 17, 1876, Marchant, *Wallace*, p. 239. The strength of this feeling is illustrated by the following comment by Darwin in the recently published complete edition of his autobiography: "I have almost always been treated honestly by my reviewers, passing over those without scientific knowledge as not worthy of notice. My views have often been grossly misrepresented, bitterly opposed and ridiculed, but this has generally been done, as I believe, in good faith. I must, however, except Mr. Mivart, who as an American expressed it in a letter has acted towards me

'like a pettifogger', or as Huxley has said 'like an Old Bailey lawyer'."
The Autobiography of Charles Darwin, edited by Nora Barlow, (London,
Collins, 1958), pp. 125–26.

40. Leonard Huxley, *Life and Letters of Thomas Henry Huxley* (2 vols.,
London, Macmillan and Co., 1900), I, 426.

41. December 27, 1874, Huxley papers.

42. Thomas H. Huxley, "Review of *Anthropogenie, Entwicklungsgeschichte des Menschens* von Ernst Haeckel," Academy, V (1875), 16–17.

43. Leonard Huxley, *Huxley*, I, 425.

44. F. St. George Mivart to Sir Shane Leslie, August 30, 1923, in the
possession of the latter.

45. December 11, 1874, Huxley papers.

46. December 12, 1874, *ibid.*   47. December 19, 1874, *ibid.*
48. December 20, 1874, *ibid.*   49. December 23, 1874, *ibid.*
50. December 24, 1874, *ibid.*   51. December 24, 1874, *ibid.*
52. December 28, 1874, *ibid.*   53. January 6, 1875, *ibid.*

54. An indication of the persistence and depth of the antipathy, as well
as of Huxley's personal feelings, toward Mivart is apparent in a letter
from Huxley to Charles Darwin, February 3, 1880, in the midst of the
Butler-Darwin controversy.   Inexplicably to Darwin, his family, and his
friends, Samuel Butler had launched a vicious personal attack on Darwin.
In the course of the hectic consultations as to what should be done, Huxley wrote: "I am astounded at Butler—who I thought was a gentleman
though his last book appeared to me to be supremely foolish.   Has Mivart
bitten him and given him Darwinophobia?   It is a horrid disease and I
would kill any son of a [here there is a drawing of a dog—presumably fe-
male] I found running loose with it without mercy.   But don't you worry
about these things.   Recollect what old Goethe said about his Butlers and
Mivarts: 'Hat doch der Wallfische seine Laus/Muss auch die Meine
haben.' " *Autobiography*, ed. Barlow, p. 211.

55. L. Huxley, *Huxley*, I, 258.

56. Membership in the Athenaeum could be gained in either of two
ways.   The first and usual method was election by the membership.
Blackballing by ten percent of the membership was sufficient to bar a
candidate on the theory that the congeniality of the Club would otherwise
suffer.   The Governing Committee, however, had the power of electing
yearly from the list of candidates for admission a limited number of persons not to exceed nine who were distinguished in science, literature, the
arts, or public service.   Because of the probability of too many blackballs,
Mivart, in at least one instance, preferred to stand for election by the
Committee.

57. P. L. Sclater, long-time secretary of the Zoological Society of London.   The reference is to the recent sale of one of the public's favorites at
the Society's Gardens, Jumbo the Elephant, to P. T. Barnum.   *L'affaire
Jumbo* exercised the emotions of the public and brought down upon the
Zoological Society the wrath of press, pulpit, and populace.

58. Herbert Paul, ed., *Letters of Lord Acton to Mary Gladstone*, (London, Macmillan, 1904), p. 236.

59. October 23, 1883; I am indebted to Sir Shane Leslie, who kindly provided me with a copy of this letter.

60. Huxley papers.

NOTES TO VII: INTERLUDE

1. St. George Mivart, "Modern Catholics and Scientific Freedom," *Nineteenth Century*, XVIII (1885), 47.

2. No date, but probably during 1887; Meynell papers.

3. See, for instance, his controversy with Romanes in the pages of the *Fortnightly Review* and the *Forum* between 1885 and 1888.

4. St. George Mivart, "Where Darwinism Fails," *Forum*, VII (1888), 264–73; "Prof. Weismann's Hypothesis," *Dublin Review*, XXII (1889), 269–96; "Darwinism," *Dublin Review*, XXIII (1890), 33–47; "Evolution in Professor Huxley," *Nineteenth Century*, XXXIV (1893), 198–211.

5. Had Mivart lived a few years into the twentieth century, he would have enjoyed the violent controversies which raged between the mutationists, Mendelists, and selectionists as the result of the birth of genetics. These were controversies whose virulence was not ameliorated by the distortions utilized by both lay and professional advocates to support their respective positions.

6. Professor H. Charlton Bastian had, during the late 1860s, sought to demonstrate experimentally that the spontaneous generation of microorganisms is a constant occurrence in nature. His eager support of this ancient doctrine led to a series of violent controversies with both Huxley and John Tyndall, both of whom accused Bastian of incompetence as an investigator through the lack of care allegedly employed in the construction of his experiments and the inferences drawn from their results.

7. February 19, 1888, in the collection of papers and correspondence of Edward Bagnall Poulton in the possession of the Hope Laboratory of Oxford University (hereafter referred to as the Poulton papers). In actual fact, Poulton was one of Darwinism's most persistent defenders. In the controversies which attended the synthesis of the new genetics with the older Darwinism to produce the structure of contemporary evolution theory, it was Poulton who consistently and vehemently upheld Darwinism against the enthusiastic claims and the barely concealed derogations of younger investigators already at least a generation removed from the author of the *Origin*.

8. Unpublished correspondence of the Zoological Society of London.

9. Mivart's three papers were "What Is the Good of Truth?" read at the meeting on June 13, 1876; "Matter and Force," read May 8, 1877; and "The Religion of Emotion," read April 8, 1879, a few months before the society was dissolved. An excellent account of the Metaphysical Society, its formation, its members, and the tenor of its discussions is contained in Allan Brown's valuable study, *The Metaphysical Society* (New York, Columbia University Press, 1947).

10. "Professor St. George Mivart: Obituary," *Nature*, LXI (1900), 569–70.

11. St. George Mivart, "Anatomy of the Lobster (Homarus)," *Popular Science Review*, VII (1868), 345.

12. St. George Mivart, "On the Study of Natural History," *Contemporary Review*, XXXV (1879), 251–52.

13. March 5, 1883, Meynell papers.

14. David Duncan, ed., *Life and Letters of Herbert Spencer* (2 vols., D. Appleton and Co., 1908), I, 228–29.

15. St. George Mivart, "The Meaning of Life," *Nineteenth Century*, V (1879), 488–512; "The Government of Life," *Nineteenth Century*, V (1879), 690–713.

16. May 5, 1879, in the archives of the publishing firm of John Murray, London, England.

17. "Review of *The Cat*," *Popular Science Review*, n.s., V (1881), 260.

18. St. George Mivart, "On the Use of the Term 'Homology'," *Annals and Magazine of Natural History*, VI (1870), p. 114.

19. *Ibid.*, pp. 117–18.

20. St. George Mivart, "On the Vertebrate Skeleton," *Transactions of the Linnean Society of London*, XXVII (1871), 392.

NOTES TO VIII: REASON

1. *Encyclopaedia Britannica*, 9th ed. (25 vols., Chicago, Werner Co., 1895; original English ed., 1875–89), XXIV, 820.

2. St. George Mivart, *The Origin of Human Reason* (London, Kegan Paul, Trench and Co., 1889), p. 299.

3. St. George Mivart, *Man and Apes* (London, Robert Hardwicke, 1873), p. 188.

4. A. R. Wallace, for example, broke with Darwin—although in friendly fashion—on the same issue. Wallace too believed that man was unique and could not be accounted for *in his totality* by natural selection. Unlike Mivart, however, Wallace based his claim for man's uniqueness upon his putative possession of extrasensory powers of whose existence he was fully convinced. While Mivart was sometimes inclined to accept these powers as part of the human mentality, he recognized too well the hopelessness of using such powers alone, undemonstrated as they were, as proofs for his position.

5. St. George Mivart, "Darwin's Descent of Man," *Quarterly Review*, CXXXI (1871), 67–68.

6. St. George Mivart, *On Truth: A Systematic Inquiry* (London, Kegan Paul, Trench and Co., 1889), pp. 200–1.

7. *Ibid.*, pp. 204–5.   8. *Ibid.*, p. 223.

9. St. George Mivart, "The Rights of Reason," *Fortnightly Review*, XLV (1886), 65–6; to these arguments Romanes, speaking for science, could reply that Mivart was abdicating his role as a scientist in setting up certain areas which could never be explained through scientific investigation. In using the arguments Mivart was, of course, combating the realistic empirical philosophy which from Berkeley through Hume and Mill had come so to dominate English philosophy and, through it, the science of the nineteenth century. It was the denial, for any practical purposes,

of absolute reality implicit in empiricism and the emphasis upon the operational reality of the perceived and experienced which provided the empirical sciences of the nineteenth century with the stimulus they required. An absolute, divorced from the senses of perception, was no longer an important goal for the investigator. If an absolute reality was admitted to exist, it was relegated to an area of the unknowable and formed no part of science, a science which was concerned with observable phenomena as if these phenomena were reality. Working hypotheses were erected to explain segments of reality without assuming that the hypotheses themselves represented truth; for Truth—so important to the eighteenth-century savant —was not the goal of the nineteenth-century scientist. Mivart, who related the significant aspects of the human mind to absolute reality, was accused by his opponents of eliminating that phenomenal area from the scope of empirical investigation and placing it in a category of the unknowable through empirical means. In denying such a charge, he maintained that, far from removing the human mind from the possibility of investigation, he was attempting to explain it and to define its problems in the only terms in which this could be done—by rational inquiry rather than empirical examination—because its relationship to reality demanded that approach alone. To the empirical techniques of the physical scientist he attempted to add the rational approach of traditional philosophy. That he never succeeded in this attempt is due primarily to the success of empiricism as a basis for scientific investigation. In short, the philosophical frame of reference within which Mivart worked was incongruent with that of the majority of his colleagues in science; and so, whatever the force of his arguments, *within that frame of reference,* those whom he wished to persuade were unable to understand what he was talking about.

10. John Herman Randall, Jr., *The Making of the Modern Mind* (revised ed., Boston, Houghton Mifflin, 1940), pp. 598–99.

NOTES TO IX: DIFFICULTIES

1. "A Candid Friend," *The Tablet,* April 19, 1884, pp. 82–83.

2. "Dr. Mivart's Heresy," *The Tablet,* January 6, 1900, p. 5.

3. St. George Mivart, "Genesis of Species," *The Tablet,* June 1, 1888, last of a series of ten articles attacking anew the Darwinian theory of evolution, a series written at the request of the editor of this Catholic weekly.

4. St. George Mivart, "Correspondence with Cardinal Vaughan," printed in *The Times* (London), January 25, 28 and February 1, 1900.

5. *The Academy,* London, April 7, 1900, p. 284.

6. Francis Aveling, "St. George Mivart," *The Catholic Encyclopedia* (15 vols., New York, The Encyclopedia Press, 1913), X, 408.

7. J. G. Snead-Cox, *The Life of Cardinal Vaughan* (2 vols., Herbert and Daniel, London, 1910), II, 301–2.

8. William Barry, *Memories and Opinions* (Putnam, New York, 1926), pp. 220–21.

9. Mivart's letters to Father David Fleming during 1896 and 1897 indicate that at this time he was already freely expressing to his friends

ideas which, when contained in his published articles, led to his difficulties with Vaughan. Thus, in a letter dated December 27, 1896, he could write: "The absolute necessity of making use of Evolution as an explanation of the development of dogma seems to me more and more plain the more I think about it." Nor was Fleming a friend without consequence. As a member of the Inquisition at Rome, he had the ear of the pope; and Mivart felt that a great future in the Church lay before him, perhaps the papacy itself. The comfort with which Mivart expressed his views in these letters, as well as in those to Bishop, would suggest that his position was generally known and that his friends agreed with it. His eventual fault, it would seem, was his publication of these views in the popular periodicals. (Copies of the letters of Mivart to Fleming were kindly provided me by Sir Shane Leslie.)

10. W. R. Brownlow, "Letter," *The Tablet,* August 8, 1887.

11. Benedict Williamson, "Letter," *The Tablet,* January 20, 1900, p. 100.

12. J. F. Stephen, "Mr. Mivart's Modern Catholicism," *Nineteenth Century,* XXII (1887), 591.

13. December 31, 1887, in letters of St. George Mivart to Edmund Bishop (hereafter referred to as the Bishop papers), in the possession of Downside Abbey, Stratton on the Fosse, Bath, England.

14. Bertram C. A. Windle, *The Church and Science,* 3rd ed. (London, Catholic Truth Society, 1924), p. 397.

15. "Evolution and Faith," *Dublin Review* LXI (1871), 1–38.

16. John A. O'Brien, *Evolution and Religion* (New York, Century, 1932), p. 113.

17. St. George Mivart, *Contemporary Evolution: An Essay on Some Recent Social Changes* (New York, D. Appleton and Co., 1876), pp. 120–21.

18. *Ibid.,* p. 77.

19. W. G. Ward, "Civil Intolerance of Religious Error: Professor Mivart on Liberty of Conscience," *Dublin Review,* LXXX (1877), 2 (published anonymously).

20. W. G. Ward, "Professor Mivart on the Rights of Conscience," *Dublin Review,* LXXIX 1876), 3.

21. This exchange between Ward and Mivart reads strangely—it has an almost eerie quality—in the midst of the twentieth century when totalitarianisms, whether of the state, the church, or the mind, are of so immediate a concern. The inevitable consequence of Ward's arguments was a totalitarianism, albeit a theocratic one, as hard and as uncompromising as any that the modern world has seen. Mivart's voice was that of a nineteenth-century English liberal, a voice that has softened almost to the point of extinction through the pressures of the succeeding century.

22. St. George Mivart, "Liberty of Conscience," *Dublin Review,* LXXIX (1876), 563–64.

23. *Ibid.,* p. 567.

24. W. G. Ward, "Professor Mivart on The Rights of Conscience," *Dublin Review,* LXXIX (1876), 32.

25. St. George Mivart, "Liberty of Conscience," *Dublin Review,* LXXIX (1876), 563–64.

26. St. George Mivart, "Catholicity in England Fifty Years Ago—A Retrospect," *American Catholic Quarterly Review,* XVII (1892), 161–75, 773–85; XVIII (1893), 53–77.

27. Newman papers. 28. April 22, 1877, *ibid.*

29. St. George Mivart, "Liberty of Conscience," *Dublin Review,* LXXIX (1876), 560.

30. Newman papers. 31. March 6, 1884, *ibid.*

32. March 8, 1884, *ibid.* 33. March 9, 1884, *ibid.*

34. March 10, 1884, *ibid.*

35. In 1873 the Fourth Provincial Synod of Westminster, under the leadership of Cardinal Manning, laid down disciplinary regulations against the attendance by Catholics of non-Catholic universities. Manning's ideal was to found a Catholic university; and, after the Westminster Synod, he did establish the Catholic University at Kensington, whose doors were opened in 1875. "A very distinguished body of professors," wrote Wilfrid Ward, one of the few students who enrolled, "was got together. . . . They were almost as numerous as the undergraduates. They were worthy of a more promising field for the exercise of their great attainments." Despite his reservations about the merits of such a provincial enterprise in education, Mivart was persuaded by Manning to become a member of the faculty as a physiologist and biologist along with Barff, the chemist, Paley, the Cambridge classical scholar, and others of equal note. As an experiment in education, the Catholic University was an utter failure. "A few young men besides myself," Ward continued, "hardly any of them with any intellectual tastes or appetite, responded to the Cardinal's advertisement. They were hardly the anxious and profoundly intellectual doubters whom my father pictured. Some did not know how to spell, others were backward boys of whom their schools had despaired. I don't recall one of a speculative turn of mind." Saddled by debts and surrounded by scandal, the university closed in 1877. Maisie Ward, *The Wilfrid Wards and the Transition* (London, Sheed and Ward, 1934), pp. 47–48.

36. March 11, 1884, Newman papers.

37. March 12, 1884, *ibid.* 38. May 9, 1884, *ibid.*

39. This refers to Mivart's criticism of the scientific ignorance of the clergy which formed the central theme of his article entitled "The Conversion of England," *Dublin Review,* n.s., XII (1884), 65–86. The issue raised led to Murphy's rebuttal (see note 41 below) and the subsequent controversy provided the opportunity for "Modern Catholics and Scientific Freedom" a year later.

40. May 9, 1884, Newman papers.

41. Jeremiah Murphy, "Evolution and Faith," *Irish Ecclesiastical Record,* XV (1884), 756–77.

42. Mivart considered Murphy's article not only an opportunity but a challenge as well. The case of Galileo and his intellectual difficulties with Church authority, then subject to popular airing, paralleled too closely an emergent reaction to the Church's previously liberal policy with reference to evolution and its spokesmen; and Murphy's attack was but a single symptom. In the columns of the *Tablet,* where the Murphy-Clarke arguments had reached a plateau of scholastic rarification far removed from

the immediate issues, Mivart addressed his public with a promise: "Permit me through your columns, to ask those persons interested about Evolution, and who have read Mr. Murphy's letter, to suspend their judgment for a while. I deeply regret the controversy Mr. Murphy has initiated, for I am strongly persuaded such writings as his do great injury to the Catholic cause. The dispute has now extended beyond the limits of the Catholic press, and I am already reproached with having declared peace when there was no peace; for it is known to very many outside the Church how long and earnestly I have striven to reconcile science and religion. They now see my arguments disputed, my position denied, and my very words quoted against me. Priests whose opinions I value tell me I cannot keep silence. Mr. Murphy challenges me again, and questions are put to me by him and by others. I promise that they shall be answered." The *Tablet,* June 6, 1885, p. 898.

43. St. George Mivart, "Modern Catholics and Scientific Freedom," *Nineteenth Century,* XVIII (1885), 38–39.

44. *Ibid.,* pp. 40–41.

45. Jeremiah Murphy, "The Case of Galileo," *Nineteenth Century,* XIX (1886), 722–39.

46. The *Tablet,* July 18, 1885, pp. 82–83.

47. Quoted in the *Tablet,* August 8, 1885, p. 220.

NOTES TO X: SECOND CONFLICT

1. St. George Mivart, "Organic Nature's Riddle," *Fortnightly Review,* XLIII (1885), 323–37; "The Rights of Reason," *Fortnightly Review,* XLV (1886), 61–68; "An Explanation," *Fortnightly Review,* XLV (1886), 525–27; George J. Romanes, "Professor Mivart on Intellect," *Fortnightly Review,* XLIV (1885), 90–101; "Mr. Mivart on the Rights of Reason," *Fortnightly Review,* XLV (1886), 329–38. Mivart's final summation was reserved for his book *The Origin of Human Reason* (London, Kegan Paul, 1889), in which he developed a point-by-point critique of the emerging "evolutionary psychology," using Romanes as his main antagonist.

2. St. George Mivart, "The Catholic Church and Biblical Criticism," *Nineteenth Century,* XXII (1887), 31–51.

3. *Ibid.,* p. 32.

4. No date, Meynell papers. The occasion was a meeting of the Council of the Catholic Union during which support of that body was urged for an International Science Congress of Catholics. Mivart addressed the body on the importance of increasing the knowledge of science among Catholics, since, as he was often to maintain, the "battleground" between science and Christianity was the most important problem facing the Church. His complaint with regard to Cox, however, has little justification. The editor of the *Tablet* did report (February 26, 1887, pp. 339–41) the address with extensive extracts; and three weeks later, he ran a leader ("Catholics and Science," March 19, 1887, pp. 442–44) which was friendly to Mivart's general point of view. In neither case, however, did he emphasize Mivart's concerns with the subject of Biblical criticism and his views toward "this most important subject." Although Cox noted that

that subject, in Mivart's opinion, was the next battleground between science and faith, he interpreted the address to mean that Catholics should know about that which they would refute if they were to hold out any hope of successful refutation. As conciliator and harmonizer, Mivart intended not to refute or to reject a priori but to integrate the findings of the new science into an evolved faith. He evidently felt that Cox's handling of the address would dispose the Catholic community to oppose, without reason and without a hearing, the arguments of the exegetists, many of which Mivart himself was willing to accept as scientifically documented truths.

5. August 6, 1887, Meynell papers.

6. St. George Mivart, "The Catholic Church and Biblical Criticism," *Nineteenth Century,* XXII (1887), 33.

7. *Ibid.,* p. 50.

8. April 20, 1888, Newman papers.

9. John C. Hedley, Bishop of Newport, "Mivart on Faith and Science," *Dublin Review,* CI (1887), 401–19.

10. St. George Mivart, "Letter in Reply to Bishop Hedley," *Dublin Review,* CII (1888), 180–87.

11. January 9, 1888, Bishop papers.

12. December 31, 1888, *ibid.*

13. F. St. George Mivart to Sir Shane Leslie, August 30, 1923.

14. St. George Mivart, "Happiness in Hell," *Nineteenth Century,* XXXII (1892), 899.

15. *Ibid.,* p. 899.   16. *Ibid.,* p. 900.

17. St. George Mivart, "Roman Congregations and Modern Thought," *North American Review,* CLXX (1900), 566–68.

18. December 8, 1892, Meynell papers.

19. St. George Mivart, "Roman Congregations and Modern Thought," *North American Review,* CLXX (1900), 570.

20. This criticism was not confined to Catholics. Most orthodox Christians were shocked at this apparent weakening of the terrors of hell and saw in it the opening of the floodgates of immorality. For example, the venerable Gladstone commented in a letter, "What is more grave in my view is that 'the terrors of the Lord' are fading and dying out of orthodox preaching. A bad sign of the times was Mivart's 'Happiness in Hell'." W. E. Gladstone to S. E. Gladstone, February 3, 1896, in D. C. Lathbury, ed., *Correspondence on Church and Religion of W. E. Gladstone* (2 vols., New York, Macmillan, 1910), II, 123.

21. St. George Mivart, "Roman Congregations and Modern Thought," *North American Review,* CLXX (1900), 570.

22. December 17, 1892, Meynell papers.

23. R. F. Clarke, "Happiness in Hell: A Reply," *Nineteenth Century,* XXXIII (1893), 83–92.

24. *Ibid.,* pp. 83–84.

25. St. George Mivart, "The Happiness in Hell: A Rejoinder," *Nineteenth Century,* XXXIII (1893), 320–38.

26. *Ibid.,* p. 320.   27. *Ibid.,* p. 332.   28. *Ibid.*

29. David Mathew, *Catholicism in England 1535–1935* (London, Longmans, Green and Co., 1936), p. 224.

30. Maisie Ward, *The Wilfrid Wards and the Transition* (London, Sheed and Ward, 1934), pp. 50–51.

31. Quoted in R. F. Clarke, "The Verdict of Rome on 'The Happiness in Hell'," *Nineteenth Century,* XXXIV (1893), 500.

32. August 6, 1893, Bishop papers.

33. St. George Mivart, "Roman Congregations and Modern Thought," *North American Review,* CLXX (1900), 570.

34. August 11, 1893, Bishop papers.

35. St. George Mivart, "The Index and My Articles on Hell," *Nineteenth Century,* XXXIV (1893), 979–90.

36. Quoted in a letter from Mivart to Vaughan, January 23, 1900, printed in *The Times* (London), January 28, 1900.

NOTES TO XI: EXCOMMUNICATION

1. The *Tablet,* January 14, 1889, p. 227. See also a discussion of further recantations in the *Tablet* of June 24, 1899, under the title, "Evolution and its Upholders."

2. January 23, 1900, in *The Times* (London), January 28, 1900.

3. January 21, 1898, Bishop papers.

4. September 11, 1897, Meynell papers.

5. St. George Mivart, "Scripture and Roman Catholicism," *Nineteenth Century,* XLVII (1900), 426.

6. St. George Mivart, "Roman Congregations and Modern Thought," *North American Review,* CLXX (1900), 571.

7. *Ibid.*

8. Nicholas Halasz, *Captain Dreyfus* (New York, Simon and Shuster, 1955).

9. The quotations in this paragraph are from Mivart's long letter to the *Times* of October 17, 1899.

10. *Ibid.*   11. Meynell papers.

12. November 27, 1899, *ibid.*   13. December 3, 1899, *ibid.*

14. St. George Mivart, "Roman Congregations and Modern Thought," *North American Review,* CLXX (1900), 571–72.

15. St. George Mivart, "The Continuity of Catholicism," *Nineteenth Century,* XLVII (1900), 51–72; "Some Recent Apologists," *Fortnightly Review,* LXVII (1900), 24–44.

16. Bishop papers.   17. *Ibid.*   18. *Ibid.*

19. St. George Mivart, "Some Recent Apologists," *Fortnightly Review,* LXVII (1900), 24.

20. St. George Mivart, "The Continuity of Catholicism," *Nineteenth Century,* XLVII (1900), 61–62.

21. Nigel J. Abercrombie, "Edmund Bishop and St. George Mivart," *The Month,* CXCIII (1952), 176–80.

22. "Dr. Mivart's Heresy," the *Tablet,* January 6, 1900, p. 7.

23. *Ibid.*

24. "Mivart's Correspondence with Cardinal Vaughan," in *The Times* (London), January 25, 28, and February 1, 1900. When the correspondence had almost been completed (with Mivart's categorical refusal to sign

the profession of faith demanded by Vaughan), Mivart sent the entire series to *The Times* for publication. Cardinal Vaughan followed with his last letter, written on January 25, and Mivart submitted his reply to complete the series. The extracts which immediately follow are from *The Times* of January 25. A short time later the whole correspondence was reprinted, along with the two articles which had touched off the controversy, in a volume entitled *Under the Ban,* by the Tucker Publishing Co., of New York, a firm with a "free-thinking" orientation.

25. St. George Mivart, "Roman Congregations and Modern Thought," *North American Review,* CLXX (1900), 572.

26. Mivart to Vaughan, January 23, 1900.

27. The *Tablet,* January 27, 1900.

28. The *Tablet,* February 10, 1900, p. 216.

29. Alice Meynell to St. George Mivart, Meynell papers.

30. Mivart to Alice Meynell, March 23, 1900, *ibid.*

NOTES TO: EPILOGUE

1. Henry F. Osborn, *Impressions of Great Naturalists* (New York, Scribners, 1928), p. 95.

2. August 16, 1888, Poulton papers.

3. July 12, 1885, Meynell papers.

4. St. George Mivart, "Evolution and Its Consequences; A Reply to Professor Huxley," in *Essays and Criticisms,* II, 90.

5. The *Tablet,* March 11, 1871.

6. December 31, 1886, Huxley papers.

7. St. George Mivart, "The Rights of Reason," *Fortnightly Review,* XLV (1886), 67.

8. George G. Simpson, "The Principles of Classification and a Classification of Mammals," *Bulletin of the American Museum of Natural History,* Number 85, 1945.

9. Marcus W. Lyon, Jr., "Tree Shrews: an Account of the Mammalian Family *Tupaiidae,*" *Proceedings of the United States National Museum,* XLV (1913), 1–188.

10. "Professor St. George Mivart: Obituary," *Nature,* LXI (1900), 569–70.

11. G. B. H[owes], "St. George Mivart," *Proceedings of the Royal Society of London,* LXXV (1905), 97.

12. Reading Jones, particularly his *Hallmarks of Mankind* (Baltimore, Williams and Wilkins, 1948), is little more than a rereading of Mivart. He adopts not only the Mivartian view as to man's place among the Primates, but he reaffirms as well almost the entire classification with its particular phylogenetic meanings which Mivart set forth in 1873. It is little wonder then that Jones, as Sir Arthur Keith wrote (personal correspondence) "has been laying laurels on the brow of Mivart and hails him as the Great Primatologist."

13. E.g., his emphasis on an internal force regulating the growth of the individual as well as the development of the species, a view which can be regarded as a shadowy anticipation of contemporary genetics.

14. George Tyrrell to Baron von Hugel, March 11, 1900, in Maud Petre, *Von Hugel and Tyrrell* (London, J. M. Dent and Sons, 1937). Tyrrell, an English Jesuit, was the leader of the Modernist movement in England which reached its climax and virtual end in 1907 with the Papal Encyclical denouncing its point of view and calling upon its advocates to recant. Von Hugel, an ardent Catholic as well as an erudite Biblical scholar, also played a prominent role as a Modernist. It was he, friend and confidant, who provided Tyrrell's mysticism with its intellectual support. His judgment of Mivart's approach in the common struggle to modernize the Church is illustrative of the gap which separated the Modernists as such from the modernism, almost secular in its foundations, of Mivart. "The thing that in all this strikes me as so instructive," von Hugel wrote of Mivart's difficulties with Vaughan, "is how near, how remarkably near, he and his neo-scholastic adversaries stand to one another, not in their conclusions, but in their tone and habit of mind; for both he and they are strangely irreverent, without history and development, without apprehensions, intuitions, instincts, trusts—without a shred of 'atmosphere'— moon-landscapes, both of them" (p. 127). And in another letter: "Though I do not deny that Mivart is a sincere believer in his own manner and degree, I cannot help being struck by his apparently complete absense of all response to even the most general and mystical Incarnation doctrine" (Michael de la Bedoyere, *The Life of Baron von Hugel* [London, J. M. Dent and Sons, 1951], p. 115). It was just such an "atmosphere" and such "mystical" responses—irrational and unscientific—that Mivart sought to strip from the Faith. It was just that gradualism and gentlemanliness in the face of error, which the Modernists maintained, that Mivart could not condone. Ideas and practices were either true or false, right or wrong—and if the latter, they must be condemned without hesitation. In Mivart's excommunication, however, there was warning for the more moderate Modernists themselves, had they been able to read it. Although it was Tyrrell to whom Vaughan had sent Mivart for aid in his last protest against Church authority, it was the same Tyrrell who, seven years later, was himself excommunicated for his continued advocacy of Modernist views in the face of papal censure.

15. W. S. Blunt, *My Diaries* (2 vols., London, Secker, 1919–20), I, 367.

16. St. George Mivart, *Nature and Thought* (London, Burns and Oates, 1882), pp. 1–2.

17. St. George Mivart, *The Groundwork of Science* (London, John Murray, 1898), p. 31. See also J. W. Gruber, "Hexicology: a Note for the History of Ecology," *Ecology*, XXXV (1954), 415–17.

18. Alfred R. Wallace, *My Life* (2 vols., New York, Dodd, Mead and Co., 1905), II, 43.

19. F. St. George Mivart to Sir Shane Leslie, August 30, 1923.

20. St. George Mivart, "Difficulties of the Theory of Natural Selection," *The Month*, XI (1869), 288.

21. "Correspondence with Cardinal Vaughan," January 23, 1900. *The Times* (London), January 25, 1900.

BIBLIOGRAPHY OF THE WORKS OF
ST. GEORGE JACKSON MIVART

I have mentioned in the text only those of Mivart's articles or books which have some pertinence to the main currents of his intellectual life. To appreciate the varied nature of his interests and the sheer mass of his published work, however, one must see his bibliography in its entirety. I have no doubt that there are items which are missing from this list, either because of the obscurity of the medium of publication or because of the anonymity which traditionally cloaked the identity of the contributor to many of the reviews of the period, although articles anonymously published but known to have been written by Mivart are included. Mivart often wrote letters to the popular press, notably the *Tablet* and the London *Times;* only those which etch clearly some particular phase of his life or thought are listed here.

The following abbreviations or short titles have been used:

Amer. Cath. Quar. Rev.	The American Catholic Quarterly Review
Ann. Mag. Nat. Hist.	Annals and Magazine of Natural History
Ann. Sci. Nat. Paris	Annales des sciences naturelles (zoologie)
Brit. Quar.	The British Quarterly Review
CR	The Contemporary Review
DR	The Dublin Review
Edin. Rev.	The Edinburgh Review
FR	The Fortnightly Review
Harpers	Harper's Magazine
JAP	Journal of Anatomy and Physiology
Jour. Lin. Soc.	Journal of the Linnean Society of London
Month	The Month: a Magazine and Review
Nat. Sci.	Natural Science
NC	Nineteenth Century
No. Am. Rev.	North American Review
Pop. Sci. Rev.	Popular Science Review
Proc. Brit. Assoc.	Proceedings (Records) of the British Association for the Advancement of Science
Proc. Roy. Inst.	Proceedings of the Royal Institution
Proc. Roy. Soc.	Proceedings of the Royal Society of London

PTRS   Philosophical Transactions of the Royal Society
                              of London
PZS   Proceedings of the Zoological Society of London
QR   Quarterly Review
Rev. Quest. Sci.   Revue des questions scientifique (Société Scien-
                              tifique de Bruxelles)
Times   The Times, London
TLS   Transactions of the Linnean Society of London
TZS   Transactions of the Zoological Society of London

1864

"Notes on the Crania and Dentition of the *Lemuridae*," *PZS*, XXXII,
611–48.

1865

"Contributions towards a More Complete Knowledge of the Axial Skele-
ton of Primates," *PZS*, XXXIII, 545–92.
"Notes on the Myology of a Specimen of *Cercopithecus sabaeus*," *PZS*,
XXXIII, 43–46.
With James Murie. "Observations on the Anatomy of *Nycticebus tardi-
gradus*," *PZS*, XXXIII, 240–56.
With James Murie. "On the Myology of *Hyrax capensis*," *PZS*, XXXIII,
329–52.

1866

"Contributions towards a More Complete Knowledge of the Skeleton of
Primates: Part I, The Appendicular Skeleton of Simia," *TZL*, VI, 175–
225 (read December 13, 1866).
"On Some Points in the Anatomy of *Echidna hystrix*," *TLS*, XXV, 379–
403.
"On the Structure and Affinities of *Microrhynchus laniger*," *PZS*, XXXIV,
151–67.
With James Murie. "On the Anatomy of the Crested Agouti (*Disprocta
cristata*)," *PZS*, XXXIV, 383–417.

1867

"Notes on the Myology of *Iguana tuberculata*," *PZS*, XXXV, 766–97.
"On the Skull of *Indris diadema*," *PZS*, XXXV, 247–56.
"On the Appendicular Skeleton of the *Primates*," *PTRS*, CLVII, 299–429.
"Additional Notes on the Osteology of the Lemuridae," *PZS*, XXXV,
960–75.
"Notes on the Osteology of the Insectivora," *JAP*, I, 280–312; II, 117–54.
"Notes on the Osteology des insectivores," *Ann. Sci. Nat. Paris* (series 5),
VIII, 221–84; IX, 311–72.
"On *Plethodon perisimilis* Gray," *PZS*, XXXV, 695–99.

1868

"Anatomy of the Lobster (*Homarus*)," *Pop. Sci. Rev.*, VII, 345–53.
"On *Pachybatrachus robustus,* a New Genus of Anurous Batrachians,"
PZS, XXXVI, 557–60; XXXVII, 227–28.

1869

"Notes on the Myology of *Menobranchus lateralis,*" PZS, XXXVII,
450–66.
"Anatomy of the Cuttle-fish (*Sepia*)," *Pop. Sci. Rev.*, VIII, 111–20.
"Notes on *Menopoma allegheniense,*" PZS, XXXVII, 254–71.
"On the Classification of the Anurous Batrachians," PZS, XXXVII, 280–95.
"Difficulties of the Theory of Natural Selection," *The Month,* XI, 35–53,
134–53, 274–89 (anonymous).

1870

"Letter from the Author of the Articles on the Theory of Natural Selec-
tion," *Month,* XII, 639 (anonymous).
"On the Axial Skeleton of the *Urodela,*" PZS, XXXVIII, 260–78.
"On the Myology of *Chamaelon parsonii,* PZS, XXXVIII, 850–90.
"On the Vertebrate Skeleton," TLS, XXVII, 369–92.
"On the Use of the Term 'Homology'," *Ann. Mag. Nat. Hist.*, VI, 113–21.
"The Vertebrate Skeleton," *Nature,* II, 291–92.
"On the Echinus or Sea Urchin," *Pop. Sci. Rev.*, IX, 366–77.

1871

On the Genesis of Species, London and New York, Macmillan and D. Ap-
pleton.
"Darwin's *Descent of Man,*" QR, CXXXI, 47–90.
"On *Hemicentetes,* a New Genus of Insectivora, with Some Additional
Remarks on the Osteology of That Order," PZS, XXXIX, 58–79.
"Ape Resemblances to Man," *Nature,* III, 481.
"On the Axial Skeleton of the Ostrich (*Struthio camelus*)," TZS, VIII,
385–451.

1872

"Evolution and its Consequences: A Reply to Professor Huxley," CR,
XIX, 168–97.
"Specific Genesis," *No. Amer. Rev.*, CXIV, 451–68.
With James Murie. "Anatomy of the Lemuroidea," TZS, VII, 1–113
(communicated March 27, 1866).

1873

Lessons in Elementary Anatomy, London, Macmillan.
Man and Apes, London, Hardwicke.
"On *Lepilemur* and *Cheirogaleus* and on the Zoological Rank of the
Lemuroidea," PZS, XLI, 484–510.

"Man and Apes," *Pop. Sci. Rev.*, XII, 113–37, 243–64.
"The Assumptions of Agnostics," *FR*, XIII, 718–31.
"Contemporary Evolution I," *CR*, XXII, 595–614.
"Herbert Spencer," *QR*, CXXXV, 509–39 (anonymous).
"The Common Frog," *Nature*, VIII, 470–71, 510–12; IX, 10–13, 28–30, 67–69, 107–9, 147–50, 186–89, 264–66, 305–7, 367–69, 406–8.

1874

The Common Frog, London, Macmillan.
"One Point in Controversy with the Agnostics," in Manning, ed., *Essays in Religion and Literature,* 3rd series, London.
"Primitive Man: Tylor and Lubbock," *QR*, CXLVII, 40–77.
"Examination of H. Spencer's Psychology I," *DR*, XXIII, 476–508.
"Axial Skeleton of the *Struthionidae*," *TZS*, X, 1–52 (read November 17, 1874).
"Reply to George Darwin," *QR*, CXXXVII, 588–89.
"Contemporary Evolution II," *CR*, XXIII, 345–62.
"Contemporary Evolution III," *CR*, XXIII, 599–620.
"Contemporary Evolution IV," *CR*, XXIV, 360–73.
"Contemporary Evolution V," *CR*, XXIV, 772–93.

1875

"On Instinct and Reason," *CR*, XXV, 763–88.
"Examination of H. Spencer's Psychology, II," *DR*, XXV, 143–72.
"The Natural History of the Kangaroo," *Pop. Sci. Rev.*, XIV, 372–94.
"Likenesses, or Philosophical Anatomy," *CR*, XXVI, 938–57.
"Ape," *Encyclopaedia Britannica* (9th ed.), II, 148–69.

1876

Contemporary Evolution, London, Henry S. King & Co.
Lessons from Nature as Manifested in Mind and Matter, London, Murray.
"Liberty of Conscience," *DR*, XXVII, 555–68.
"What Are Bats?" *Pop. Sci. Rev.*, XV, 225–40.

1877

"Examination of H. Spencer's Psychology, III," *DR*, XXVIII, 193–219.
"Examination of H. Spencer's Psychology, IV, *DR*, XXVIII, 479–502.
"Axial Skeleton of the *Pelecanidae*," *TZS*, X, 315–77 (received May 1, 1877).
"Grenouilles et Crapauds" [Frogs and toads], *Rev. Quest. Sci.*, II, 612–34.

1878

"Force, Energy and Will," *NC*, III, 933–48.
"Emotion," *Amer. Cath. Quar. Rev.*, III, 301–20.
"Examination of H. Spencer's Psychology, V," *DR*, XXX, 158–94.

"Examination of H. Spencer's Psychology, VI," *DR*, XXXI, 412–39.
"Notes Touching Recent Researches on the Radiolaria," *Jour. Linn. Soc.*, XIV, 136–86 (read before Linnean Society, January 17, 1878).
"Notes on the Fins of Elasmobranchs, with Considerations on the Nature and Homologies of Vertebrate Limbs," *TZS*, X, 439–84 (received February 5, 1878).
"Notes on the Fins of Elasmobranchs, with Considerations on the Nature and Homologies of Vertebrate Limbs" (abstract), *PZS*, XLVI, 116–20.
"The Genesis of Limbs," *Nature*, XVIII, 282–84, 309–11, 331–34.
With Robert Clarke. "On the Sacral Plexus and Sacral Vertebrae of Lizards," *Jour. Linn. Soc.*, XIII, 370–73; *TLS*, I (1879), 513–32 (read May 3, 1877).

1879

"Examination of Herbert Spencer's Psychology, VII," *DR*, XXXII, 141–63.
"The Meaning of Life," *NC*, V, 488–512.
"Examination of H. Spencer's Psychology, VIII," *DR*, XXXII, 368–96.
"The Government of Life," *NC*, V, 690–713.
"Buffon's Place in Natural History," Presidential Address to the Biological Section of the British Association at Sheffield, August 21, 1879, *Proc. Brit. Assoc.*, XLIX, 354–69; *Nature*, XX, 393–400.
"On the Study of Natural History," *CR*, XXXV, 251–68.
"What are Living Beings?" *CR*, XXXV, 688–718.
"Animals and Plants," *CR*, XXXVI, 13–41.
"The Forms and Colours of Living Creatures," *CR*, XXXVI, 313–31.
"Tails," *Nature*, XX, 509–12, 537–40.

1880

"Herbert Spencer's 'System of Philosophy'," *DR*, XXXIV, 26–73.
"Notes on Spain," *Amer. Cath. Quar. Rev.*, V, 288–304, 453–67, 615–35.
"Note on the Discovery of Living Medusae in the Botanical Society's Gardens," *PZS*, XLVIII, 454.
"The Relation of Animals to Time," *CR*, XXXVII, 99–122.
"The Geography of Living Creatures," *CR*, XXXVII, 275–99.
"The Relations of Living Beings to One Another," *CR*, XXXVII, 606–25.

1881

The Cat, an Introduction to the Study of Backboned Animals, Especially Mammals, London and New York, Murray and Scribner.
"Evolution and Intellect," *Brit. Quar.*, LXXIV, 298–332.
"The Soul and Evolution," *Amer. Cath. Quar. Rev.*, VI, 385–433.
"Popular Account of Chameleons," *Nature*, XXIV, 309–12, 335–38.

1882

"On the Classification and Distribution of the Aeluroidea," *PZS*, L, 135–208.

Nature and Thought, London, Burns and Oates.
"A Danger from Diffidence," *Month,* XLIV, 333–44.
"Notes on the Anatomy of *Erethizon dorsalis,*" *PZS,* L, 271–86.
"Notes on Some Points in the Anatomy of the *Aeluroidea,*" *PZS,* L, 459–520.

1883

"On Catholic Politics," *DR,* X, 1–25.
"Catholic Positivism," *Month,* XLVII, 170–81.
"Letter to the Editor," *CR,* XLIV, 156.
"A Limit to Evolution," *Amer. Cath. Quar. Review,* VIII, 193–221.

1884

"The Conversion of England," *DR,* XII, 65–86.
"Phases of Faith and Unfaith," *Cath. World,* XXXIX, 598–605.
A Philosophical Catechism, London, Burns and Oates.
"Notes on the Cerebral Convolutions of the Carnivora," *Jour. Linn. Soc.,* XIX, 1–25 (read December 18, 1884).
"On the Development of the Individual and of the Species as Forms of Instinctive Action," *PZS,* LII, 462–74.
"Hands and Feet," *Zoologist,* VIII, 281–95.
"A Limit to Evolution," *NC,* XVI, 263–80.
"The Downside Collection of Australian Mammals," *Downside Review,* III, 89.

1885

"Modern Catholics and Scientific Freedom," *NC,* XVIII, 30–47.
"On the Anatomy, Classification and Distribution of the *Arctoidea, PZS,* LIII, 340–404.
"Note on the Viverricula," *PZS,* LIII, 477.
"Notes on Pinnipedia," *PZS,* LIII, 484–501.
"Organic Nature's Riddle," *FR,* XLIII, 323–37, 519–31.

1886

"The Rights of Reason," *FR,* XLV, 61–68.
"A Visit to Some Austrian Monasteries," *NC,* XX, 374–90.
"An Explanation," *FR,* XLV, 525–27.
"What are Animals and Plants?" *Amer. Cath. Quar. Rev.,* XI, 58–75.
"Reptiles," *Encyclopaedia Britannica* (9th ed.), XX, 432–72.

1887

"The Catholic Church and Biblical Criticism," *NC,* XXII, 31–51.
"The Duke of Argyll and Mr. Darwin," *Tablet,* October 1, 1887.
"Catholicity and Reason," *NC,* XXII, 850–70.

"Some Notes on Colonial Zoology," *CR*, LI, 668–80.
"Laughter," *Forum*, III, 492–502.

1888

"Sins of Belief and Sins of Disbelief," *NC*, XXIV, 548–68.
"Letter of Dr. Mivart in Reply to Bishop Hedley (Bishop of Newport),"
  DR, XIX, 180–87.
"Reason and Language," *Nature*, XXVII, 364–65.
"Natural Selection and Useless Structures," *Nature*, XXIX, 127.
"Darwin's Brilliant Fallacy," *Forum*, VII, 99–105.
"Why Tastes Differ," *Amer. Cath. Quar. Rev.*, XIII, 12–27.
"Where Darwinism Fails," *Forum*, VII, 264–73.
"On the Possible Dual Origin of the Mammalia," *Proc. Roy. Soc.*, XLIII,
  372–79.
"Genesis of Species," *Tablet*, March 3–June 1 (10 articles).

1889

"On Galls" (letter), *Nature*, XLI, 175.
On Truth: a Systematic Inquiry, London, Kegan Paul, Trench & Co.
"Anapophyses" (letter), *Nature*, XL, 391.
The Origin of Human Reason, London, Kegan Paul, Trench and Co.
"Prof. Weismann's 'Essays'," *Nature*, XLI, 38–41.
"Prof. Weismann's Hypothesis," *DR*, XXII, 269–96.
"Notes of a Catholic Tourist in Central Europe," *Amer. Cath. Quar. Rev.*,
  XIV, 342–57.
"Skeleton," *Encyclopaedia Britannica* (9th ed.), XXII, 105–19.

1890

"Beginning and End of Life: Review of Weismann," *QR*, CLXX, 370–93
  (anonymous).
"Darwinism," *DR*, XXIII, 33–47.
"Notes on the Genus *Cyon*," *PZS*, LVIII, 88–92.
"Notes on the South American *Canidae*," *PZS*, LVIII, 98–113.
"Note on Canine Dental Abnormalities," *PZS*, LVIII, 376–78.
Dogs, Jackals, Wolves and Foxes—A Monograph on the Canidae, London,
  R. H. Porter.
"Eimer on Growth and Inheritance," *Edin. Rev.*, CLXXII, 316–49 (anony-
  mous).
"Birds," *QR*, CLXXI, 503–31 (anonymous).

1891

"Herbert Spencer on Justice," *DR*, XXVI, 245–65.
"Professing Themselves to Be Wise, They Become Fools," *Amer. Cath.
  Quar. Rev.*, XVI, 309–29.
*Introduction générale à l'Etude de la Nature: Cours professé à l'Uni-
  versité de Louvain*, Louvain and Paris.

"Taine on Napoleon I," *QR*, CLXXIII, 438–67 (anonymous).
"The Implications of Science," *Proc. Roy. Inst.*, XIII, 428–42 (delivered in 1891); *Nature*, XLV, 60–62, 82–84.

1892

The Elements of Ornithology, London, R. H. Porter.
Essays and Criticisms, 2 vols., London, Osgood, McIlvaine & Co.
"Happiness in Hell," *NC*, XXXII, 899–919.
"Beasts and Reptiles of India," *Edin. Rev.*, CLXXV, 469–99 (anonymous).
"Snakes," *QR*, CLXXIV, 423–52 (anonymous).
"Catholicity in England Fifty Years Ago—a Retrospect," *Amer. Cath. Quar. Rev.*, XVII, 161–75, 773–85; XVIII, 53–77.
"The Limits of Animal Intelligence," *Nature*, XLVI, 466.
"Pearson's *Grammar of Science*" (letter), *Nature*, XLVI, 269.

1893

Types of Animal Life, London, Osgood, McIlvaine & Co.
"Sir Richard Owen's Hypothesis," *Nat. Sci.*, II, 18–23.
"The Happiness in Hell: A Rejoinder," *NC*, XXXIII, 320–38.
"Last Words on the Happiness in Hell," *NC*, XXXIII, 637–51.
"The Index and My Articles on Hell," *NC*, XXXIV, 979–90.
"Evolution in Professor Huxley," *NC*, XXXIV, 198–211.
"Christianity and Roman Paganism," *NC*, XXXIV, 822–38.
"Fall of the Ancien Régime," *QR*, CLXXVII, 212–34 (anonymous).
"L'Ancien Régime," *Amer. Cath. Quar. Rev.*, XVIII, 518–38; XIX, 368–87.
"Evolution and Ritual," *Downside Review*, XII, 192.

1894

An Introduction to the Elements of Science, London, Osgood, McIlvaine & Co.
American Types of Animal Life, Boston, Little, Brown & Co.
"The Newest Darwinism," *Amer. Cath. Quar. Rev.*, XIX, 673–90.
Henry Standon (published under the pseudonym D'Arcy Drew). London, Simkin and Marshall.
"Memoirs of an Internuncio," *Edin. Rev.*, CLXXX, 61–79 (anonymous).

1895

The Helpful Science, New York, Harper.
"The Evolution of Evolution," *Amer. Cath. Quar. Rev.*, XX, 673–97.
"A Century of Science," *QR*, CLXXX, 381–405 (anonymous).
"Science in Fetters," *DR*, CXVI, 158–78; CXVII, 1–15.
"Bateson on Variation of Organic Life," *Edin. Rev.*, CLXXXII, 78–105 (anonymous).
"Denominational Science," *FR*, LXIV, 423–38.
"Heredity," *Harpers*, XC, 631–41.

"Spencer vs. Balfour," *NC*, XXXVIII, 261–77.
"On the Hyoid Bone of Certain Parrots," *PZS*, LXIII, 162–74.
"The Skeleton of *Lorius flavopalliatus* Compared with That of *Psitaccus erithacus*," *PZS*, LXIII, 312–37, 363–99.

1896

"On the Hyoid Bones of *Nestor meridionalis* and *Nanodes discolor*." *PZS*, LXIV, 236–40.
A Monograph of the Lories, London, R. H. Porter.
"Balfour's Philosophy," *Amer. Cath. Quar. Rev.*, XXI, 53–80, 294–320, 541–57, 763–806.
"Life from the Lost Atlantis," *FR*, LXV, 801–7.
"Are Specific Characters the Result of 'Natural Selection'?" *Nature*, LIV, 246–47.

1897

"Dr. F. H. Beadley's Appearance and Reality—Primary and Secondary Qualities," *Amer. Cath. Quar. Rev.*, XXII, 531–53.
"The Human Mind and Animal Intelligence," *QR*, CLXXXV, 477–502 (anonymous).
"Reminiscences of T. H. Huxley," *NC*, XLII, 985–98.
"Burial Service," *NC*, XLI, 38–55.
"Monkeys," *QR*, CLXXXVI, 394–419 (anonymous).

1898

"Moral Sense and Ethic" (letter), *Nature*, LVIII, 294.
The Groundwork of Science: a Study of Epistemology, London and New York, Bliss, Sands & Co. and Putnam's.
"What Makes a Species?" *Amer. Cath. Quar. Rev.*, XXIII, 28–44.
"Another Catholic's View of 'Helbeck of Bannisdale'," *NC*, XLIV, 641–55.
"Review of Ward's Cardinal Wiseman," *Amer. Cath. Quar. Rev.*, XXIII, 358–81.
"Notes on Some Lories," *Jour. Linn. Soc.*, XXVI, 620–22.
"Living Nature," *Amer. Cath. Quar. Rev.*, XXIII, 673–91.

1899

"The New Psychology," *NC*, XLV, 261–72.
"What Church Has 'Continuity'?" *NC*, XLVI, 203–12.
"The Dreyfus Affair and the Roman Catholic Church" (letter), *Times* London), October 17, 1899.

1900

"The Continuity of Catholicism," *NC*, XLVII, 51–72.
"Some Recent Catholic Apologists," *FR*, LXVII, 24–44.
"Scripture and Roman Catholicism," *NC*, XLVII, 425–42.

"Roman Congregations and Modern Thought," *No. Amer. Rev., CLXX,* 562–74.

Castle and Manor, London, Sands & Co. (reissue of Henry Standon).

"Correspondence with Cardinal Vaughan," *Times* (London), January 25, 28, and February 1, 1900.

Under the Ban, New York, Tucker Publishing Co.

"Letter to the Editor," *Tablet,* February 10, 1900.

"The Cathedral of Vannes," *Downside Review,* XIX, 33.

INDEX